introduction to

biomechanic analysis of sport

introduction to

biomechanic analysis of sport

John W. Northrip
Southwest Missouri State University

Gene A. Logan
University of Southern California

Wayne C. McKinney
Southwest Missouri State University

WM. C. BROWN COMPANY PUBLISHERS
Dubuque, Iowa

PHYSICAL EDUCATION

Consulting Editor

Aileene Lockhart
Texas Woman's University

HEALTH

Consulting Editor

Robert Kaplan
The Ohio State University

PARKS AND RECREATION

Consulting Editor

David Gray
California State University, Long Beach

Copyright © 1974 by Wm. C. Brown Company Publishers

Library of Congress Catalog Card Number: 73—83970

ISBN 0—697—07121—9

Printed in the United States of America

contents

preface

Introduction to Biomechanic Analysis of Sport is written for the student without a physics background who is taking a course in biomechanics at the college or university level for the first time. This text may also be used for kinesiology courses required in the professional-preparation program for students majoring in physical education. Or, it may be used for general education courses taught by instructors concerned with physics of sport and designed for students interested in basic physics. The main purpose of this book is to assist the physical educator in utilizing subject matter from biomechanics in daily teaching-coaching situations.

Kinesiology is the scientific study of human motion. Comprehension of kinesiology involves detailed study and subsequent synthesis of anatomic kinesiology and biomechanics. The primary emphasis in this book lies in the area of biomechanics. Biomechanic analysis is one vital aspect of kinesiology and is a necessary tool for the physical educator attempting to improve performances in sport, exercise, and dance. There is a secondary emphasis on anatomic kinesiology. Chapter two contains minimal descriptive information on motion for the student who has not had courses in human anatomy or anatomic kinesiology. There is a description of anatomic planes, landmarks, and motions. For the study of biomechanics, it is imperative that the student have this introduction to anatomic kinesiology in order to locate points on levers and joints as accurately as possible within the limitations of cinematographic analysis and to develop the vocabulary necessary to describe human body motion. This is necessary, as examples, to calculate angular and linear velocities of limbs or body segments, to describe force interactions which occur in sport, and to communicate ideas related to human motion to professional peers and students.

The book is divided into three parts. Part One is "Human Motion Analysis." This part introduces the student to essential concepts of biomechanic analysis and anatomic kinesiology. It serves as an introduction to anatomic kinesiology for the student who has not had course work in this area, or it can be used as a review for students who have had courses in human anatomy and/ or anatomic kinesiology.

Part Two, "Physics of Sport," is written for the student who has not had college course work in mathematics and physics. This part serves as the theoretical foundation for comprehending biomechanic analysis. Elements of physics are presented. These are the fundamental physics required to describe motions observed in exercise, sport, and dance whether the performances are on land, in air, or in water. The last chapter of Part Two, "Principles of Biomechanics," summarizes those concepts from physics in a nonmathematical framework.

Part Two of the book is designed primarily to assist the reader in gaining an understanding of biomechanic analyses through the intermediate cinematographic level. Three procedures are used to convey biomechanic principles to the readers. First, principles are explained in a fundamental manner to facilitate comprehension. Second, to reinforce the word description of principles, graphic illustrations are included where applicable. Third, where deemed necessary to facilitate comprehension and add precision, mathematical formulae and examples are included to further reinforce the ideas conveyed. Numerals as symbols do have a distinct advantage over words as symbols. Words, especially in the English language, do have some degree of ambiguity; whereas mathematical symbols are more precise ways of expressing ideas. Some people tend to succumb to a syndrome known as "symbol shock" if they are asked to work extensively in the field of mathematics. As a consequence, it is believed the best way to convey ideas regarding biomechanics to the majority of potential users of subject matter from biomechanics on a regular basis in teaching-coaching is to delimit the mathematics to the very essential equations necessary to describe motion adequately through the intermediate cinematographic analysis level.

Part Three, "Techniques of Biomechanic Analysis," leads the student to practical applications of biomechanics for teaching-coaching situations. In order to accomplish the practicality objective for utilizing biomechanics subject matter in instruction situations, *a hierarchy for biomechanic analysis is introduced.* Each level is designed to increase the degree of precision in controlled observations of performers in classes, athletic situations, or as research subjects. The four levels of biomechanic analysis are (1) noncinematographic analysis, (2) basic cinematographic analysis, (3) intermediate cinematographic analysis, and (4) biomechanic research. This text provides the student with the potential for a functional understanding of the first three levels within the hierarchy of biomechanic analysis. The first two levels should be used in day-to-day teaching and coaching by physical educators in elementary, secondary, and undergraduate university positions. Intermediate cinematographic analysis can be applied in special teaching-coaching situations on a less frequent basis.

Conducting biomechanic research requires extensive multidisciplinary professional preparation at both undergraduate and graduate levels. This involves course work in mathematics through calculus, advanced physics, computer science, human engineering, and other related course work. As a consequence, the most advanced analytic step in the hierarchy, biomechanic research, is beyond the scope of this book except to inform the reader that this level does exist and logically follows after the student has attained an understanding of the first three levels of biomechanic analysis. Most professional physical educators will utilize the first three levels of biomechanic analysis within the hierarchy and be consumers as opposed to producers of biomechanic research.

Acknowledgment is made to Don Anderson (USC Athletic News Service), Dick Bank and Phil Bath of Visual Track and Field Techniques, Mark Stillwell (SMSU Sports Information Director), and Bill Rowe for their assistance in helping to obtain the photographs used throughout the text. In addition, the authors would like to acknowledge the athletes who appear in the photos.

David Andereck contributed the vector diagrams and line drawings. Bill Armstrong and Philip J. Van Voorst provided the plane of motion and anatomic drawings, respectively, which appear in chapter two.

Acknowledgment is given to the following people for their assistance: John G. Boelter, Dr. Roger K. Burke, Dr. Alberto Calb, Dr. John Callaghan, Peggy Cramer, Dr. Herbert A. deVries, Mark Logan, Mike McKinney, Debbie Malpee, Sandra Malpee, Kenneth Matsuda, John D. Northrip, Nathalie Smith, Janice Stevenson, Jeffrey Spencer, Michael J. Swiderski, Josephine Tromba, Joseph D. Weiss, and Dr. Ron Witchey. Finally, the invaluable assistance of Susan Welsch and Rita Needham in preparing the manuscript is appreciated.

The content and purposes of this book, together with possible errors, are the sole responsibility of the authors.

John W. Northrip, Ph.D.
Gene A. Logan, Ph.D.
Wayne C. McKinney, Ph.D.

part one

human motion analysis

Chapter 1

Kinesiology

The scientific study of human motion is known as *kinesiology*. Kinesiology has many dimensions; however, it is most commonly divided into two special study fields: (1) anatomic kinesiology and (2) mechanical kinesiology. During recent years, the term *mechanical kinesiology* has been replaced by *biomechanics*. The term *biomechanics* more accurately describes this field of study. The prefix *bio* is from the Greek, and it means "life." The suffix *mechanics* is an area of Newtonian physics designed to study the effect of forces on bodies and motion. The bodies studied by people concerned with physics per se are mostly of the inanimate variety. Physical educators concern themselves primarily with forces and motions of human beings. A body in motion may literally be a performer's body, or it may be a sport object projected into motion by a series of sequential joint and lever actions by the performer. *Studying and analyzing humans in motion, sport object motion, and forces acting upon these animate and inanimate bodies is known as biomechanics.*

It is desirable that a thorough understanding of anatomic kinesiology precede the study of biomechanics. That is to say, an understanding of anatomic planes of motion, motions possible at major joints of the body, ranges of motion possible at each body joint, and comprehension of the myologic internal force components for controlling the extent of motion with and against gravity at each major joint is of utmost importance. There is a positive and reciprocal relationship between anatomic kinesiology and biomechanics. This functions in both directions, i.e., an understanding of anatomic kinesiology assists the learner in comprehending aspects of biomechanics and vice versa. A review of anatomic planes of motion, bony landmarks, and major joint motions is presented in chapter two.

BIOMECHANIC ANALYSIS OF PERFORMANCE

One of the major objectives of physical education often cited in the literature is to improve skill levels of students. In order to obtain this objective, the physical educator must be thoroughly cognizant of a variety of analytic techniques. Analyzing performers in motion to improve the efficiency of their movements, whether it be with males or females in the context of sport, exercise, or dance, always precedes the communicative process between teacher and student known as *teaching*. The physical educator, therefore, must have a variety of professional experiences and course work at both undergraduate and graduate levels to prepare to analyze motion by using a variety of scientifically based procedures. One of these procedures is known as biomechanic analysis. Anatomic and biomechanic analyses of sport skills are ongoing processes and integral functions for a physical educator performing professional responsibilities in instructional as well as athletic situations with students of all ages, both sexes, and varying skill levels. Biomechanic analysis is another vital "working tool" for all physical educators.

Biomechanic analyses should be used any time a physical educator is attempting to improve performances of students so they may attain their full potentials as performers. Quality instruction in physical education always includes some form of kinesiologic analysis. One purpose of biomechanic analysis is to increase the precision of the instructor's observations for teaching-coaching. Some have advocated the point of view that biomechanic analysis procedures and techniques which do not meet scientific detail and precision based on research criteria cannot be used in teaching-coaching situations. The contention is that data obtained would be limited to the point of negating the findings of the analysis. This is a point of view limited to the research situation. Significant biomechanic analyses can be made in instructional and athletic situations with and without cinematographic equipment. Furthermore, the findings of these analyses will greatly assist the physical educator in communicating to students, in language understandable to them, exact changes which should be made to improve their performances. In this context, the fact that research criteria were not met for biomechanic analysis is irrelevant. *Utilization of the subject matter from biomechanics is not restricted to the research laboratory.*

Techniques for performing analyses will be presented herein with and without photographic equipment. Techniques will be shown to implement analyses without high-speed research cameras, sophisticated projection equipment which needs to be connected to computers, and timing equipment accurate into the range of nanoseconds. Obviously, this type of equipment is not available in the physical education department of the average secondary school. Therefore, since analyses are so basic to the teaching process, adjustments must be made in analytic techniques to compensate for the type of instrumentation available to physical educators in elementary and secondary schools as well as in colleges and universities. Biomechanic research is an important aspect of physical education, but not all biomechanic analyses made by every coach or physical educator are going to attain a publishable level. The vast majority of biomechanic analyses will not attain the precision of research conducted in the laboratory. The precision and control of the observations made by physical educators who are teaching and coaching differ considerably from analyses made by physical educators conducting research. Although differences do exist, these two analytic levels are compatible.

During the professional preparation of a physical educator, a gradual change must occur from being a fan of sport to becoming a teacher-coach of students involved in sport. What are the basic differences between being a fan and being a physical educator responsible for teaching and coaching? One of the main differences lies in the fact that the physical educator understands motion so thoroughly that a detailed analysis of any sport skill can be undertaken. The physical educator, unlike the fan, observes a skill in terms of its component parts as well as its subsequent outcomes. The average sport fan appears to be interested only in the outcome of a given performance. As an example, during a field goal attempt in American football, the average fan tends to watch the trajectory of the ball as it moves toward the goalpost. The fan's only concern is whether or not the ball passes between the uprights and over or under the crossbar. On the other hand, the physical educator, watching from the sidelines and subsequently viewing the same field goal attempt on game film, is fully aware of the fact that sequential movements by the kicker are of utmost importance. Once the ball has been contacted by the kicker's foot, the end result is very predictable. The physical educator, unlike the fan, is very much aware of the summation of motions generating forces to be applied to the ball. The relationships of biomechanic principles to these sequential motions are understood by the physical educator, and the implications of using them either effectively or ineffectively during the execution of a performance are known. Unlike the sport fan, the physical educator—and the performer, for that matter—does not have to follow the flight of the football in the example to know whether or not the kick was successful. The kinetic chain of sequential movement by the performer indicates to the skilled observer, most of the time, whether the performance was effective or ineffective.

The type of observations indicated in the aforementioned example is used in the noncinematographic analysis technique. The basic criterion for doing this type of analysis or any other analysis of a performer is for the physical educator to understand the scientific principles and techniques of the skill under analysis. That is to say, the physical educator should be professionally aware of what constitutes the stereotype of perfect form for the skill being analyzed. The so-called techniques or technical aspects of any skill must be thoroughly understood by the physical educator prior to undertaking a scientific analysis. In the place-kicking example, the coach would have to be fully aware of what constitutes perfect field goal kicking form in order to do an adequate job of analyzing the kicker. Understanding the stereotype of perfect form for a skill serves as the basis for analysis and teaching. Once the performer has achieved an adequate level of skill, individual differences at times necessitate unique changes in form. Changes of this type require thorough applications of biomechanic analysis. Kinesiologic knowledge by physical educators is an absolute necessity when stereotypes of sport skills change as a result of pragmatic experiences by athletes or coaches. Evaluation of a new performance technique such as the Fosbury Flop form of high jumping can be made by utilizing kinesiologic techniques. Improving upon newly discovered techniques is one function of the physical educator utilizing biomechanic analyses. The knowledgeable coach must utilize these analytic procedures to make individual adjustments to the form of student-athletes. Adjustment of form as opposed to radical change is recommended procedure in most teaching-coaching situations.

Physical educators must undergo professional preparation in a wide variety of sports. The actual involvement in performing and learning skills is a vital aspect of the analytic process. The physical educator who has not performed skills he attempts to analyze as a teacher or coach is at a disadvantage technically. In other words, a thorough understanding of the techniques of the sports one is attempting to teach or coach is also a prerequisite of biomechanic analysis. Once knowledge of the techniques for each skill is attained, the physical educator must be able to utilize the appropriate level of biomechanic analysis for any given teaching-coaching or research situation.

HIERARCHY OF BIOMECHANIC ANALYSES

Biomechanic analyses are divided into four levels: (1) noncinematographic analysis, (2) basic cinematographic analysis, (3) intermediate cinematographic analysis, and (4) biomechanic research. The physical educator performing routine responsibilities in elementary, secondary, and university teaching will utilize the first two levels primarily. The third level, intermediate cinematographic analysis, can also be used extensively in teaching-coaching situations to objectify analytic observations which tend to be subjective in nature. The first three levels of biomechanic analyses are of prime concern within this book because they are applicable to the physical educator outside the research laboratory.

Biomechanic research production is actually a function of a small number of individuals throughout the world. A detailed description of research procedures and instrumentation is beyond the scope of this book; consequently, only a brief introduction to research is presented in chapter nine. An effort to understand biomechanic research is important because the professional physical educator, although he may not be a research producer, should be a consumer of research published in the area of biomechanics. Courses beyond the introductory level in biomechanics should be designed to facilitate an understanding of biomechanic research.

Noncinematographic analysis is the most common analytic technique used by physical educators. As the term implies, no film or videotape is utilized during this type of observation of performers. This means that the physical educator must have a disciplined approach to observing and analyzing motions at various body articulations. This type of approach is presented in chapter eight. Noncinematographic techniques are literally used the majority of time during the teaching-coaching process. Therefore, knowing how to observe human motion without the assistance of film or videotape is of utmost importance to teaching and obtaining the skill-improvement objective of physical education.

The implications of utilizing biomechanic principles in the noncinematographic technique are often overlooked. The reason for this lies in the fact that many people involved in the professional preparation of physical educators believe that biomechanic ideas can only be transmitted by using intricate mathematical calculations of physics principles. From the standpoint of time, it is not always feasible in teaching-coaching situations at the high school level, for example, to undertake detailed mathematical analyses of performances being observed. A detailed mathematical analysis would be desirable to greatly objectify the observation. However, if the underlying biomechanic principles are fully understood by the teacher-coach, communication of ideas for improving performance based on biomechanic principles can be conveyed to the performers in succinct, nonscientific terms. This applies regardless of which biomechanic analysis level is being utilized. It is often more difficult to communicate to a performer an idea regarding the implications of adhering to a biomechanic principle without having the assistance of making calculations from film. Noncinematographic analysis and the subsequent teaching from the observations are challenging!

The physical educator must have a systematic approach for viewing human performances while utilizing his own field of vision. If this is not accomplished, teaching-coaching suggestions to the performer will result in considerable guesswork. Communication of violated biomechanic principles by the physical educator to the performer should be conveyed in a positive manner. In the context of the learning situation, it is not always necessary for the student to fully understand the physics principle being violated and adversely affecting the performance. The physical educator, however, must have an in-depth understanding of the biomechanic principles underlying the performances observed and the implications these principles have to the ultimate outcome of the performance. The communication (teaching) with the student should be a positive recommendation designed to eliminate the performance problem. *A good teacher never dwells on the negative aspects of performance.*

As an example, a track-and-field coach should be fully aware of the biomechanic principle which states, "When horizontal distance is the primary objective in a skill, the highest velocity obtainable by the performer should be observed at the takeoff point." If a long jumper appears to have negative acceleration at the time he hits the takeoff board, the coach will take this biomechanic principle into consideration as he makes a positive coaching suggestion to the long jumper. The idea to eliminate the problem of negative acceleration at takeoff could be communicated very simply to the student by telling him, "Run through the takeoff." This type of observation and recommendation can be made on a subjective or qualitative basis while on the field or observing film during a basic cinematographic analysis. Furthermore, the professional physical educator might possibly want to objectify his observations by undertaking an intermediate biomechanic analysis of film taken of the long jumper. This would give the coach quantitative information with which to work. Such quantitative or numerical information regarding, for example, the velocity of the runner in feet per second may or may not be communicated to the athlete. As a matter of fact, most communications between physical educator and performer are in the context of words to convey meanings as opposed to the use of mathematical symbols to convey ideas. This very salient point is often overlooked by biomechanics teachers and researchers in universities.

In summary, the noncinematographic analysis technique involving the use of biomechanic principles is a vital function of the physical educator, because it is the technique utilized the majority of time in all teaching-coaching situations.

Basic cinematographic analysis involves utilization of film or videotape specifically for the purpose of improving the performances observed. This level of biomechanic analysis does not involve any mathematical calculations. The use of film tends to objectify, substantiate, or refute what has been seen through noncinematographic techniques. For all practical purposes, the way performers are visualized through basic cinematographic and noncinematographic techniques is essentially the same. One major limitation of noncinematographic analysis is the difficulty in seeing detailed movements when ballistic or fast-moving limb or body actions are being observed. Many coaches, for example, give very profound suggestions to performers on what they think they observed noncinematographically as opposed to what they actually observed without the aid of film. *Film allows the observer to see what has actually occurred versus what he thinks took place*. The implications for quality teaching-coaching are obvious.

Film has the distinct advantage of holding permanent images of even the fastest limb actions, and projection techniques enable the physical educator to stop these images on a timed, frame-by-frame basis. This adds precision to the basic cinematographic analysis process over the noncinematographic technique.

To return to the example of the field goal kicker, the coach utilizing noncinematographic techniques on the practice field or during a game has severe limitations in regard to what he can observe during a once-only performance of the skill. At best, since place-kicking is a ballistic action of the lower limb, the coach would only observe the pendular action of the kicking leg and its linear force; whereas while viewing game film, the coach could make a much more detailed analysis of all major joint components utilized during the kicking process. In addition, various biomechanic principles should serve as a frame of reference for the development of questions as the coach watches film: (1) What are the force-counterforce components between upper and lower body segments of the kicker? (2) Was conservation of angular momentum utilized at the knee joint within the kicking limb? (3) Was an optimum position of the foot applied to the ball at the point of contact for force to be transferred from the kicking limb to the ball? (4) Was transformation of linear motion of the body and angular motion of the kicking limb adequate to effectively execute the skill? and (5) What was the angle of projection and subsequent trajectory and flight pattern of the ball? It is rather obvious that all of these questions could not be answered during a noncinematographic observation.

Basic cinematographic techniques are also very important in any learning situation whether it be in a physical education class at the elementary- or secondary-school level or in competitive athletics. The physical educator who relies strictly on an undisciplined, noncinematographic technique has a tendency to do a considerable amount of guessing during analysis and subsequent teaching. Therefore, film and videotape should be utilized as much as possible during the teaching-coaching process. Most elementary- and secondary-school districts as well as colleges and universities have communications media or audiovisual departments. A wide variety of eight-millimeter and sixteen-millimeter cameras and projectors are obtainable in most school situations. In addition, there is a trend toward having portable videotape cameras and monitors available for use by school personnel. Since this type of cinematographic equipment is available in most school situations, basic cinematographic analyses should be made, as much as possible, during instructional and athletic situations.

Basic cinematographic analysis does not involve utilization of mathematical computations to objectify observations made on film. During this type of analysis, the physical educator must be capable of observing the performer who is effectively or ineffectively applying biomechanic principles. In the case where a student is obviously violating a biomechanic principle, or several principles, the physical educator must decide precisely what motions are causing violations of principles and which principles are being violated, and he must determine which changes or alterations must be made in the performer's style to bring about a more efficient application of biomechanic principles. Again, this is a vital aspect of the teaching-coaching process in physical education.

The basic cinematographic analysis technique should be used extensively by coaches analyzing individual skills of athletes on game film. Obviously, game film will not meet the very rigid film criteria established for biomechanic research. However, recognizing the fact that game film does have limitations, very significant and critical biomechanic analyses can be made, even on a basic level, to help improve performances. As one example of how this is done, the use of this technique has been very effective in eradicating baseball hitters' "slumps." Game film should be taken of a hitter when he is hitting for a good percentage. This film should be filed according to such factors as date, pitching situation, and the result of the swing or swings of the bat as shown on the film. This can subsequently be utilized to compare and contrast with film taken during a game situation when the same hitter is performing poorly. Similar or identical game situations can be analyzed independently or concurrently. For example, two single-action projectors can be utilized concurrently, and the hitter's form can be analyzed frame by frame at synchronized times during both hitting processes. Motion variations can be noted in such factors as total body position in the stance, motion variations during the preparatory phase of the swing, angular velocity of the pelvic and spinal column rotations, bat trajectories and accelerations, and variations in the follow-through actions. On the basis of this type of basic cinematographic analysis, positive decisions can be reached by the coach with regard to adapting the individual's hitting style back to its previous form when he was hitting for a good batting average. These coaching adjustments would be made during the next practice. Having a permanent record of both performances on film tends to eliminate any guesswork on the part of the coach. By using noncinematographic techniques only, the coach would have to rely on his memory regarding what he thought the student-athlete was doing as a hitter several weeks previously. The human brain is not capable of maintaining precise images over a period of time. This is one reason the physical educator must rely on film periodically for analytic purposes, especially in athletic situations.

Intermediate cinematographic analysis involves some mathematical computation to enhance the precision of observations by the analyzer. All procedures and knowledge utilized by the physical educator in performing noncinematographic and basic cinematographic analyses are employed during intermediate cinematographic analyses. Intermediate cinematographic techniques are capable of being utilized on film taken in instructional situations or from game film taken during athletic contests. There are distinct advantages for the physical educator to make mathematical computations at times to assist in communicating ideas to performers. This is particularly true in those sports not requiring measurements in precise units. As an example, a diving coach may have some difficulty communicating the importance of an extreme "tuck position" to a diver who is attempting to improve a two and one-half somersault diving maneuver. From an intermediate cinematographic analysis of the dive, calculations could be made to indicate the diver's angular velocity in precise units. When the diver follows the coach's suggestions regarding the basic body movements to "tighten the tuck" and, therefore, increase the subsequent angular velocity by conserving angular momentum, film can again be made and subjected to intermediate analysis techniques. Following this, the change in velocity achieved by the performer can be communicated to him in precise units. This type of communication plus actual viewing of the film helps motivate some student-athletes.

Biomechanic research techniques for analytic purposes involve highly sophisticated instrumentation. Most of this equipment can be found in only a very few specialized laboratories in universities throughout the United States. High-speed cameras for triaxial cinematographic analysis with associated velocity measurement devices, stroboscopic devices, electromyographic units, electrogoniometers, force plates, force transducers, and computers are not commonly found in elementary- and secondary-school situations. These and other types of equipment are absolutely essential to conducting biomechanic research.

Biomechanic research techniques bring a great amount of precision to the task of solving a motion problem. Also, research facilitates discovery of new knowledge in the area of biomechanics. When research techniques are utilized, considerable attention is given to working with a delimited portion of the motion problem. This facilitates a deeper understanding of the factors underlying the motion observed. In order to conduct biomechanic research properly, a background of very specialized professional preparation is needed for the person undertaking this type of research. At the present time, this preparation usually involves earning a doctorate in biomechanics. Research workers in this field have available to them very costly "hardware," or instruments, to solve various motion problems. In addition, biomechanic research takes a vast amount of time to solve rather minute motion problems. The latter factor alone makes it very unrealistic to think that all people in physical education will perform biomechanic research.

To study and describe motions of a single shot-putter in a research situation, for example, the researcher might very well have to utilize triaxial cinematographic techniques. One way this is accomplished is to synchronize three cameras at precise angles relative to three critical planes of motion traversed by the shot-putter. These cameras would have to be of sufficient quality to include precision-timing on the film. A scaling device within the photographic background would have to be included to help determine limb velocities. A special shot-putting ring would have to be set up with a variety of force transducers to determine weight-shifting factors by the shot-putter as he traversed the ring. If ranges of motion were studied, electrogoniometers would be required. If the electromyographic parameters were to be evaluated concurrently, this equipment would have to be set up to determine precisely the internal forces generated by specific muscles or muscle groups during the execution of the skill. This, in turn, would necessitate a fourth camera being synchronized with the three cameras for triaxial analysis. The fourth camera would be set on the oscilloscope for reading muscle-action potentials elicited by the muscles during various points within the execution of the skill. It is rather obvious that it takes considerable time to work out the electronic details and actually set up for an experiment of this nature with the type of equipment indicated. An electronic technician is an absolute must as a member of the biomechanic research team.

To continue with the example of researching the shot put, after data are collected following the performance, these data are usually processed through a computer and synthesized within the construct of the statistical model established prior to the start of the experiment within the experimental design. It is unrealistic to believe that biomechanic research could be effectively conducted at elementary- and secondary-school levels on a regular basis. It is entirely realistic, however, that most professionally prepared physical educators at elementary- and secondary-school levels, as well as college or university physical educators, could utilize biomechanic analysis through the intermediate level on a day-to-day basis in teaching-coaching situations in their schools. Biomechanic research will be discussed briefly in chapter nine. *The main emphasis in this textbook, however, is on the more practical applications of biomechanic analysis in teaching-coaching situations.*

Chapter 2

Anatomic Planes, Landmarks, and Motions

In order to communicate adequately, it is essential to have a thorough comprehension of the vocabulary commonly used by people working in a given field. All specialized areas of endeavor, whether they be scientific or nonscientific, have specialized vocabularies. This is just as true for anatomic kinesiology and biomechanics as it is for American football. A specialized vocabulary is necessary to enable individuals working in a common area to adequately and precisely communicate ideas to each other. Those same ideas conveyed in the very specialized vocabulary of a given area may not have meaning to someone untrained in the discipline.

Scientific terminology has the distinct advantage of being more precise and meaningful when taken completely out of context of the discipline. As examples, let us take the terms *biomechanics* and *love* out of their respective areas of kinesiology and tennis. As one views these two terms out of context, *biomechanics* informs the reader who has not been trained in the area of biomechanics that it is an area having some relationship with life—*bio*—and a relationship between force and motion of this living matter—*mechanics*. Most scientific terms have meaningful prefixes and suffixes of Latin or Greek derivation which help clarify their meaning; whereas terms or words from other disciplines do not have this communication advantage. For example, the term *love* taken out of a tennis context connotes to the reader many different ideas which may be completely unrelated to tennis! There is no hint in the term *love* that would lead an individual without a tennis background to deduce that it is defined as a zero score in tennis. While many of the basic scientific terms relevant to motion may be new to the reader and somewhat confusing at first, they do have the advantage of a logical, semantic rationale.

One purpose of this chapter is to assist the student in the development of a motion-description vocabulary for all basic joint movements of the body. This chapter contains many of the basic concepts from anatomic kinesiology necessary to understand, describe, and communicate ideas related to human motion.

PLANES AND AXES OF MOVEMENT

A plane may be defined as an imaginary two-dimensional surface. Body segments and limbs always move through a plane of motion. The important thing to remember regarding a plane is the direction in which it lies relative to the body as opposed to the point at which it intersects the body. For example, a transverse plane can intersect the body at the knee, hip, pelvic girdle, and spinal column. Since all joint motions are angular in nature, motions occurring through the traditional or cardinal planes may be considered as being rotational around the line perpendicular to that plane. *This line is known as the axis of motion.* In this context, there is always a ninety-degree relationship between a traditional plane of motion and its axis of motion. This ninety-degree relationship also applies to the diagonal planes of motion described later in this chapter.

The anteroposterior, lateral, and transverse planes are known as the traditional or cardinal anatomic planes of motion (figs. 2.1, 2.2, and 2.3). The origin of these planes can be traced almost directly to the ancient Greeks. These three planes of motion serve a very important descriptive function for movement, but they are limited in regard to describing ballistic or high-velocity actions of limbs. It is rather interesting to note that formally organized and historic sport activities utilized movements primarily through the traditional planes. These activities were commonly observed in physical education curricula early in the twentieth century. They included mass calisthenics, marching, wand and Indian club drills, Swedish gymnastics, and German Turnverein activities. These activities have decreased in popularity in American physical education programs since 1927.

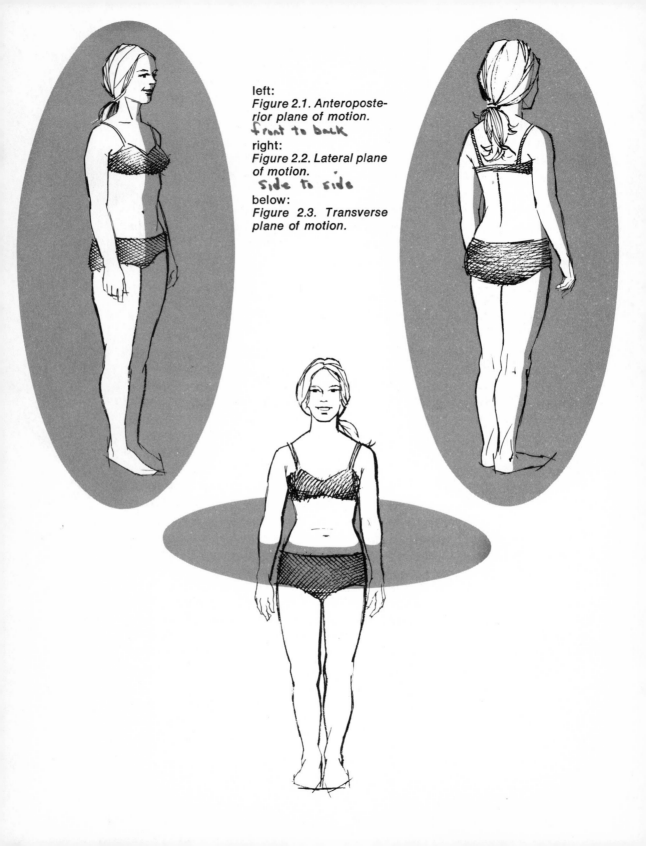

left:
Figure 2.1. Anteroposterior plane of motion.
front to back
right:
Figure 2.2. Lateral plane of motion.
Side to side
below:
Figure 2.3. Transverse plane of motion.

Traditional planes of motion and subsequent joint motion terminology based on these planes do not always allow precise analyses and descriptions of living, moving performers. One reason for this lies in the paradoxical fact that early anatomists described active joint movements for living individuals by detailed study of human cadavers. This procedure, obviously, has rather severe limitations in regard to accurate descriptions of movements by living human beings. There is very little resemblance between motion of a manipulated joint of a cadaver when compared to dynamic motion observed in an articulation of a living individual.

To add to descriptive terminology for analytic kinesiology, three new diagonal planes of motion were introduced in 1970 (Logan and McKinney) to describe ballistic limb actions: (1) the high diagonal plane of motion involving the glenohumeral or shoulder articulation, (2) the low diagonal plane of motion involving the same articulation, and (3) the diagonal plane of motion involving the coxal or hip articulation. Most movements of upper and lower limbs during ballistic actions are through one of the diagonal planes at shoulder or hip joints, i.e., these motions are diagonal to the longitudinal axis of the body (figs. 2.4, 2.5, and 2.6).

One reason that motions are diagonal to the longitudinal axis of the body when one limb is used to impart force to an object is that the opposite limb is involved in maintaining equilibrium when the performer is in an upright position. This is intricately related to the biomechanic principle of force-counter-force. Another reason that diagonal movements are the rule for most ballistic actions is that pendular levers revolving on multiaxis articulations do involve angular momentum, i.e., as an attempt is made to move a limb through a range of motion in one plane, there is also a tendency for a lever or limb to describe a circular action. Therefore, the limb moves in an arc diagonal to the longitudinal axis of the body because the joint involved is also moving through space. Finally, the spatial relationships of the musculature to the enarthrodial shoulder and hip joints also add credence to the concept of diagonal planes. Major muscles of the lower limb and upper limb attach to the femur and humerus respectively to provide diagonal lines of pull. This results in internal forces during contraction to pull the limb levers through the commonly observed diagonal limb action of skills requiring ballistic actions.

There also appears to be some neurologic basis for diagonal movement patterns in man. One reflex adds some credibility to the diagonal movement pattern. This is known as the crossed-extensor reflex. Simply stated, this reflex is

upper left:
Figure 2.4. High diagonal plane of motion—left shoulder joint.

upper right:
Figure 2.5. Low diagonal plane of motion—right shoulder joint.

left:
Figure 2.6. Diagonal plane of motion—right hip joint.

a combination of a flexion reflex in one limb and an extensor reflex occurring almost simultaneously in the opposite limb. This crossed-extensor reflex is responsible for an "automatic relationship" in diagonal-type movements. There is a constant reciprocal relationship between flexion and extension of alternating limbs as observed in most locomotor activities. Figure 2.7 shows this type of relationship in upper and lower limbs of the football player.

Courtesy USC Athletic News Service

Figure 2.7. Crossed-extensor reflex limb action—Mike Garrett, USC Heisman Trophy winner.

ANATOMIC LANDMARKS

Figure 2.8 provides a minimal list of bones and skeletal landmarks. This list is delimited to include the most frequently used anatomic references related to human motion. Figures 2.9 through 2.30 provide illustrations of the bones, skeletal landmarks, and major joints which must be observed during a bio-

FOOT	Talus, calcaneus, navicular, cuboid, medial, lateral and intermediate cuneiforms, tuberosity of fifth metatarsal, sustentaculum tali
LEG	Fibula—lateral malleolus, styloid process Tibia—medial malleolus, anterior border-medial surface, tibial tuberosity, medial and lateral condyles
THIGH	Femur—medial and lateral condyles, linea aspera, lesser trochanter, greater trochanter, head, neck
PELVIS	Pelvis—Ilium, ischium, pubis—pubic crest, crest of ilium, anterior and posterior, superior and inferior spines, ischial tuberosity, acetabulum
SPINE	Vertebrae—cervical, thoracic, lumbar—body, transverse and spinous processes—atlas and axis
CHEST	Ribs, Sternum—body, manubrium, and xiphoid process
SHOULDER	Scapula—spine, acromion process, infra and supraglenoid tubercles, superior border, vertebral border, inferior angle, glenoid fossa, coracoid process, superior angle, subscapular fossa, supraspinatous fossa and infraspinatous fossa
ARM	Humerus—greater tubercle, lesser tubercle, head, anatomical neck, surgical neck, medial and lateral epicondyles, olecranon fossa, trochlea, capitulum, deltoid tuberosity, intertubercular groove
FOREARM	Ulna—olecranon process, coranoid process, styloid process, trochlear notch Radius—head, neck, radial tuberosity, styloid process
HEAD	Skull—mastoid process, zygomatic arch, mandible, maxilla, superior nuchal line, occipital protuberance

From Logan-McKinney, *Kinesiology*

Figure 2.8. Selected bones and skeletal landmarks

mechanic analysis. For biomechanic purposes, it is imperative that these bones, skeletal landmarks, and joints be known in order to locate points on levers or within the joints as accurately as possible within the limitations of cinematographic analysis. This is necessary, as examples, to calculate such factors as angular and linear velocities of limbs or body segments, to describe force interactions which occur in sport, and to communicate ideas related to human motion to professional peers and students.

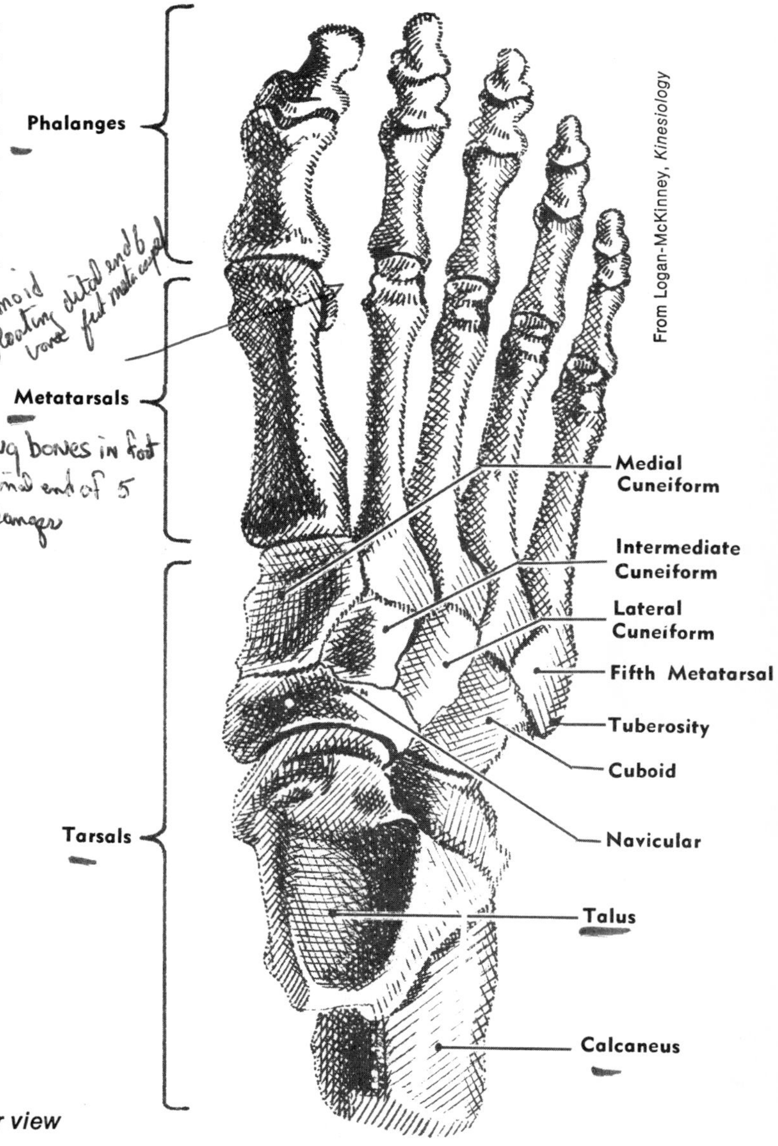

Phalanges

Sesmoid floating bone distal end of vone fut medicap

Metatarsals

Long bones in foot
Proximal end of 5
phalanges

Medial Cuneiform

Intermediate Cuneiform

Lateral Cuneiform

Fifth Metatarsal

Tuberosity

Cuboid

Navicular

Talus

Calcaneus

Tarsals

From Logan-McKinney, *Kinesiology*

Figure 2.9. Right foot—superior view

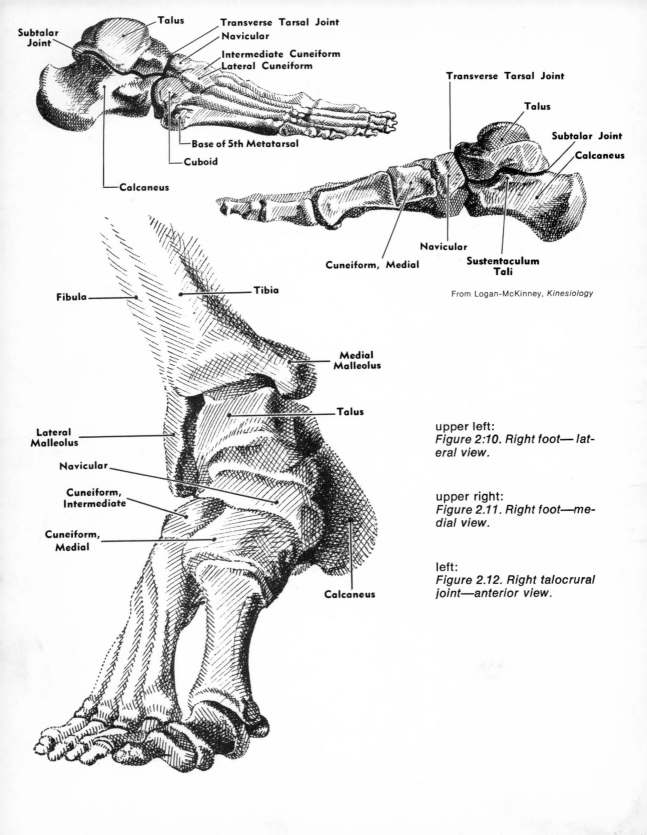

Subtalar Joint

Talus

Transverse Tarsal Joint

Navicular

Intermediate Cuneiform

Lateral Cuneiform

Base of 5th Metatarsal

Cuboid

Calcaneus

Transverse Tarsal Joint

Talus

Subtalar Joint

Calcaneus

Cuneiform, Medial

Navicular

Sustentaculum Tali

From Logan-McKinney, *Kinesiology*

Fibula

Tibia

Medial Malleolus

Talus

Lateral Malleolus

Navicular

Cuneiform, Intermediate

Cuneiform, Medial

Calcaneus

upper left:
Figure 2:10. Right foot— lateral view.

upper right:
Figure 2.11. Right foot—medial view.

left:
Figure 2.12. Right talocrural joint—anterior view.

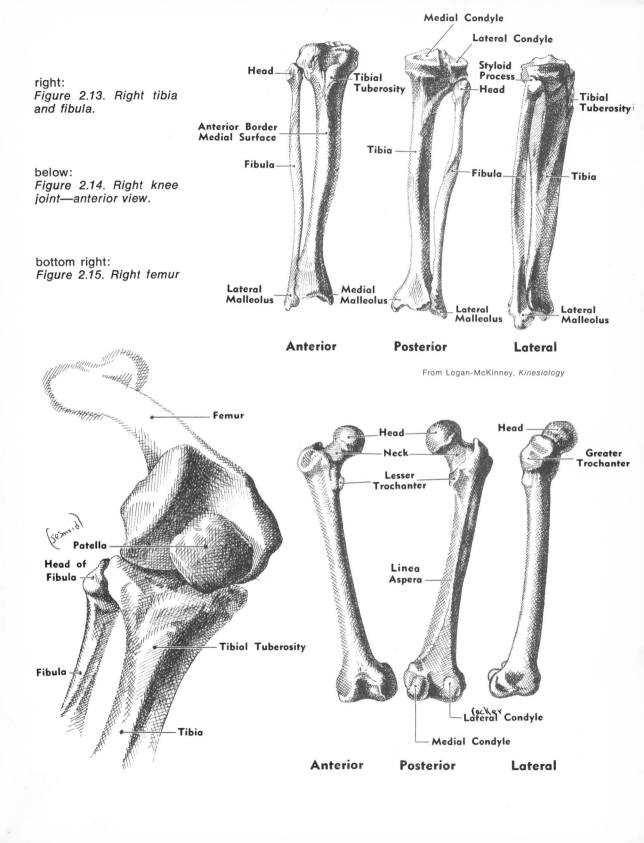

right:
Figure 2.13. Right tibia and fibula.

below:
Figure 2.14. Right knee joint—anterior view.

bottom right:
Figure 2.15. Right femur

Head

Medial Condyle

Lateral Condyle

Tibial Tuberosity

Styloid Process

Head

Anterior Border Medial Surface

Tibia

Tibial Tuberosity

Fibula

Fibula

Tibia

Lateral Malleolus

Medial Malleolus

Lateral Malleolus

Lateral Malleolus

Anterior

Posterior

Lateral

From Logan-McKinney, *Kinesiology*

Femur

Head

Head

Neck

Greater Trochanter

Lesser Trochanter

(sesmoid)

Patella

Head of Fibula

Linea Aspera

Fibula

Tibial Tuberosity

(socket)

Lateral Condyle

Tibia

Medial Condyle

Anterior

Posterior

Lateral

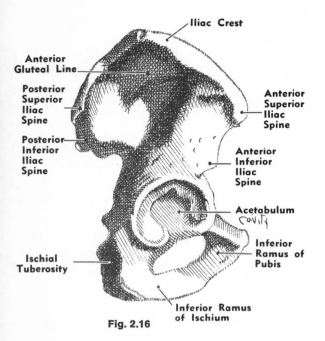

Iliac Crest

Anterior
Gluteal Line

Posterior
Superior
Iliac
Spine

Anterior
Superior
Iliac
Spine

Posterior
Inferior
Iliac
Spine

Anterior
Inferior
Iliac
Spine

Acetabulum
cavity

Ischial
Tuberosity

Inferior
Ramus of
Pubis

Inferior Ramus
of Ischium

Fig. 2.16

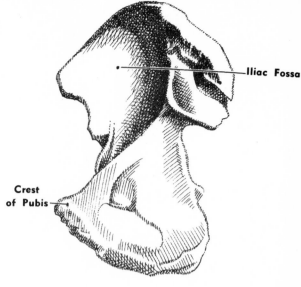

Iliac Fossa

Crest
of Pubis

Fig. 2.17

From Logan-McKinney, *Kinesiology*

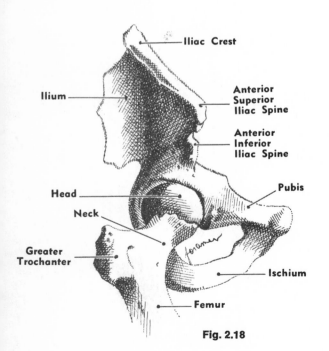

Iliac Crest

Ilium

Anterior
Superior
Iliac Spine

Anterior
Inferior
Iliac Spine

Pubis

Head

Neck

foramen

Greater
Trochanter

Ischium

Femur

Fig. 2.18

Figure 2.16. Right half of pelvic girdle—lateral view.

Figure 2.17. Right half of pelvic girdle—medial view.

Figure 2.18. Right hip joint

Figure 2.19. Spinal column—lateral view

Figure 2.20. Vertebrae—diagonal view

Figure 2.21. Rib cage—anterior view

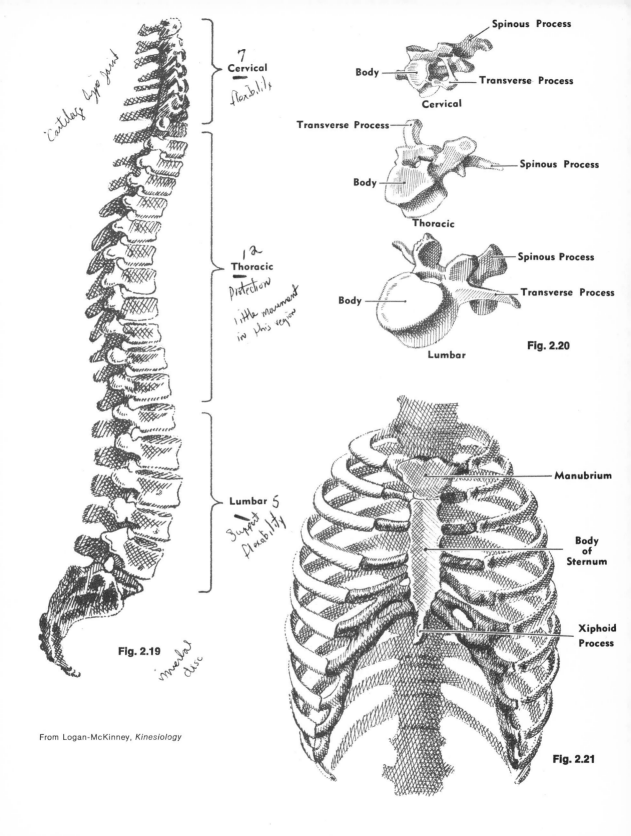

Spinous Process

Body

Transverse Process

Cervical

7
Cervical
flexibility

Transverse Process

Body

Spinous Process

Thoracic

12
Thoracic

Protection

little movement
in this region

Body

Spinous Process

Transverse Process

Lumbar

Fig. 2.20

Lumbar 5
Support
flexibility

cartilage type joint

Manubrium

Body
of
Sternum

Xiphoid
Process

Fig. 2.19

metal
disc

From Logan-McKinney, *Kinesiology*

Fig. 2.21

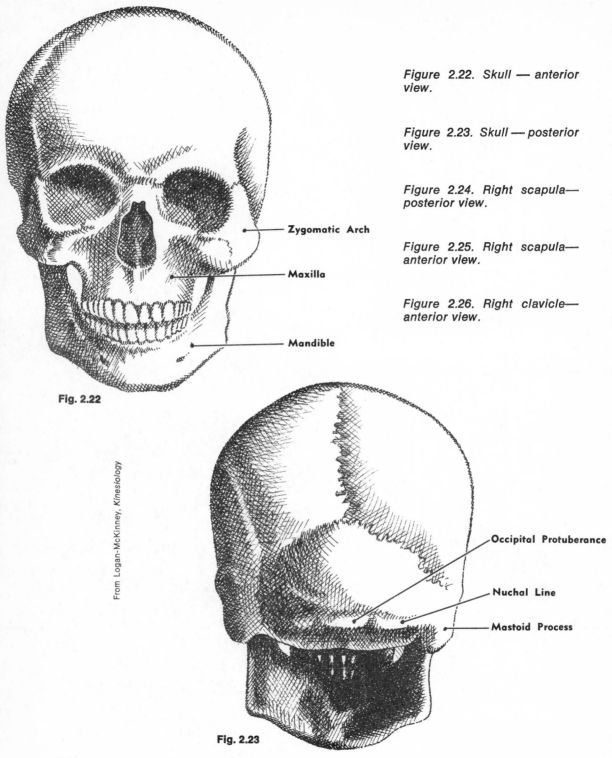

Figure 2.22. Skull — anterior view.

Figure 2.23. Skull — posterior view.

Figure 2.24. Right scapula—posterior view.

Figure 2.25. Right scapula—anterior view.

Figure 2.26. Right clavicle—anterior view.

Zygomatic Arch

Maxilla

Mandible

Fig. 2.22

Occipital Protuberance

Nuchal Line

Mastoid Process

Fig. 2.23

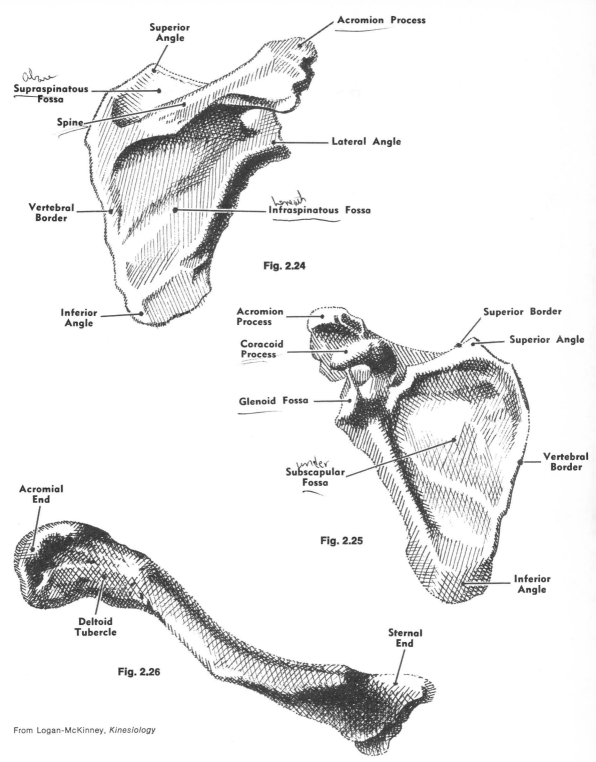

Superior Angle

Acromion Process

above

Supraspinatous Fossa

Spine

Lateral Angle

Vertebral Border

beneath

Infraspinatous Fossa

Fig. 2.24

Inferior Angle

Acromion Process

Coracoid Process

Glenoid Fossa

Superior Border

Superior Angle

Vertebral Border

under

Subscapular Fossa

Fig. 2.25

Inferior Angle

Acromial End

Deltoid Tubercle

Sternal End

Fig. 2.26

From Logan-McKinney, *Kinesiology*

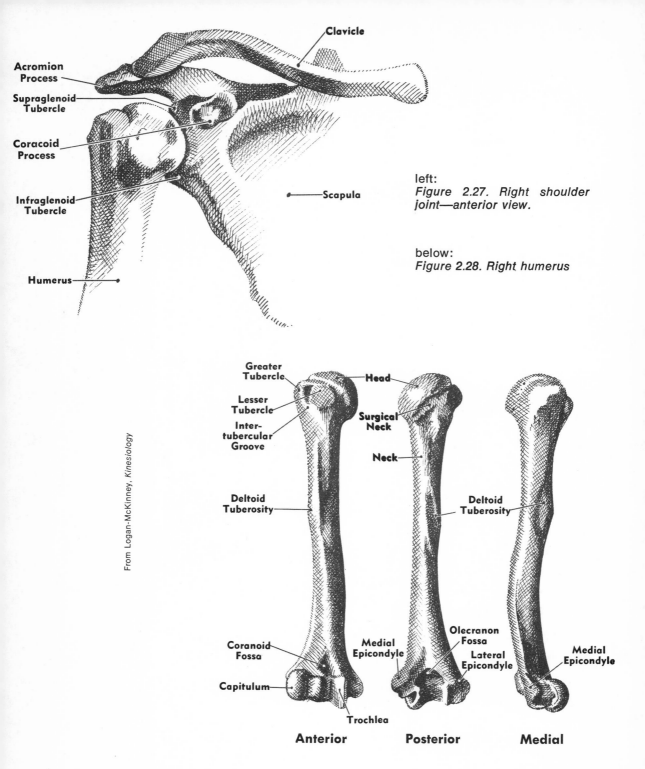

Clavicle

Acromion
Process

Supraglenoid
Tubercle

Coracoid
Process

Infraglenoid
Tubercle

Humerus

Scapula

left:
*Figure 2.27. Right shoulder
joint—anterior view.*

below:
Figure 2.28. Right humerus

From Logan-McKinney, *Kinesiology*

Greater
Tubercle

Head

Lesser
Tubercle

Surgical
Neck

Inter-
tubercular
Groove

Neck

Deltoid
Tuberosity

Deltoid
Tuberosity

Coranoid
Fossa

Olecranon
Fossa

Medial
Epicondyle

Lateral
Epicondyle

Medial
Epicondyle

Capitulum

Trochlea

Anterior

Posterior

Medial

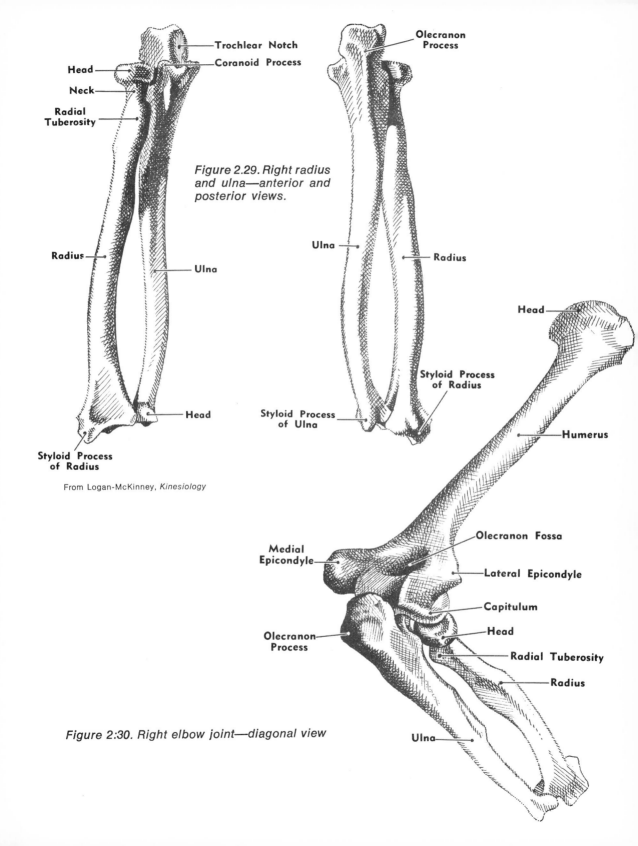

Trochlear Notch

Coranoid Process

Head

Neck

Radial Tuberosity

Figure 2.29. Right radius and ulna—anterior and posterior views.

Radius

Ulna

Head

Styloid Process of Radius

From Logan-McKinney, *Kinesiology*

Olecranon Process

Ulna

Radius

Styloid Process of Radius

Styloid Process of Ulna

Head

Humerus

Medial Epicondyle

Olecranon Fossa

Lateral Epicondyle

Capitulum

Head

Radial Tuberosity

Radius

Olecranon Process

Ulna

Figure 2:30. Right elbow joint—diagonal view

MAJOR JOINT MOTIONS

Motion within the human organism occurs in angular patterns around joints. Although a sprinter is progressing in a linear direction during a 100–yard dash, the critical motions involved are angular in nature at the ankle, knee, hip, and shoulder joints. The individual analyzing motion must be capable of recognizing which joints and motions are actually involved in the action, the planes of motion being traversed, and the extent of joint motion being utilized. In

Joint or Segment	Bones Involved	Motions Possible
Ankle	Tibia, fibula, talus	Dorsiflexion, plantar flexion
Knee	Tibia, femur, patella	Flexion, extension, rotation (when knee is flexed)
Hip	Femur, pelvis	Flexion, extension, adduction, abduction, diagonal adduction, diagonal abduction, medial and lateral rotation, circumduction
Pelvis	Ilium, ischium, pubis (pelvic rotations)	Anterior rotation, posterior rotation, lateral rotation left and right, transverse rotation left and right
Intervertebral (spine)	Vertebrae	Flexion, extension, rotation, lateral flexion, hyperextension, circumduction
Shoulder	Humerus, scapula	Flexion, extension, adduction, abduction, diagonal adduction, diagonal abduction, medial and lateral rotation, circumduction, hyperextension, horizontal adduction, horizontal abduction
Sternoclavicular (shoulder girdle)	Clavicle, sternum, scapula	Elevation, depression, protraction, retraction, rotation, circumduction
Sternoclavicular (scapula)	Scapula (scapular movements)	Elevation, depression, adduction, abduction, upward and downward rotation
Elbow	Humerus, radius, ulna	Flexion, extension
Radio-ulnar	Radius, ulna	Pronation, supination
Wrist	Radius, navicular, lunate, triangular	Flexion, extension, adduction, abduction, circumduction (adduction and abduction also called ulnar and radial flexion, respectively)
First carpometacarpal (thumb)	Multiangular first metacarpal	Flexion, extension, adduction, abduction, rotation, opposition

After Logan, *Adapted Physical Education*

Figure 2.31. Major joints and their motions

order to accomplish this, one must have an elementary understanding of the major joints of the body and the motion capabilities within each of these joints. This is a necessity when analyzing even the simplest types of movements.

The physical educator must be fully aware that internal forces generated by the human organism to move itself against resistances are a result of strong muscle contractions. These internal forces cause motion to occur in a sequential fashion within the joints of the body. In biomechanic analysis, these are the human body forces and motions analyzed during performances. In many sport activities, the summation of these internal or muscular forces is transferred to impart force and motion to sport implements or objects such as rackets and balls. Unless the physical educator has this basic understanding of the anatomic processes involved, it is difficult to comprehend biomechanic analysis techniques and outcomes of performances. These types of professional understandings from anatomic kinesiology with reciprocal relationships to biomechanics are vital aspects of a professional physical educator's knowledge. This knowledge will enable him to improve performances by students and student-athletes.

Figure 2.31 describes all motions possible at selected joints of the body. The anatomic position serves as a reference point for the initiation of all body movements (fig. 2.32).

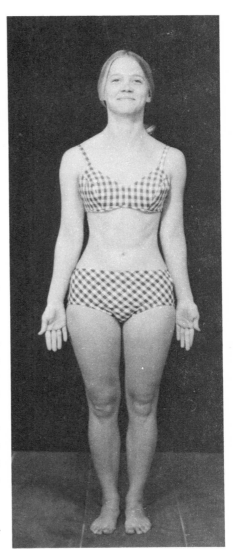

Figure 2.32. Anatomic position—anterior view.

Abduction is movement of a body part or limb away from the midline of the body. An example of abduction is movement of the upper limb away from the side of the body through the lateral plane of motion. Figure 2.33 shows shoulders in the abducted position.

Figure 2.33. Shoulder joint abduction in a stabilized condition by Don Elshire, USC gymnast.

Courtesy USC Athletic News Service

Adduction is movement of a body part toward the midline of the body. Adduction is the return of the abducted limb to the anatomic position through the lateral plane of motion.

Circumduction is movement of a limb or body part in a manner which describes a cone. Circumduction involves a combination of four basic movements: (1) flexion, (2) extension, (3) abduction, and (4) adduction. Also, circumduction is a combination of diagonal adduction and diagonal abduction.

Depression is downward movement of the shoulder girdle. Very little depression within the shoulder girdle can occur from the anatomic position. Depression is the return movement of the shoulder girdle from elevation to the anatomic position. Figure 2.34 illustrates depression of the shoulder girdle.

Figure 2.34. Shoulder girdle depression during a ring maneuver by Gareth Burk, USC gymnast.

Diagonal abduction is movement by a limb through a diagonal plane across and away from the midline of the body. Figure 2.35 illustrates diagonal abduction of the left shoulder joint during the back-crawl stroke in swimming.

Diagonal adduction is movement by a limb through a diagonal plane toward and across the midline of the body. Figure 2.36 shows diagonal adduction of the right shoulder joint at the completion of the follow-through by the baseball pitcher.

Dorsiflexion is movement at the ankle joint of the "top" of the foot toward the lower limb, i.e., flexion of the ankle or talocrural joint. The dancer's right ankle in figure 2.37 is in a dorsiflexed position.

Figure 2.35. Diagonal abduction of the left shoulder joint by Steve Cameron, USC swimmer, during the back crawl.

Courtesy USC Athletic News Service

right:
Figure 2.36. Diagonal adduction of the right shoulder joint by Randy Scarbery, USC pitcher.

pectoralis
major

below:
Figure 2.37. Dorsiflexion of the right ankle adds to the aesthetic quality of this modern dancer's position.

Courtesy USC Athletic News Servic

Scapula

Elevation is upward movement of the shoulder girdle. Elevation occurs within the shoulder girdle during the execution of the "fly" swimming stroke as shown in figure 2.38.

Eversion is movement of the sole of the foot outward. This movement takes place within the subtalar and transverse tarsal joints. It is not an ankle-joint movement.   *Soccer type kick*   *Lateral plane - satyall*

Extension is any movement resulting in an increase of a joint angle. Most major joints are in extension while the individual is in the anatomic position. Complete extension of a body part approximates 180 degrees of motion. Figure 2.39 shows extensions in the defensive basketball player's elbow, hip, and knee joints.

Flexion is any movement resulting in a decrease of a joint angle. For example, when the elbow is being flexed from the 180–degree extended position, the number of degrees within the joint angle is decreased as the hand moves toward the shoulder. The cyclist in figure 2.40 is flexing the right knee and moving the left knee from a position of flexion to extension.

Figure 2.38. Elevation of the shoulder girdle occurs during the "fly stroke" as executed by Jim McConica, USC swimmer.

Courtesy USC Athletic News Service

Figure 2.39. Extension of elbow, hip, and knee joints during a defensive move by Mike Westra, USC center.

Figure 2.40. Knee flexion-extension is a vital aspect of cycling, as shown by Jeff Spencer, member of the U.S.A. Olympic cycling team.

Courtesy USC Athletic News Servic

Horizontal abduction is movement of an upper limb through the transverse plane at shoulder level away from the midline of the body.

Horizontal adduction is movement of an upper limb through the transverse plane at shoulder level toward the midline of the body. Figure 2.41 illustrates horizontal adduction of both shoulder joints by the performer working against resistance provided by an ExerGenie Exerciser.

Hyperextension is movement of any joint beyond the joint's normal position of extension. The gymnast in figure 2.42 is hyperextending at both shoulder joints.

Inversion is movement of the sole of the foot medially. If both feet are *inward* inverted, the soles of the feet will be toward each other. Inversion occurs at the subtalar and transverse tarsal joints. Inversion and eversion are both inefficient movements for many performers during the process of running.

Lateral flexion is movement of the head and/or trunk laterally away from the midline of the body. Figure 2.43 shows lateral flexion of the cervical spine of the pole-vaulter, and figure 2.39 shows lateral flexion of the lumbar-thoracic spine of the defensive basketball player.

From Logan-McKinney, *Kinesiology*

Figure 2.41. Horizontal adduction of both shoulder joints by Mike McKinney, SMS wrestler, working against resistance of an ExerGenie Exerciser.

above:
Figure 2.42. Hyperextension of both shoulder joints by Don Elshire, USC gymnast, during a ring maneuver.

right:
Figure 2.43. Lateral flexion of the cervical spine during a vault by Robert Pullard, USC pole-vaulter.

Opposition of the thumb is a diagonal movement of the thumb across the palmar surface of the hand. This is commonly observed in the grips utilized to handle sport implements or objects. Figure 2.44 shows a catcher's grip on a baseball; opposition of the thumb is utilized.

Pelvic anteroposterior rotation is movement of the pelvic girdle through the anteroposterior plane of motion. In *anterior pelvic rotation* the iliac crests move forward. Conversely, *posterior pelvic rotation* results in the iliac crests being moved posteriorward. Figure 2.45 shows posterior rotation of the pelvic girdle.

Pelvic lateral rotation is movement of the pelvic girdle through the lateral plane of motion. Lateral pelvic rotation takes place either right or left through the lateral plane, and the axis is anteroposterior. Lateral rotation occurs unilaterally when the weight is borne either by the hands or one leg. This is a common pelvic girdle motion during the pivoting actions observed in sport. Figure 2.46 shows left lateral pelvic rotation.

Figure 2.44. Opposition of the right thumb by Sam Ceci, USC catcher, while gripping the baseball.

Courtesy USC Athletic News Service

Pelvic transverse rotation is movement of the pelvic girdle through the transverse plane of motion. Transverse pelvic rotation can occur either right or left through the transverse plane around the longitudinal axis of the body. Transverse rotation of the pelvic girdle is an absolute necessity for high ballistic performances such as javelin throwing and baseball pitching. For the right-handed athlete throwing the javelin, for example, left transverse pelvic rotation must be an integral aspect of the sequential body motions for optimum results. Figure 2.47 below and figure 3.2, frame 21, on page 56 show left pelvic transverse rotation.

Figure 2.45. Posterior pelvic girdle rotation.

Figure 2.46. Left lateral pelvic girdle rotation.

Figure 2.47. Left transverse pelvic girdle rotation.

pointing toe

Plantar flexion is movement at the ankle joint of the sole of the foot downward. The term *plantar flexion* is an exception to the previous definition of flexion. In reality, plantar flexion is extension of the ankle. Most body movements from the vertical or erect body position begin with plantar flexion. The sprinter crossing the finish line in figure 2.48 has plantar-flexed both ankle joints.

Pronation is movement of the "back of the hand" forward. Pronation takes place at the radio-ulnar joint. The swimmer in figure 2.49 has pronated both radio-ulnar joints.

Courtesy USC Athletic News Service

Figure 2.48. Plantar flexion of both ankle joints by Willie Deckard, USC sprinter.

Prone position is the face-downward position by the entire body. The body does not have to be lying face downward on the ground or on some other supportive surface to be in a prone position. The prone position can be assumed, for example, in midair while rebound tumbling or diving.

media flexion

Radial flexion is movement at the wrist on the thumb side of the hand toward the forearm. Figure 2.49 also illustrates radial flexion of both wrist joints. *radial line*

Figure 2.49. Pronation of both radio-ulnar joints by Jim McConica, USC swimmer, prior to the racing start.

Courtesy USC Athletic News Service

to midline of body

Rotation downward is rotary movement of the *scapula,* with the inferior angle of the scapula moving medially and downward. The glenoid fossa is moved downward to accommodate the head of the humerus. Downward rotation of the scapula always accompanies any downward movement of the upper limb. Figure 2.50 shows downward rotation of both scapulae during the downward pull on the latissimus bar.

Rotation laterally is movement around the longitudinal *vertical* axis of a bone away from the midline of the body. Lateral rotation of the humerus, for example,

Figure 2.50. Downward rotation of both scapulae occurs concurrent with shoulder joint adduction during a latissimus pull.

must occur prior to executing the overhead serve in volleyball, serving a tennis ball, or throwing a baseball. This action helps place muscles on stretch and increases the range of motion. In arm wrestling, figure 2.51, lateral and medial rotations of the shoulder are very important.

Rotation medially is movement around a longitudinal axis of the bone toward the midline of the body. As an example, a well-timed throw through the high diagonal plane of motion usually involves medial rotation of the humerus immediately prior to the release of the thrown object. Medial rotation of the humerus is the most critical movement in the sport of arm wrestling as seen in figure 2.51.

Figure 2.51. Lateral and medial rotations of the humerus at the shoulder joint are critical in arm wrestling.

Rotation upward is rotary movement of the scapula, with the inferior angle moving laterally and upward. The glenoid fossa is being moved upward to accommodate the head of the humerus. Upward rotation of the scapula always accompanies any upward movement of the upper limb.

Supination is the "palms forward" position of the hands in the anatomic position (fig. 2.32). Supination is the return movement from pronation, and it occurs at the radio-ulnar joint. A flat handball serve involves a supinated hand.

Supine position is lying with the body in a face-up position. The body does not have to be lying face upward on a supportive surface. It may be suspended in air in a supine position. This is observed in diving and rebound tumbling.

Ulnar flexion is movement of the little finger side of the hand toward the forearm. Ulnar flexion of the wrist is a vital movement for the baseball pitcher throwing a curve ball. The left wrist of the pole-vaulter in figure 2.43 is ulnar-flexed through its complete range of motion.

Part Two of the book in hand is designed primarily to assist the reader in gaining an understanding of biomechanic analyses through the intermediate cinematographic level. Three procedures are used to convey biomechanic principles to the readers: (1) Principles are explained in a fundamental manner to facilitate comprehension; (2) To reinforce the word description of principles, graphic illustrations are included where applicable; and (3) Where deemed necessary to facilitate comprehension and add precision, mathematical formulae and examples are included to further reinforce the ideas conveyed. Numerals as symbols do have a distinct advantage over words as symbols. Words, especially in the English language, do have some degree of ambiguity; whereas mathematical symbols are more precise ways of expressing ideas. Some people tend to succumb to a syndrome known as "symbol shock" if they are asked to work extensively in the field of mathematics. As a consequence, it is believed the best way to convey ideas regarding biomechanics to the majority of potential users of subject matter from biomechanics on a regular basis in teaching-coaching is to delimit the mathematics to the very essential equations necessary to describe motion adequately through the intermediate cinematographic analysis level. This procedure is followed in Part Two.

part two

physics
of sport

Chapter 3

Understanding Basic Physics

Confusion sometimes arises regarding the use of four major terms in biomechanics and physics literature which categorize the study of motion. The student should be aware of an author's basic definitions of these terms, and others, in order to compare statements which appear in the literature in textbooks as well as professional journals. As indicated in chapter one, *mechanics* is the most general term used to describe the study of the behavior of objects or fluids under gravitational and contact forces. *Kinematics* technically refers to the study of motion without reference to the forces causing motion. *Dynamics* is the term used for the study of relationships which exist between forces and motion. *Kinetics* refers to the description of a system in terms of the motions of its component parts. With the exception of "kinematics," these terms are used as defined in this text.

In the same sense that each sport within physical education has a specialized vocabulary to describe motions and techniques, the field of biomechanics also utilizes a unique vocabulary in describing various aspects of the relationship between forces and motion. This scientific vocabulary gives students problems at times because they may be unfamiliar either with the terms or with the precise meaning scientists give to these terms. In science, every effort is made to keep terms unambiguous so a given statement can have only one possible interpretation. In order to do this, terms are used in a much more restricted sense than they are in everyday life. In a few cases, scientific terms can be used in a much more general sense. An example of the more restricted usage is the scientific definition of the word *power*. In everyday usage this term connotes everything from muscular strength to social authority. *To the scientist utilizing biomechanics, however, the term "power" means precisely the total amount of work accomplished in one unit of time.* For example, a 220-pound man running up a ten-foot flight of stairs in four seconds would be exerting one horsepower. In order to exert two horsepower, he would have to run up the same flight of stairs, accomplishing the same amount of work, in two seconds.

On the other hand, it is found that the term *acceleration* is used in a much more generalized sense in scientific description of motion than during everyday usage of the word. Most people who use the term *acceleration* imply that an increase in velocity of a moving object is occurring. In a biomechanic description of motion, however, *acceleration* refers to any change of motion whether it represents a speeding up, a slowing down, or simply a change in direction of a moving body. For example, a football back in broken field running may give himself a positive acceleration at times to escape a pursuing player. He may next provide a negative acceleration (change of pace), more commonly called deceleration, to allow blocking to occur in front of him. Following this, he may provide an acceleration, changing the direction of motion in order to follow his blocking.

It is the purpose of this chapter to define many of the important terms of biomechanics as they are used in the scientific sense. Examples will be given of the use of these concepts, and in some cases numerical calculations will indicate the relation between mechanical quantities.

DESCRIPTION OF LINEAR MOTION

In order to describe the effect of forces upon motion of bodies, a precise set of terms and relationships to describe motion itself is needed. Motion is generally described in terms of velocities and accelerations.

Velocity

Velocity is defined as the change of position of a body per unit of time. When an object is moving, it is constantly changing position. Its velocity is defined by determining how much this position changes within a certain time span.

Experimentally, velocities are measured as follows: A certain amount of time is taken, and a measure of the change of position in that time is calculated. Or, a certain amount of change of position is taken, and a measure of the amount of time necessary to effect this change is performed. Mathematically, this relationship is simply stated: Velocity equals the distance traversed divided by the elapsed time:

$$\text{Velocity} = \frac{\text{Distance}}{\text{Time}} = \frac{d}{t}$$

When stating scientific quantities, it is always necessary to have a universally accepted set of units. In the case of distances, the English system expresses these units either in feet or miles. The Metric system states distance units either in meters or kilometers. The commonly accepted unit of time is the *second* in both systems. Thus, the quantities of velocity would normally be expressed in such units as feet per second (ft/sec), meters per second (m/sec), or miles per hour (mi/hr). These units may be converted from one to the other by the use of multiplying factors (see Appendix for a more extensive conversion table):

$$1 \text{ ft/sec} = .305 \text{ m/sec} = .682 \text{ mi/hr}$$

$$1 \text{ m/sec} = 3.28 \text{ ft/sec} = 2.24 \text{ mi/hr}$$

As an example, the highest average velocity achieved by a runner in N.C.A.A. championship track-and-field competition occurs in the 220-yard dash. A performer who can run this distance in 20 seconds flat would be considered a potential champion in most college or university meets. In terms of velocity, this represents a distance covered of 660 feet in 20 seconds:

$$V = \frac{660 \text{ ft}}{20 \text{ sec}} = 33 \text{ ft/sec}$$

$$33 \text{ ft/sec} = 22.5 \text{ mi/hr}$$

It should be noted that this 33 ft/sec is an *average velocity* over the distance and not maximum or minimal velocities achieved by the performer at various points during the race. This type of velocity calculation does not take into account the fact that the performer is actually starting from a velocity of zero. This, of course, decreases the sprinter's total average velocity. Theoretically, a maximum velocity for the human body during a running event would seem to be about 40 ft/sec or approximately 27 mi/hr.

As another example, the present listed world record for running 30,000 meters is 1 hr. 31 min. 30.4 sec. The average velocity for this feat would be:

$$V = \frac{30,000 \text{ meters}}{(1 \times 3600) + (31 \times 60) + 30.4 \text{ sec}} = \frac{30,000}{5490.4} = 5.46 \text{ m/sec}$$

When converted into familiar units, this means the performer ran nearly 18⅔ miles at an average speed of 12.24 mi/hr.

Velocities encountered in sport motions vary from a few feet per second in slow precision movements to nearly 150 ft/sec in ballistic **movements** of body parts. The head of a golf club may reach a speed over 200 ft/sec at the point of impact.

It should be emphasized that within the area of biomechanics there is a slight scientific distinction between the terms *velocity* and *speed*. Velocity is known as a vector quantity. *A vector quantity has both magnitude and direction associated with it.* The units expressed above actually represent the magnitude of the velocity. This is referred to as *speed*. In order to completely define a velocity, speed must be indicated along the direction in which the motion is taking place. Examples of describing vector quantities are (1) a baseball moving at 100 ft/sec into a head wind and (2) a motion in which a performer moves his hand upward at 50 ft/sec as a result of shoulder flexion. In these simple examples, both the amount of motion and a direction in which motion occurs have been specified. Both are necessary for velocity calculations.

There are times when the direction of motion is not exceptionally important. For example, in the previous question regarding average velocity for a man performing a 220-yard dash, the reference was actually to speed and not to the total components of velocity. The direction of motion in this case is clearly defined in terms of such things as rules governing the race and the way running lanes are marked on the track. In the case of distance races performed on a 440-yard track, the path (direction) is a closed loop. In fact, from the previous definition of velocity, the average velocity over a closed loop must add up to zero because the performer ends at the same point he started. In this case, it is actually the speed, i.e., the total linear distance covered divided by the time, which is important.

Since velocity is a vector quantity, there are certain properties of vectors considered important in analyzing velocities. The fact that a vector has direction as well as magnitude means that it can be calculated geometrically. For example, a vector quantity in a certain direction also has components in other directions. As an example, a ball thrown or batted into the air has a certain component of its velocity in a linear or horizontal direction. There is also a certain component of velocity in a vertical direction both up and down. These would be referred to as the horizontal and vertical components, respectively, of the velocity (fig. 3.1).

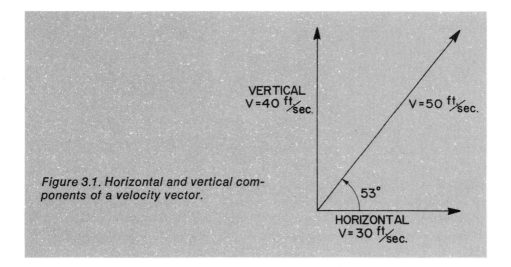

VERTICAL
V = 40 ft/sec.

V = 50 ft/sec.

53°

HORIZONTAL
V = 30 ft/sec.

Figure 3.1. Horizontal and vertical components of a velocity vector.

This concept of the relationship between direction of the velocity vector and other components involved will be discussed in greater detail in chapter four when important trajectories which occur during sport events are presented.

The directional nature of velocity enables calculations of what is known as *vector addition,* i.e., a series of motions all generally in the same direction will sum together to give a greater total velocity vector. For example, a javelin thrower in his run to the "scratch line" gives his body a velocity in the direction of the intended throw. Prior to the act of throwing, the shoulder joint is moved with respect to this body motion. This causes the total arm to move through a high diagonal plane at the shoulder. With the final flexion motion of the wrist, the javelin is propelled forward away from the arm and torso. The final velocity vector of the javelin is the sum of these and other critical joint and body-segment motions during the performance (fig. 3.2).

Figure 3.2. Development of the final velocity vector for the javelin by Janis Lusis of the USSR

It is seen that the final velocity of most sport objects is actually the result of a summation of several previous velocities developed sequentially in moving joints. The concept that there is a stereotype of perfect form for any sport skill, adjusted to allow for individual differences, is that procedure which will allow these individual velocities to sum together most effectively to provide an optimum result. For example, a deviation from perfect form for a javelin throw results in some motions which would cancel a part of the optimum summation of velocities. Therefore, a lower final velocity would be transferred to the javelin itself. This would result in a decrease in total distance which the javelin travels through the air. This same principle applies in the case of a pitched base-ball, tennis serve, shot put, long jump, and many other skills of a ballistic nature.

Acceleration

As mentioned previously, the term *acceleration* is used to connote any change of velocity occurring during motion. *Acceleration is defined as the change of velocity occurring per unit time.*

$$\text{Acceleration} = \frac{\text{Change of velocity}}{\text{Time}} = \frac{V_{(final)} - V_{(initial)}}{\text{Time}} = \frac{V_f - V_i}{t}$$

These changes of velocity may result in an increase in speed or magnitude of the velocity; they may result in a decrease in speed or magnitude of the velocity; or, they may simply result in a change of direction. Acceleration is also expressed in terms of precise scientific units. These will be the units of velocity divided again by units of time normally expressed in seconds. Quantities of acceleration are usually expressed in terms of feet per second per second (ft/sec²) or meters per second per second (m/sec²).

Acceleration may be either positive or negative. As an example of positive acceleration, a shot-put performer in his move across the ring may change the motion of the shot from near rest to a final velocity of 40 ft/sec. If he performs this motion in one second, the acceleration is:

$$a = \frac{40 - 0}{1} = 40 \, \text{ft/sec}^2$$

Again, this represents an *average acceleration* for the motion of the shot across the circle, and not necessarily the acceleration occurring at any specific point in the maneuver.

An example of negative acceleration is given by a trampoline performer stopping motion at the end of a rebound by flexion of knee and hip joints. As the performer falls to the trampoline from a height of about six feet above the bed, a velocity of 20 ft/sec is acquired. If the motion is stopped within one-third of a second of contact with the trampoline bed, the acceleration is:

$$a = \frac{0 - 20}{1/3} = -60 \, \text{ft/sec}^2$$

The negative sign in this case simply indicates that the direction of acceleration was such as to oppose the initial velocity; consequently, it is decreased to zero. In a motion such as this, the magnitude of the acceleration depends strongly on the time used in stopping the motion. Motions stopped in very short times lead to very high negative accelerations.

Still a third example of acceleration is the case of a baseball runner taking a wide turn at second base at a constant speed (figs. 3.3 and 3.4). Actually calculating the acceleration in this case is more complex, since geometrical relations must be used to determine the magnitude of change of velocity and time. If speed is 20 ft/sec, for instance, normal relations of a triangle reveal that the change of velocity in this example is slightly over 28 ft/sec. Actually, it can be shown that for a circular path traversed at constant speed, this acceleration can

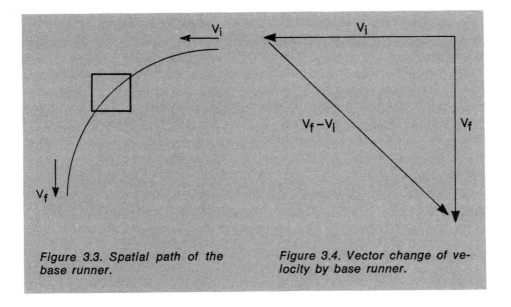

Figure 3.3. Spatial path of the base runner.

Figure 3.4. Vector change of velocity by base runner.

be calculated by the equation $a = v^2/r$ where r is the radius of the circle of curvature. If a radius of 16 feet is used in the foregoing example of a runner rounding second base at 20 ft/sec, the acceleration is:

$$a = \frac{V^2}{r} = \frac{20 \times 20}{16} = 25 \text{ ft/sec}^2$$

In this special case of a change of direction at constant speed, the term *radial acceleration* is used. It can be seen that either an increase in speed or a decrease in radius leads to a larger acceleration. Large radial accelerations are often observed in athletic skills requiring sharp turns at high speed.

   It will be noted from these examples that acceleration, like velocity, is a vector quantity, i.e., both the direction of the acceleration and its magnitude are important. There is no special term for the magnitude of acceleration analogous to the term *speed* used to describe the magnitude of velocity. The direction of acceleration is of utmost importance. This is especially true as it relates to the direction of velocity. An acceleration in the same direction as the velocity produces an increase in speed; an acceleration in the opposite direction produces a decrease in speed; and an acceleration perpendicular to the velocity produces a change of direction. For these reasons, consideration is given to the components of the acceleration vector parallel and perpendicular to those of the velocity vector. The component of acceleration parallel to the velocity is normally called the *tangential acceleration*. The component perpendicular to the velocity is called the *radial acceleration* (fig. 3.5).

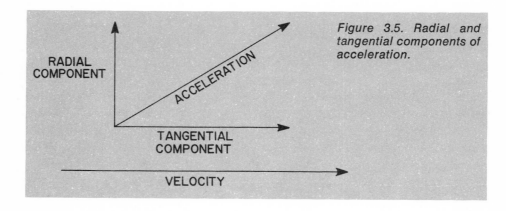

Figure 3.5. Radial and tangential components of acceleration.

RADIAL COMPONENT

ACCELERATION

TANGENTIAL COMPONENT

VELOCITY

In the example of the shot put, acceleration was in the same direction as movement of the shot. Therefore, the shot was increasing in speed. In the example of the trampoline performer, acceleration was opposite to the direction the performer was moving through a series of flexions at the major joints. Consequently, he slowed to a stop. In the example of the baseball runner, acceleration was perpendicular to the direction of movement. This was the causative factor for the change in direction with no change of speed.

One very important acceleration commonly observed in sport events is acceleration due to gravity. Neglecting the effects of air resistance, all falling bodies will accelerate toward the center of the earth with an acceleration of 32 ft/sec² or 9.8 m/sec². Because of the importance of this acceleration, other accelerations are often expressed in comparison with *gravitational acceleration. An acceleration of 32 ft/sec² is sometimes called one g.* If, for example, during the start of a 50-yard dash, a performer were to experience an acceleration of 64 ft/sec², it could be stated that this acceleration was equal to two *g*'s. It should be noted that the term *g* as used here refers to an acceleration and not to a force. Gravitational force will be discussed more fully in the next section of this chapter.

Concepts of Force and Mass

The concept of force is one with which everyone is familiar. Force is usually thought of in terms of "pushes and pulls." From the viewpoint of biomechanic analysis, the concept of force is extremely important because it represents the way in which various bodies or parts of bodies interact with each other.

There are two effects produced by forces acting on bodies. First, the action of force may distort the shape of the body being acted upon. This phenomenon will be discussed when the concept of energy is presented. The second effect—the one which is most important—is that application of an unbalanced force to a body or body part results in an acceleration of the body or body segment. The term *unbalanced* is used in this context to represent those forces not being counteracted by any other opposing force on the body. Many times a performer has forces acting on him which seem to produce no effect simply because there is some counteracting force. For example, when a person is standing virtually motionless, there is a force from air tending to push him backward, but there is no acceleration backward of the body because there is an equal and opposite counteracting force from air pushing against his back.

This relationship between force and acceleration is one of the two most important relationships to be found in biomechanics. Not only are forces always associated with changes of motion of bodies, but the amount of acceleration is always directly proportional to the force. If there is a force twice as great, it will produce an acceleration of the same degree. If there is a force only one-half as great, it will produce only one-half as much change of motion per unit time. Also, the acceleration is always in the same direction as the force with which it is associated. It is this basic relationship which allows detection and measurement of effects of forces by observing changes in motion of bodies or body parts.

This proportional relationship between force and acceleration introduces another very important concept in biomechanics. *The ratio between force and the acceleration which it causes is called the mass of the body. Mass is equal to force divided by acceleration. Or, force is equal to mass times acceleration:*

$$\text{Mass} = \frac{\text{Force}}{\text{Acceleration}} = \frac{F}{a} \text{ or } F = ma$$

A body having a large mass will require a large force to produce a given acceleration. For a body with a small mass, only a small force is required to produce the same acceleration.

There is a difference between the use of the terms *mass* and *weight*. Oftentimes these two terms are used synonymously and incorrectly. In the scientific sense, each has a specialized meaning. As indicated, mass is the ratio of the force acting on a body to the acceleration which it produces. *Weight is the force with which the earth attracts a body gravitationally.* Thus, weight is a force dependent not only on the mass of the body but on gravitational attraction. For example, if a body were taken to the moon where gravitational force is six times less than earth's, its mass would remain the same. Its weight would decrease by a factor of six, since the force of gravity is associated with this unique gravitational acceleration known as g. "The force equals mass times acceleration" relationship can be written as "Weight is equal to mass times g ($w = mg$)," or inversely, "Mass is equal to weight divided by g ($m = \frac{w}{g}$)." In making calculations involving forces, masses, and accelerations, the mass of a body is replaced by its weight divided by g (32 ft/sec² in English units). For example, the mass of a 16-pound shot is given by:

$$\text{Mass} = \frac{\text{Weight}}{g} = \frac{16}{32} = \frac{1}{2} \text{ mass unit}$$

A second major characteristic regarding forces in biomechanics is called the *Law of Action and Reaction.* This law states simply that when an object exerts a force on a second object, the second object exerts an equal and opposite force on the first. Forces never occur singly or in isolation, but always in a force-counterforce situation. One object cannot affect the motion or condition of a second without itself also being affected. In the context of applying biomechanics to human motion, it should be noted that an object may be the whole human body or may represent only certain individual body parts. Also affected would be sport implements and sport objects. *A sport implement is anything utilized to increase force application to a sport object.* Examples are bats, rackets, and hockey sticks. *A sport object is anything propelled into motion by a performer using a sport implement or body part at the point of impact or time of release.* Balls, pucks, and the human body, at times, are examples of sport objects.

The Law of Action and Reaction is of great importance in the study of human motions because of the forces and counterforces various body parts exert on one another. For example, this force interaction is noticed during a runner's arm motion. As the left shoulder joint is being flexed, the right shoulder joint is being extended or hyperextended. This force-counterforce relationship of the arms helps maintain the body in an equilibrium position from which the legs can function most effectively to accelerate the runner.

Force, like velocity and acceleration, is a vector quantity. Force has both magnitude and direction. As stated above, the direction of a single operating force is usually the same as the direction of acceleration which it produces. As in all other vector quantities, components of a force can be identified. At times, a single diagonal force vector will be replaced by a horizontal force vector plus a vertical force component. Also, force vectors may be additive at a given point to produce a resultant force which has magnitude and a direction given by summing the individual force vectors. The proper sequential production of these individualized forces at joints to produce an optimum resultant is what the physical educator sometimes refers to as *timing* in a wide variety of sport and dance skills.

In anatomic kinesiology the term *summation of internal forces* is sometimes used to denote sequential motion within joints of a performer. From the viewpoint of biomechanics, this is termed a *summation of motions,* since an optimum motion either of the sport implement, such as a golf club or tennis racket, or at the body part responsible for the final motion of the skill, such as the hand in handball, is actually produced. The difference in this terminology occurs because the internal forces produced by the muscle contractions of the performer result in an optimum series of motions whose forces are additive. In a kinesthetic sense, what the performer experiences is actually a summation of internal forces. To the observing physical educator doing a biomechanic analysis, this is seen as a sequential set of additive motions executed by the performer to produce a given skill. From the standpoint of biomechanics, objectivity and precision of motion description are attained by mathematical calculations of summing motion as viewed cinematographically.

Pressure and Frictional Forces

Within the area of biomechanics, *the term "pressure" refers to the force applied per unit area across a surface.* A moderate force applied over a large area may produce a very low pressure. On the other hand, this same moderate force on a very small area of a body or implement may result in pressures high enough to cause tissue damage or great pressure on body parts. Boxing gloves are designed to spread the force of a blow over a large area. This avoids large pressures. Without the gloves, the smaller area of the hand or knuckles striking in regions such as the orbital ring of the eye may apply the force of the blow to an extremely small area. Such a blow would produce extensive pressures resulting in traumatic laceration and contusions of the skin and underlying tissue.

Another type of force extremely important in biomechanic analysis is the force of *friction*. This force always occurs between two surfaces in contact. When these surfaces attempt to move in a sliding condition across one another, the amount of frictional force gained between the two surfaces depends on the amount of force pressing them together. This is sometimes called *normal force*. Frictional force is also dependent on the condition of the surfaces, generally expressed in terms of a *coefficient of friction:*

$$\text{Coefficient of friction} = \frac{\text{Frictional force}}{\text{Normal force}}$$

Coefficient of friction depends on such things as smoothness of surface areas, dryness of contacting surfaces, characteristics of the composition of which the surfaces are constructed, and, to a small extent, the total surface area of the contacting surface.

Friction is often thought of as something leading to loss of motion or to other problems in athletic events. To the contrary, friction is a very necessary force for skilled performance. Without it, athletic events as we know them would not be possible. Friction is needed in order to hold onto something. Performers need friction in order to exert forces against the ground, floor, or other performers. In some instances, the problem is to get more frictional force, not less. The latter is particularly true during periods of high acceleration as seen in athletic and dance skills. As examples, very fast starts, quick stops, or rapid changes of direction of motion—all require considerable frictional force.

Many times performers will use materials such as rosin or pine tar in order to increase the coefficient of friction while handling sport implements. This is a common practice in baseball. The hitter uses pine tar on his hands or hitting gloves to increase the coefficient of friction between the hands and bat during the very high, positive acceleration of the bat at the time of the swing. Without friction between hands and bat at this point, bat control would be extremely difficult. Without bat control, hitting averages tend to be low. Therefore, friction is a very vital factor in this particular skill.

As a numerical example of frictional calculations, consider the following situation. A performer is attempting to move laterally from rest on a floor with a coefficient of friction of 0.5. What is the maximum acceleration which he can obtain if body weight is 160 pounds?

If it is assumed that weight provides the entire normal force, then,

$$\text{Frictional force} = \text{Coefficient of friction} \times \text{Normal force}$$
$$= \quad 0.5 \quad \times \quad 160$$
$$= 80 \text{ pounds lateral force}$$

Using the relation between force and acceleration:

$$\text{Force} = \frac{\text{Weight}}{g} \times \text{Acceleration}$$

$$80 = \frac{160}{32} \times a$$

$$\text{Acceleration} = \frac{80}{5} = 16 \text{ ft/sec}^2$$

An increase in the coefficient of friction to 0.8 through the use of rosin or pine tar would allow an increase in acceleration as follows:

$$\text{Frictional force} = 0.8 \times 160 = 128 \text{ pounds}$$

$$= 5 \text{ mass units} \times \text{Acceleration}$$

$$\text{Acceleration} = \frac{128}{5} = 25.6 \text{ ft/sec}^2$$

In actual performance, it is possible for a short period of time to push off against the floor and exert a normal component of force greater than the weight of the body. This allows frictional forces and accelerations even greater than those calculated above. This, however, also lifts the body. The leg will eventually reach full extension at the hip and knee, resulting in lifting the foot from the floor, and no lateral forces are possible.

Energy and Momentum

There are certain quantities important in biomechanics because they can be conserved. The two most important conserved quantities in biomechanics are *energy* and *momentum*. Within an isolated system, a constant amount of these quantities will be present throughout a performance or interaction. Because of this, they can be used for accounting purposes. If the change of a conserved quantity within one part of the system is known, it will also be known that this must be offset by an opposite change of this quantity in some other part of the system.

Work and Energy

Energy is another term which has multifaceted connotations when found in common usage. For the scientist, however, the term *energy* has a specific meaning, and this is directly related to a specific definition of the term *work*. In biomechanics, *work is accomplished by the operation of a force through a distance in the direction of the force.* For example, the amount of work can be defined during weight training. During a bench-press workout, the average college football lineman should be able to press 240 pounds through a distance of approximately three feet. Since the direction of motion is exactly the same as the direction of force, the total amount of work performed is 240 pounds times three feet, or

720 foot-pounds of work during each repetition. Work = force × distance = 240 × 3 = 720 foot-pounds. Since this weight load would be handled for ten repetitions, 7,200 foot-pounds of work would be performed at the bench-press station. If three sets were performed, this would amount to a total of 21,600 foot-pounds.

Another unit of work often used in biomechanics is the Calorie. Although originally defined as a unit of heat, the importance of this unit in food conversion within the human body has caused its wide acceptance in many areas of physical education. *The Calorie is equal to 3087.4 foot-pounds.* In the preceding example, the 21,600 foot-pounds of work done is equivalent to seven Calories. It should be noted here that the human body is far less than 100 percent efficient in converting food energy into work. To do seven Calories of external work might require ten to twelve Calories of fuel consumption.

From the point of view of biomechanics, if the student-athlete simply holds this 240 pounds in the air during a repetition, no further work is being performed. This is where the big difference lies between the scientist's concept of work and the common connotation of work. *The important thing in performing work is maintaining a motion against a resisting force.* For example, if during a relay race at a picnic a 120-pound girl carries another 120-pound girl over a fifty-yard distance, the total amount of work accomplished would be zero unless she met with some force resistive to the horizontal motion. Since, in carrying the girl, she is exerting the force upward but is moving horizontally, there is no component of motion in the direction of the force. No work from the standpoint of biomechanics has been performed. From a *physiologic* standpoint, however, energy is being expended in both examples above through all aspects of the weight-training exercise and the run.

The conservation properties regarding work and energy come from the observation that every force has an equal and opposite counterforce. When there is a motion in the direction of one force, causing that force to do work, the opposite counterforce is having motion against it. Therefore, it is receiving the same quantity of work. *The term "energy" is used to represent the ability of a body to perform work.* Thus, one body doing work and losing energy implies that a second body receives work and gains that amount of energy. In this way, the total amount of energy within any system remains the same. This concept has some limitations in regard to the human system's ability to store energy.

To return to the example of the bench-press exercise, when the athlete has pressed the weight upward, he has performed work. Therefore, he has 720 foot-pounds less energy. The weights, on the other hand, have been lifted higher in the air and are capable of doing work as they return to their original position. This capability to perform work is called *potential energy*. Therefore, the 720 foot-pounds lost to the man are counterbalanced by a 720 foot-pound gain of potential energy by the weights themselves. In this way, energy within the system is conserved.

When the man returns the weights to their original position through flexion at the elbow and extension of the shoulder joint, a new phenomenon occurs. The weights now have lost the energy, and the 720 foot-pounds of work were transferred to the man. Unfortunately, the human system is incapable of storage of energy received mechanically. Within the human, this energy is transformed to the form of heat and serves only to elevate the temperature of the body and its surroundings. This energy is lost mechanically to the system and is dissipated as heat energy.

Within the context of sports, the principal energy interactions are the change from chemical energy within the body into mechanical energy and the change from received mechanical energy into heat within the human body. It should be noted that transformation of energy into the form of heat does not represent a total loss, since the generation of heat within the body triggers many other physiologic processes. These include an increased rate of perspiration, heart rate, and mechanical breathing rate which facilitates biochemical respiratory actions. It is precisely this property of energy being transformed from one form to another which makes it such a useful and important quantity in the field of biomechanics.

Within the human body, the conservation of energy is illustrated by the relation between work, food consumption, and body fat. Energy input into the body is in the form of food and in oxygen to burn it. This energy may be used in the basic life processes or may be expended during work. Most of the energy for basic metabolism is dissipated in the form of heat. If the heat loss plus the work performed does not equal the input energy, the body stores the excess in the form of fat. At times, some of this fat may then be burned to provide a greater expenditure of energy over input.

There are two types of mechanical energy of concern within this text. *The first of these is kinetic energy or energy due to motion.* Any moving object has the ability to do work simply because it is moving. In slowing this object to a stop, some force must be exerted against the motion. As a consequence, the object does work, and the body exerting force receives energy. For example, following the striking of the ball in a tennis serve, the arm and racket have a great amount of kinetic energy. The muscles posterior to the racket arm and shoulder absorb this energy by eccentric contraction. This eccentric contraction serves the dual purposes of stopping the total motion in order to prepare for the next motions at these joints by placing critical muscles on stretch and of protecting the elbow joint against hyperextension. It may be noted here that the units of work and energy in the English system are simply the units of distance, feet, times the unit of force, pounds; and the unit of energy then becomes the foot-pound.

The numerical calculation of the kinetic energy uses the equation:

$$\text{Kinetic energy} = \tfrac{1}{2} \times \text{Mass} \times (\text{Velocity})^2 = \tfrac{1}{2}mv^2$$

Thus, a bowling ball weighing 16 pounds and moving at 20 ft/sec has a kinetic energy given by:

$$\text{Kinetic energy} = \tfrac{1}{2}mv^2 = \tfrac{1}{2}\,\frac{16}{32}\,(20)^2 = 100 \text{ ft-lb of kinetic energy}$$

and a 160-pound runner moving at 30 ft/sec has a kinetic energy of:

$$\text{Kinetic energy} = \tfrac{1}{2}\,\frac{160}{32}\,(30)^2 = 2{,}250 \text{ ft-lb}$$

It can be seen that kinetic energy increases dramatically as either the mass of the body or the speed increases.

The other principal mechanical type of energy mentioned previously is *potential energy*. This is the ability to work which an object possesses because of its position within the gravitational field or because of an elastic change of the object's shape. An example of potential energy is observed in the approach of a diver to his final step on the diving board. This step is calculated to impart an optimum amount of potential energy into the bending of the board so the board will release this energy back to the diver and provide an optimum angle for the trajectory of the dive.

Numerical calculation of the gravitational potential energy is given by:

$$\text{Gravitational potential energy} = \text{Weight} \times \text{Distance raised or lowered}$$

$$= W \times h$$

Thus, as in the previous example of the bench press, the potential energy gained by the weight equals:

$$\text{P.E. (grav.)} = W \times h = 240 \text{ pounds} \times 3 \text{ feet} = 720 \text{ ft-lb}$$

As another example, a 190-pound pole-vaulter raising his center of gravity 16 feet acquires a gravitational potential energy of:

$$\text{P.E. (grav.)} = W \times h = 190 \times 16 = 3,040 \text{ ft-lb}$$

Calculation of potential energy due to elastic distortion depends so much on the characteristics of the object that there are no simple equations which have a wide range of application. Usually, a graph of the force versus distortion needs to be made, and energy is calculated from this curve.

In many sport events there is a long chain of energy transformations from one type to another before the conclusion of the performance. For example, a pole-vaulter uses the running approach to produce a large amount of kinetic energy. During the early part of the vault immediately following the pole plant, much of this energy is stored in the bending of the pole. The good vaulter then moves himself into a position to enable the pole to deliver this potential energy to his body in the form of kinetic energy. This aids motion in an upward direction. Kinetic energy is transformed into gravitational potential energy as the vaulter goes high enough to clear the bar. Following clearance of the bar, gravitational potential energy is then retransformed into kinetic energy of the fall. The purpose of the padding in the pole-vault pit is to absorb this kinetic energy in a harmless form of work and finally dissipate it as heat.

The area of elasticity within biomechanics is a study of the interplay between kinetic and potential energies. During a collision involving an elastic object such as a tennis ball, the kinetic energy which the ball has before the collision is stored as elastic potential energy in the deformation of the ball. As the ball returns to its original shape, most of this energy is reconverted into kinetic energy. *The term "coefficient of restitution" is used to denote the ratio of the amount of kinetic energy after the collision to the amount of kinetic energy prior to the collision.*

Many times the rules of a sporting event specify either air pressure or materials of the sport objects in order to limit the coefficient of restitution to an acceptable level. As an example, the United States Handball Association's rules specify that the handball should be made of rubber $1\frac{7}{8}''$ in diameter with a $\frac{1}{32}''$ variation. It should weigh no more than 2.3 oz. with a variation of 0.2 oz. The rebound from a 70-inch drop at 68°F shall be no more than 42–48 inches. This means that the coefficient of restitution of the handball is limited to the ratio of the final height to the initial height or approximately 45 divided by 70, or 0.64. Although not specified in the rules, it is assumed that the handball should be dropped on a nonresilient surface as found on a handball court.

Limitation of the coefficient of restitution for a handball and regulations for the size of the court allow the strategy of the game to fall within the competency of a skilled performer. There are available other balls of the same size as regulation handballs but made of a modern silicone plastic composition. These are sold to children under the trade name of "Super Ball." The coefficient of restitution of these balls is approximately 0.95. If we were to attempt to play handball with one of these extremely lively balls, the velocities and trajectories of the rebounds would necessitate a complete change of strategy and body motion for the handball performer. It would literally be "a new ball game!" With the present size of the handball court, the reaction and movement time limitations of the performer would make it very difficult to play the game of handball as it is now played.

Impulse and Momentum

The other important conserved property is momentum. Historically, momentum has been known as the "quantity of motion." *Scientifically, it is represented by the product of the mass of a body times the velocity with which that body is moving.* Large momenta are associated with large bodies or bodies moving at high velocity. Units of momentum are simply units of mass times units of velocity. As an example of a momentum calculation, let us return to the example of the sprinter in the 220-yard dash. If the athlete has a weight of 160 pounds, his momentum can be calculated by:

$$\text{Momentum} = \text{Mass} \times \text{Velocity} = mv = \frac{wv}{g} = \frac{160}{32} \times 33 \text{ ft/sec}$$

$$= 165 \text{ momentum units}$$

During recent years, the term *momentum* has received increasing usage in a wide variety of contexts in the field of sport. It has become almost a cliché with sportscasters to use the term *momentum* in a psychological sense to describe a positive expectation of a team on the field. Momentum has also been used as a synonym for positive acceleration. For example, a ski-jumper moving down a slope may be referred to as having positive acceleration, or it can be stated that he is gaining momentum.

The latter statement is not inaccurate and represents a very important relationship between momentum and the previously discussed quantities of acceleration and force. If we consider the concept of change of momentum, the following relation can be shown:

$$\frac{\text{Change of momentum}}{\text{Time}} = \frac{\text{Mass} \times \text{Change of velocity}}{\text{Time}} = \text{Mass} \times$$

$$\text{Acceleration} = \text{Force}$$

$$\text{Force} = \frac{\text{Mom}_{(final)} - \text{Mom}_{(initial)}}{\text{Time}}$$

It can be observed that another concept of force lies in the fact that it requires a force to provide a change of momentum. Forces cause accelerations and changes of momentum, and accelerations represent changes of momentum. As an historic footnote, it is of interest that when Newton first proposed the laws of mechanics, his statement was simply that a force was linearly related to the change of quantity of motion of an object. "Quantity of motion" was simply Newton's term for what is called momentum in present-day terminology.

Just as work is related to the transfer of energy between objects, there is also a quantity called *impulse* which represents the transfer of momentum between objects. *Impulse is scientifically defined as the product of force and time.* It can be observed that this product of force and time actually represents the change of momentum of a body. Work represents transfer of energy, and impulse represents change of momentum between bodies.

The fact that forces and counterforces always occur in equal and opposite direction leads to the concept of conservation of momentum. For every force acting in one direction, there is a force in the opposite direction for the same period of time representing an opposing change of momentum. For every change of momentum occurring in one direction on one body, another body is receiving an equal and opposite change of momentum, so the total momentum of the system remains a constant.

It should be noted that there are really two types of momentum. What has been discussed thus far is termed *linear momentum*. There is also a quantity, *angular momentum,* related to rotating bodies. It is equally important in describing total motion. Angular momentum will be discussed later in this chapter, following a discussion of rotational motion.

The impulse of a collision within the context of sport action may be of different types. The total effect of the impulse is to produce a change of momentum equal to the product of force and time. However, this product may be formed by a large force for a very short time period or by a smaller average force existing over a longer time period to produce the same total change of momentum. Examples of these two types of impulses are commonly observed in boxing. A jab to the head generally exerts a very large force over a very short contact time; whereas the time of contact for a body hook is much longer. The forces for the two punches may actually be the same. However, the hook does require a longer period of time and a greater distance of motion. Most of the impulse differences between these two punches lie in the type of body tissue with which contact is made. The mandible or jaw area is the most common contact point for the jab. The amount of collision motion is minimal because of the relative hardness of the surface; therefore, the time of contact is very short. In contrast, owing to the relatively softer abdominal area where the hook is often landed, there is a much greater elastic motion. As a consequence, the collision or contact time is greater. There are many other examples in sport where a motion is produced by a sharp contact or by a more sustained force. As one other example, in a pass-protection block in football, the emphasis is on a short, hard block in repetitive sequence by the offensive lineman; whereas during line blocking to "open a hole" for a running play, a sustained block must be used, i.e., contact time for this type of blocking must be longer than for blocking for pass protection.

As a numerical example of impulse-momentum calculations, if a bowling ball is delivered at a velocity of 20 ft/sec, the total momentum of the ball would be:

$$\text{Momentum} = \text{Mass} \times \text{Velocity} = \frac{16}{32} \times 20 = 10 \text{ momentum units}$$

If the time of approach and delivery were 2 seconds, then:

$$\text{Avg. force} \times \text{Time} = \text{Change of momentum} = 10 \text{ momentum units}$$

$$\text{Avg. force} = 10/2 = 5 \text{ pounds}$$

For a second example, consider the case of a softball batter who receives a pitch at 140 ft/sec and hits it back to the pitcher at 200 ft/sec with a total time of contact with the bat of 1/50 sec. In this case, the direction of motion of the ball is reversed. The change of momentum is the numerical sum of the magnitudes of the original and final momenta (weight of a softball is about 6 ounces):

$$\text{Change of momentum} = \text{Mass} \times \text{Change of velocity}$$

$$= \frac{\text{Weight}}{\text{Gravity}} \times \text{Change of velocity}$$

$$= \frac{6/16}{32} \times (140 + 200)$$

$$= 3.98 \approx 4 \text{ momentum units}$$

$$\text{Avg. force} = \frac{\text{Change of momentum}}{\text{Time}} = \frac{4}{1/50} = 200 \text{ pounds}$$

The concepts of impulse and momentum are extremely important in situations involving collisions of the type presented in the previous example. In chapter four various types of collisions which occur in sport will be considered, and the interactions which take place will be analyzed.

Power

Power represents the amount of work performed per unit time. It is related to energy in the same way that momentum is related to force. Power is energy expended or energy gained per unit time; whereas, force represents the change of momentum per unit time. The normal units for expressing power are in units of energy per second or foot-pounds per second. Traditionally, however, power is expressed in terms of horsepower. *One horsepower is defined as 550 foot-pounds per second.* Power can also be expressed as energy expenditure in Calories per minute. One horsepower is equal to 10.7 Cal/min.

For calculations involving power, the "snatch lift" from the sport of weight lifting serves as a good example. In this event, the performer in one motion lifts the weight from the ground to a position overhead. This involves considerable power (horsepower), especially in A.A.U. and Olympic competitions.

A heavyweight world-class competitor can "snatch" about 300 pounds. If he lifts this weight a total distance of 7 feet during a ¾-second period of time, then:

$$\text{Work} = \text{Force} \times \text{Distance} = 300 \times 7 = 2{,}100 \text{ ft-lb}$$

$$\text{Power} = \frac{\text{Work}}{\text{Time}} = \frac{2{,}100}{\frac{3}{4}} = 2{,}800 \frac{\text{ft-lb}}{\text{sec}} = \frac{2{,}800}{550} \text{ hp} = 5.1 \text{ hp}$$

During the time of the lift, the performer expends energy or delivers power at a rate of about five horsepower. Most sport performances require high power expenditures for short periods, with rest intervals between.

ROTATIONAL MOTION

So far in this chapter, motion has been described from a linear motion standpoint. In describing human motion, especially motions which occur in exercise, sport, and dance, the rotation of a body about some axis within that body is of fundamental importance. As was noted in chapter two, all individual motions at joints are actually rotations from the standpoint of biomechanics.

In many ways, the description of rotational motion parallels the description of linear motion. There are rotational positions, velocities, and accelerations. The basic difference between linear and angular motion occurs in the units in which these must be specified. In rotational motion, rather than having a distance covered, there is an angle turned through. Angular description differs from linear description in one very basic way. After a certain magnitude of angle has been traversed, the position is again reproduced. Due to limitations of joint structure and body tissue, however, a rotation will be limited to far less than one complete revolution in joint motions. Each articulation of the body has a maximum rotational range of motion about its axis. In biomechanics the term *rotation* as applied to joint motion has generalized meaning as compared to the specific anatomic definition of joint rotations described in chapter two.

Because of this reproducibility at the end of the revolution, a natural way of specifying a unit of angle is the complete revolution. However, there are other units also used for the measurement of angles. The most common unit is the degree, or $\frac{1}{360}$ of a revolution. The idea that there are 360 degrees in a complete revolution has developed from an historic context, but the number does allow convenient divisions of the circle into various numbers of parts. Normally, ranges of angular motion are specified in joints in terms of the number of degrees through which the joint may be rotated without damage. For example, the average individual can rotate the bony levers about the axis of the elbow during elbow flexion through a range of approximately 150 degrees. A full 360 degrees of motion is not possible due to the structure of the joint and the size of the surrounding musculature.

The development of *flexibility* during conditioning of students actually corresponds to an increase of ranges of motion in each of the applicable joints. This is accomplished by stretching noncontractile tissue such as ligaments and tendons. The importance of flexibility is often overlooked as a biomechanics parameter by physical educators. The increase in range of motion or flexibility allows a performer to exert forces over greater distances and times. This increases velocities, energies, and momenta associated with the performance. Also, the increase of range of motion allows a greater stretch to critically involved muscles. This provides these muscle groups with the potentiality of developing larger forces. For example, a golfer who has an extensive range of motion in the backswing is able to apply a higher velocity to the club head at the point of impact because of the extra distance over which he can provide acceleration. The muscle groups which initiate the torques or motions of the downswing are placed on greater stretch during the backswing; therefore, they are capable of exerting greater force.

Another unit of angular measure is the radian. *The radian is defined as that angle which includes an arc of a circle equal to the radius of the same circle.* As an example, if an object rotates through an angle of one radian, any point located two feet from the axis of rotation will move a distance of two feet. A point located four feet from the axis of rotation will move a distance of four feet (fig. 3.6). Because the total distance traveled by an object during one complete revolution, or 360 degrees, is 2π times the radius of the circle, it follows that one radian is equal to $\frac{1}{2\pi}$ of 360 degrees. That is:

$$1 \text{ radian} = \frac{360°}{2\pi} = 57.3°$$

$$1 \text{ degree} = \frac{2\pi}{360} = 0.0175 \text{ radian}$$

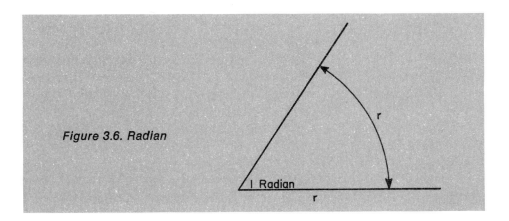

Figure 3.6. Radian

The importance of the radian will be seen later in the conversion from rotational velocities and accelerations to linear velocities and accelerations.

Angular Velocity and Angular Acceleration

Linear velocity was defined as a distance covered per unit time. *Angular velocity is the angle rotated through per unit time.* Units for angular velocity will be described in degrees per second, radians per second, or revolutions per second. Likewise, *angular acceleration is defined in terms of the change of angular velocity per unit time.* The units for angular acceleration will be degrees per second squared, radius per second squared, or revolutions per second squared.

As an example of these concepts, consider a bowling ball rolling down the lane at 18 ft/sec. Since bowling rules specify that the circumference of the ball is 27 inches, it will roll one revolution each time it travels this distance. Thus, its angular velocity will be:

$$\text{Angular velocity} = \frac{18 \times 12}{27} = 8 \text{ revolutions/sec}$$

$$= 8 \times 360 = 2{,}880 \text{ degrees/sec}$$

$$= 8 \times 2\pi = 50.3 \text{ radians/sec}$$

When released, a bowling ball is usually sliding with **no angular velocity.** The conversion from sliding to rolling involves angular accelerations—an increase of angular velocity. In the foregoing example, if the conversion from sliding to rolling required 0.7 seconds,

$$\text{Angular acceleration} = \frac{\text{Change of angular velocity}}{\text{Time}}$$

$$= \frac{8 - 0}{0.7} = 11.43 \text{ rev/sec}^2$$

$$= 4{,}114 \text{ degrees/sec}^2 = 71.86 \text{ rad/sec}^2$$

Torque

Force as a quantity is necessary to produce linear acceleration. There is also a quantity called *torque,* which is directly related to the production of angular acceleration. A torque is commonly pictured as a tendency to twist. In many cases, this is the way a torque is produced. In other cases, however, it is produced by a force applied along a line not passing through an axis of rotation; therefore, it causes a rotation of a body or body part. For example, rotation of the hand is the result of torques produced either by supination or pronation motions of the radio-ulnar joint. Hand rotation can also be caused by torques associated with medial and lateral rotations of the shoulder joint. Muscles associated with medial rotation are far more powerful than those associated with lateral rotation at the shoulder or the supination-pronation at the radio-ulnar joint. Therefore, the strongest torques achieved at the hand are produced with the elbow in a stabilized position and the shoulder joint being medially rotated. This condition is sometimes seen in the sport of arm wrestling (fig. 3.7). A winning effort is associated with the strong torques produced at the shoulder joint by the large muscle masses associated with medial rotation.

The distance from the line of action of the force to the axis about which rotation takes place is sometimes called the lever arm. The magnitude of the torque is given by the force times the length of the lever arm. A force applied far from the axis of rotation is more effective in producing torque than a force applied near the axis of rotation.

This use of various lever arms in the production of torque is commonly known as *leverage.* A performer working against a resisting force can more effectively operate if he will utilize a rotational motion and apply forces at

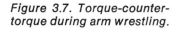
Figure 3.7. Torque-counter-torque during arm wrestling.

greater distances from the axis of rotation than the resistances. This ratio of lever arms acts as an effective multiplier of his own force. As a consequence, a force of 100 pounds applied two feet from an axis of rotation is capable of holding or moving a force of 200 pounds applied only one foot from the axis.

One application of this principle is in the widened stance used in many sports requiring quick body rotations. The frictional forces between the feet and the ground required for such movements with the feet planted three feet apart are only one-third those required if the feet are placed one foot apart. Within the limits of efficient use of the muscle-joint actions, performers in baseball, tennis, football, wrestling, and other sports use as wide a stance as practical to execute the skills.

In the initial contact in the "up position" in a wrestling match, the wrestler often endeavors to move his position of hold on the opponent as far out from the body as conveniently possible (fig. 3.8). This maneuver will enable him to turn and control the opponent with a greater torque as they apply their forces. Many maneuvers are designed to work against an opponent's extended limb where his own torques are greatly hampered by the minimal lever arms obtainable due to the positions of muscle attachment. Likewise, many of the movements in judo and kung fu are designed with the most efficient use of such leverage in mind.

Figure 3.8. Application of leverage during a wrestling match.

Courtesy SMS Public Information Office

In many other sport applications, leverage is used in just the opposite sense. When applying a rotation against a resistance located much farther from the axis, the performer sacrifices the multiplication of force but gains a multiplication of speed. Many sport implements are designed to use this by effectively extending the performer's own limb distance. One of the most dramatic examples is the use of a fly rod in fishing. The object being thrown—a dry or wet fly—is so light it requires only minimal forces. The long rod is used to impart a high velocity to the fly and line in order to effectively overcome air resistances. The stereotype of perfect form in the use of such sport implements involves the application of a series of torques to produce optimum velocity of some portion or portions of the implement.

Center of Gravity

In discussing a body or sport object which has linear and rotational motions, it normally is necessary to separate these two motions. This is done by ascribing the linear motion to a fictitious point called the center of gravity. *The center of gravity is perhaps best described as that point about which a body or object would balance most perfectly.* That is, in any direction from the center of gravity, torque caused by matter on one side exactly balances torque caused by matter on the opposite side. In this context it should be noted that a body or any given part of the body has its own center of gravity, and this can be determined. At times it becomes necessary to describe motion in terms of the center of gravity for upper and lower limbs as well as for the torso and head.

In describing the center of gravity of the total human body, it should be kept constantly in mind that this center of gravity is very much a function of the position of limbs and the motions of the spinal column. There are many times during sport and dance performances when the center of gravity may actually lie outside the body. For example, a diver in a pike position has so much mass distributed in front of the trunk that the center of gravity of the total body actually lies somewhere in the triangle formed by the trunk and limbs.

In figure 3.9, the center of gravity of the body theoretically would lie at the intersection of the three cardinal planes of motion. These were discussed in

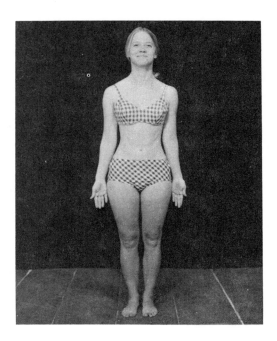

Figure 3.9. Center of gravity of the body lies at a theoretical point below the umbilicus and between the iliac fossas in the anatomic position.

chapter two. In figures 3.10, 3.11, and 3.12, the centers of gravity of the performers have been shifted to other points due to the nature of the total motion. In the cases of the high jumper and the gymnast dismounting from the horizontal bar, their centers of gravity may actually lie outside their bodies.

While executing a sport motion, the motion of the center of gravity often follows either a straight line or a parabolic gravitational arc. Meanwhile, the body or body parts are executing rotations about this center of gravity. There are times in biomechanic analysis when it becomes necessary to describe the linear motion of the center of gravity and various rotations occurring about this point by the motions of the upper and lower limbs and a variety of lumbar-thoracic and cervical spinal motions. In chapter four, the relationships between the linear motion of the center of gravity and the rotational motion of the various parts about this point will be presented in more detail.

above:
Figure 3.10. Center of gravity of the body shifts due to any change in position of its joints or segments.

right:
Figure 3.11. Center of gravity lies outside the body during a horizontal bar dismount by Gareth Burk, USC gymnast.

Courtesy USC Athletic News Service

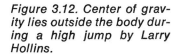

Figure 3.12. Center of gravity lies outside the body during a high jump by Larry Hollins.

Courtesy USC Athletic News Service

Moment of Inertia

Just as mass has been defined as the ratio between linear force and the observed acceleration, there is also a quantity which applies to a body to describe the ratio of angular torque to the resulting angular acceleration. This quantity has come to be known as the *moment of inertia*. It is in many ways a much more complex quantity than the mass in that the moment of inertia depends not only on the total amount of matter, but on the relative positions of each part of a body. *The total moment of inertia of a body or a sport object is calculated by summing the amount of mass contributed by each part times the square of its distance from the axis of rotation:*

$$\text{Moment of inertia} = \Sigma \, (\text{Mass}) \times (\text{Radius})^2$$

Σ means the summation over all parts of the body

For example, the moment of inertia of a football thrown or kicked with spiral rotation is much smaller than the moment of inertia when it is tumbling or rotating end over end following a kickoff or field goal attempt. The reason for this lies in the fact that the total mass tends to be located much closer to the axis of rotation in the case of spiral rotation.

The actual geometrical calculations of moments of inertia of sport objects and the human body are quite complex. However, the moment of inertia about a given axis can be measured by going back to the basic definition of determining the amount of torque necessary to provide a given angular acceleration. Although accurate numerical calculations of the moment of inertia are not always feasible, the use of the concept of a changing moment of inertia quite often allows its utilization through basic levels of biomechanic analysis. For example, when the limbs are brought in close to the longitudinal axis of the body, the moment of inertia and the torque acceleration relationship is much different than it is when the limbs are extended. The utilization or the violation of this principle can be readily observed in various gymnastic routines, ice skating rotations, and in the sport of diving.

While it is often quite difficult to numerically calculate the moment of inertia from the geometrical positions of various parts of an object, there is a term sometimes used to indicate the average distance of parts from the axis of rotation. This is called the *radius of gyration*. By definition, the radius of gyration is obtained as follows:

$$\text{Moment of inertia} = \text{Total mass} \times (\text{Radius of gyration})^2$$

$$\text{Radius of gyration} = \sqrt{\frac{\text{Moment of inertia}}{\text{Total mass}}}$$

If the radius of gyration is small, there is a small moment of inertia for a given mass. If the radius of gyration is large, there is a large moment of inertia for the same mass.

Experimentally, the moment of inertia of a man about 6'5" and 200 pounds, rotating about a longitudinal axis with his arms at his side and feet together, is about 1.5 units. If he is rotating about the same axis with arms and legs abducted, the moment of inertia is increased to about 8.5 units. In contrast, the same man will have a moment of inertia about a transverse axis through his center of gravity of about 17 units while he is in an extended position. His radius of gyration in each of these cases is calculated as follows:

Basic relationship: Radius of gyration $= \sqrt{\dfrac{\text{Moment of inertia}}{\text{Total mass}}}$

A. Longitudinal—Anatomic position

$$K = \sqrt{\frac{1.5}{200/32}} = \sqrt{0.24} = 0.49 \text{ ft} \approx 6 \text{ inches}$$

So, the average unit of mass is located about 6 inches from the axis of rotation.

B. Longitudinal—Arms and legs abducted

$$K = \sqrt{\frac{8.5}{200/32}} = \sqrt{1.36} = 1.17 \text{ ft} \approx 14 \text{ inches}$$

C. Transverse—Supine position

$$K = \sqrt{\frac{17}{200/32}} = \sqrt{2.72} = 1.65 \text{ ft} \approx 20 \text{ inches}$$

From these measurements it can be seen that the moment of inertia and radius of gyration vary greatly according to body position.

RELATION BETWEEN LINEAR AND ANGULAR MOTIONS

The interrelationship between linear and angular motions is one of the most important relationships which must be understood in biomechanics, since there is a tendency to be interested only in the linear motion of a specific body part. As examples, the velocity of the wrist joint during a throwing motion is important to calculate, and the velocity of a kicker's ankle joint is directly related to the performance outcome. In both cases, however, the final linear velocity achieved is the result of a large number of angular motions at the individual joints of the body. Therefore, the real importance of the interrelationship between angular and linear motions again lies in the fact that most human body movements are actually movements at the joints. *There must be a functional integration of linear and angular motions to produce skilled performances.*

This was pointed out in the discussion of the radian. There is a **direct** relationship between the angle turned through by a body and the distances which the various points on the body move linearly. Since the angular velocity represents the angle turned through per unit time, there is a correspondence between the angular and linear velocities of the various parts of the body doing the turning. This relationship also applies to the accelerations and is given in the following equations:

Distance = Angle (radians) × Radius (distance from axis)

Linear velocity = Angular velocity × Radius

Tangential acceleration = Angular acceleration × Radius

Radial acceleration = (Angular velocity)² × Radius

From this it should be noted that in order to achieve high linear velocities of various parts of the body, the rotations must be made either with high **angular** velocities or with a large radius of movement (fig. 3.13).

The concept of centripetal and centrifugal forces is very important to enhance understanding of the relationship between linear and angular motions. There has been considerable confusion regarding these forces in the field of physical education, as well as in many other fields of study involving angular motion. It should be remembered that the individual points on a rotating object are not moving in straight lines but are moving in circular paths. As was noted earlier during the description of acceleration, this means that their velocities are changing. This is a direction change not necessarily associated with magnitude. *This change of direction of motion is called radial acceleration.* Since these points are being accelerated, their motion is being changed. An external force must be exerted. For example, when a hammer thrower is changing the direction of motion of the hammer during the rotational phase, he is exerting a force inward on the chain in order to provide this change of motion (fig. 3.14). *The force associated with the radial acceleration is called centripetal force.*

Combining the previous expression for radial acceleration with the relationship between force and acceleration:

$$\text{Centripetal force} = \text{Mass} \times \text{Radial acceleration} = \frac{\text{Mass} \times (\text{Velocity})^2}{\text{Radius of curvature}}$$

$$F \text{ (cent)} = \frac{mv^2}{r}$$

*Figure 3.13. Integration of angular velocities
by lower limb joint motions to produce linear
velocity during running by Jim Ryun, U.S.A.
Olympic team.*

Courtesy Visual Track and Field Techniques, 292 So. LaCienaga Blvd., Beverly Hills, Calif. 90211

Figure 3.14. Centripetal force during hammer throwing by Romuald Klim of the USSR

In the previous example of a baseball player rounding second base at a speed of 20 ft/sec and a radius of curvature of 16 feet, it was found that his radial acceleration was 25 ft/sec². Assuming he weighs 192 pounds, the centripetal force necessary to accomplish this—the horizontal frictional force between his feet and ground—is then:

$$\text{Force} = \frac{w}{g} \times a \text{ (radial)} = \frac{192}{32} \times 25 = 150 \text{ pounds}$$

If he were to attempt the same maneuver with a radius of curvature of four feet (a tight turn at third base), he would need:

$$\text{Force} = \frac{w}{g} \times \frac{v^2}{r} = \frac{192}{32} \times \frac{20^2}{4} = 600 \text{ pounds}$$

This illustrates the necessity for slowing down immediately prior to executing a very sharp turn.

If a force is being exerted on objects in circular motion in order to keep them traveling along the circular path, they are in turn exerting an outward counterforce. *The counterforce to centripetal force is properly known as centrifugal force.* To return to the example of the hammer thrower, since the performer is exerting an inward force on the hammer, then the hammer itself is exerting an outward force on the performer. In fact, during the performance of this event, the outward or centrifugal force may achieve relatively high magnitude.

If a performer executes two revolutions per second with an effective radius of six feet, he achieves a hammer speed of:

$$\text{Velocity} = \text{Angular velocity} \times \text{Radius} = 2 \times 2\pi \times 6 = 75.4 \text{ ft/sec}$$

To hold the hammer in circular motion requires:

$$\text{Cent. force} = \frac{m \times v^2}{r} = \frac{16}{32} \times \frac{(75.4)^2}{6} = 474 \text{ pounds}$$

If he could increase his rotation to 2.5 revolutions per second while maintaining the same effective radius, the values would be:

$$\text{Velocity} = 2.5 \times 2\pi \times 6 = 94.25 \text{ ft/sec}$$

$$\text{Cent. force} = \frac{16}{32} \times \frac{(94.25)^2}{6} = 740 \text{ pounds}$$

The problems which performers face in handling centrifugal force are one reason that the hammer thrower is normally enclosed in a cage during track-and-field meets. Either a premature release or loss of angular orientation by the performer could result in the hammer going into an area where either spectators or other participants are located.

Rotational Kinetic Energy

Since there is a kinetic energy associated with linear motion of a body, there is also a kinetic energy associated with rotational motion of the body. This rotational kinetic energy is given by:

Kinetic energy (rotational) = ½ × (Moment of inertia) × (Angular velocity)^2

It can be calculated that the moment of inertia of a softball is about 0.00013 units. If a foul "pop up" in softball is spinning with 20 revolutions per second, its rotational kinetic energy is:

$$\text{Kinetic energy} = \text{½} \times (\text{Moment of inertia}) \times (\text{Angular velocity})^2$$

$$= \text{½} \times 0.00013 \times (20 \times 2\pi)^2 = 1 \text{ ft/lb}$$

To stop this spin during a catch, it is necessary to supply a frictional force between the ball surface and the hand or glove. If the slippage during stopping is one-half inch, the force needed is:

$$\text{Force} = \frac{\text{Energy}}{\text{Distance}} = \frac{1}{\text{½} \times \text{1/12}} = 24 \text{ pounds average frictional force}$$

The fact that rotating bodies do contain energy sometimes becomes quite important in sport events. For example, a rolling billiard ball will cause a slightly different type of collision than one which is sliding, since the rotational kinetic energy must be absorbed in the collision. Likewise, when trying to catch a rapidly spinning baseball or softball, the performer must allow for the energy associated with the spin of the ball as well as allowing for its linear motion as it approaches the glove. A failure to allow for this spinning motion of the ball sometimes causes the ball to hit the glove and "climb out." In recent years, the engineering and design of baseball gloves have tended to alleviate this problem to a degree.

Angular Momentum

As with all of the other quantities associated with linear motion, momentum also has an angular counterpart. Angular momentum is defined by the equation:

Angular momentum = Moment of inertia × Angular velocity

With a weight of about 4.4 pounds and a radius of 4.3 inches, the standard discus has a moment of inertia near 0.1 unit. To find the angular momentum of a discus spinning at five revolutions per second:

Angular momentum = Moment of inertia × Angular velocity

$$= 0.1 \times 5 \times 2\pi = 3.1 \text{ units of angular momentum}$$

Like the linear momentum, angular momentum is a conserved quantity and in the absence of external torques will remain a constant throughout the motion. The very significant fact about angular momentum is that the moment of inertia is a quantity which can be varied during motion as the angular momentum is being conserved (fig. 3.15). This means—since the product of moment of inertia and angular velocity must remain a constant—a performer can decrease his moment of inertia by flexing at the hip, knee, and lumbar spine and provide an automatic increase in angular velocity. This factor is quite often useful in the *conservation of angular momentum.*

There are many sport actions where a decrease of the distance of a part of the moving body from the axis of rotation is performed in order to increase the speed of rotation. An example is flexion of the elbow associated with diagonal abduction and adduction of the shoulder during an overhand throw. This is a common motion in almost all throwing and striking skills through the high diagonal plane. Flexion of the elbow must occur to increase limb velocity. This can be seen in figure 3.2, frames eighteen through twenty-six, where the javelin thrower moves the right elbow from extreme extension to flexion. This increases velocity of the throwing limb and is essential to obtain maximum distance for the throw.

	Weight (Pounds)	Radius (Inches)	Moment of Inertia (Pound-inch²)
BALLS			
Baseball	.31	1.5	.3
Basketball	1.31	4.8	20
Bowling	10–16	4.5	81–130
Field Hockey	.35	1.4	.3
Football—spin	.90	3.3	approx 5
tumble	.90	Ellipse 3.3 × 5.7	approx 10
Golf	.10	.81	.03
Handball	.14	.95	.08
Lacrosse	.32	1.25	.2
Ping-Pong	.006	.75	.002
Shot	16	2.5	40
Soccer	.94	4.4	12
Softball	.40	1.9	.6
Squash	.07	.88	.03
Tennis	.13	1.25	.13
Volleyball	.60	4.2	6.5
Discus—spin	4.4	4.4	approx 40
tumble	4.4	4.4	approx 20
SPORT IMPLEMENTS		(Dimensions)	
Badminton racket	.38	Handle 17 Head 10 × 7	140
Baseball bat	2.2	33–36	1900
Golf club—wood	.85	30	800
iron	1.0	28	750
Hockey stick	variable	Handle 40–53 Head 2 × 14	3000+
Softball bat	2	31–34	1100
Tennis racket	.85	27 × 9	300

Figure 3.15. Moments of inertia of selected sport objects and implements

Probably one of the most notable examples of conservation of angular momentum is the increase of rotational velocity which occurs during the tuck maneuver in diving. An angular momentum is imparted to the diver by his motion as he leaves the board. This angular momentum will be conserved during the entire interval of time in the air. As the tuck position is attained (hip and lumbar flexions), this reduces the moment of inertia and increases angular velocity. Before entering the water, the diver again extends the body in order to increase the moment of inertia and reduce angular velocity before entry.

There are also several examples of this increase of limb velocity through conservation of angular momentum by a knee flexion. For example, in the running pattern, flexions of the knee and hip joints cause a very rapid swinging of the whole leg forward in preparing for the next step. Knee flexion is also used for the same purpose in both soccer-style and traditional American football kicking patterns in order to attain a higher final foot velocity. Again, in these examples, flexion of the knee draws more of the mass near the axis of rotation taking place at the hip joint. This causes a reduction of the total moment of inertia of the leg about the hip joint and a consequent increase in angular velocity of the kicking leg.

Since angular momentum is a vector quantity, it must be conserved in direction as well as magnitude. For this reason, spinning objects have a strong tendency to keep their axis of spin in the same direction. This principle is illustrated in the stability of flight of a punted football, a discus, or a javelin. These sport objects will travel through the air without wobbling only when they have a strong, stabilizing spin.

In this context, it should be noted that each object has certain *principal axes* related to the symmetry of their bodies and about which the spin is most stable. Attempts to spin the object about other axes result in a phenomenon known as *precession* which appears in biomechanic analysis of the motion as a circular wobble. The stereotype of perfect form for throwing such objects includes the introduction of an optimum spin exactly about one of the principal axes.

In competitive diving and gymnastics, a performer often makes complex body and limb motions designed to convert a spin about one principal axis into a spin about a new axis. As examples, the change from turning to twisting motions in diving or the change from a giant swing to a flying twist dismount from the horizontal bar involves such procedures. These motions involve quite complex biomechanic analysis.

Two skills which offer interesting comparison and contrasting elements are the skills of cricket bowling and baseball pitching. The ultimate result for both of these skills is the desirability on the part of the performer of delivering the ball to a batter at a great velocity. Rules between the two sports differ considerably, and these differences in rules result in a decided difference in the way the performers are allowed to reach the ultimate objective of obtaining ball velocity. In cricket, the bowler is allowed to develop considerable linear velocity of his center of gravity prior to the time he releases the ball. In contrast to this, the baseball pitcher is greatly restricted in this context. His linear velocity of the center of gravity of the total body is lessened because he must maintain contact with the pitching plate.

Another difference between cricket bowling and baseball pitching rules has a decided impact on limb and ball velocities. The rules for cricket indicate that the throwing elbow of the cricket bowler must remain extended at all times during the delivery. This means that the cricket bowler can conserve angular momentum, but he cannot gain the added velocity which the baseball pitcher does by flexing the elbow during the pitching delivery process. In other words, the baseball pitcher increases the final velocity by decreasing the moment of inertia. The cricket bowler is not allowed to do this. A larger part of the ball velocity is due to his linear velocity attained during the approach, and a smaller part is due to the angular velocity of the throwing limb.

Chapter 4

Relationships Between Force and Motion

The purpose of this chapter is to demonstrate the interrelationships between force and motion. This chapter is especially concerned with those situations where the interaction of the sport object or body with the air is not of vital importance. Chapter five is concerned primarily with interaction between sport objects and bodies in motion in air. Chapter six is a discussion of the same types of motions of objects or bodies interacting with water.

STATIC AND DYNAMIC EQUILIBRIA

Equilibrium is one of the most important concepts for biomechanic analysis of sport events. In a purely scientific sense, *the term "equilibrium" describes those systems existing in a condition of zero acceleration.* This may be linear or rotational. If there is a system in which accelerations are zero, because of the relationship between forces and accelerations, equilibrium then specifies that every force acting on a body must be opposed by an equal and opposite counterforce. Therefore, the sum of all forces acting on the body will be equal to zero. Likewise, if the system is in rotational equilibrium, the torques will all be balanced in such a way that the total summation of torque is equal to zero.

The term *static equilibrium* is applied to objects under equilibrium at rest. The term *dynamic equilibrium* refers to those objects moving in a straight line at a constant velocity and motion. For example, a football lineman in his three-point stance before the ball is put into play displays an example of static equilibrium. A distance runner moving in a straight line at a constant velocity is demonstrating dynamic equilibrium.

The case of a body under a continuing acceleration will also be considered in this chapter. While this is not exactly a case of true equilibrium, it is of great importance in many sport and dance events. Therefore, the term *equilibrium under acceleration* is introduced. An example of this type of motion is the extreme forward lean of a sprinter coming out of the blocks at the beginning of a race. This type of motion also occurs any time a performer has an abrupt change of direction, as commonly occurs in court and field sports. The lean accompanying directional changes is especially noticeable during rapid pivoting motions of performers in such sports as soccer, field hockey, basketball, lacrosse, and football (fig. 4.1).

Courtesy USC Athletic News Service

Figure 4.1. Equilibrium under acceleration during directional change by O. J. Simpson, USC Heisman Trophy winner.

One of the most common examples of static equilibrium is the situation normally associated with the term *balance. The most important principle with respect to balance or static equilibrium is that the center of gravity of the body must lie at a point directly above the base of support.* The term *base of support* includes the entire area formed by those points at which the body is touching the ground, mat, floor, or sport apparatus. As far as the performer is concerned, the base of support may be one foot, both feet, one hand, both hands, or parts of the back or abdomen touching the mat, ground, or apparatus. In the sports of gymnastics and wrestling, as examples, the base of support is not only widely varied in terms of body parts, but also changes rapidly from one position to another. One only needs to watch a skilled gymnastic routine on uneven parallel bars to gain an appreciation of varied bases of support.

The ability to maintain equilibrium is critically a function of the type of forces which can be applied against the ground or other supporting surfaces. Support-type reactions are usually thought of as simply being totally vertical forces, i.e., the supporting parts of the body are pushing straight down against the base of support. Under these conditions, it is necessary that the center of gravity remain above some part of the base of support. If it happens to fall outside the base of support, there is no way a recovery can be effected by these forces being exerted straight downward.

Associated with this idea in many sport actions is the width of the performer's preliminary stance. A wide stance is one which offers a relatively large, stable base of support. This allows a variety of body motions while equilibrium is maintained. A wide stance also gives correspondingly larger lever arms to the vertical forces of support, thereby allowing quicker rotational motions of the entire body in beginning or changing a sport action.

Actually, in almost all contact situations the human body is capable of exerting forces not only vertically—*scientifically known as normal forces*—but forces can also be exerted parallel to the surface of contact. These are the forces discussed as frictional forces in an earlier chapter. The importance of frictional forces in maintaining equilibrium should not be overlooked. It is much easier to perform any type of action on a rough surface where slippage is diminished rather than on a smooth or slick surface where frictional forces are not available. When the center of gravity lies outside the base of support, tending to cause the object to rotate into a falling condition, frictional forces can be used to rotate body segments back into an equilibrium position.

In the case of a departure from an equilibrium condition, an important reaction of a performer is the reestablishment of a new base of support beneath the body. An excellent example of this is the situation of a "scrambling back" in football who, when he is hit and knocked out of the equilibrium condition, will rapidly move lower limbs and the upper limb not holding the football to new positions beneath the body in order to keep from falling to the ground. What he is actually doing from a biomechanics point of view is reestablishing a base of support underneath the center of gravity, enabling him to maintain equilibrium and to control volitional motions. He may use movements of the limbs to change complete body motion, enabling a return to the upright running position in another direction.

In contrast, basketball players may lose equilibrium and regain it purely by means of friction, without critical adjustments of the base of support. In order to do this, the frictional forces obtained parallel to the floor must be very large. This is the reason for the design, shape, and materials of the basketball shoe. The surfaces of the soles of the shoes and of the floor provide the basketball player with maximum coefficients of friction. The use of frictional forces in this sense requires special flexibility training and strengthening of noncontractile tissue as well as muscles most involved for controlling inversion and eversion of the subtalar and transverse tarsal joints.

Motions in dynamic equilibrium where the body is moving rather than remaining static can be described in a similar context. In fact, the example of the "scrambling back" in football better illustrates dynamic equilibrium than static equilibrium, since he will continue motion after regaining equilibrium. Again, the important point is that parts of the body in contact with the ground must be in a condition where they can establish torque to counteract any torque due to gravity. If this is not accomplished, falling will be inevitable.

In common locomotor actions such as walking, jogging, and running, linear motion of the body is maintained, in part, by a series of hip, knee, and ankle-joint actions designed to regain equilibrium when it is lost immediately after the body moves over the foot in contact with the ground. The new foot placement always occurs in front of the center of gravity in order to arrest the falling motion of the body. If this were not done, a state of complete disequilibrium would result, and the individual would fall to the ground.

This concept of arresting disequilibrium and controlling locomotor motion carries over to the earlier described idea of "equilibrium under acceleration." Consider the example of the sprinter during the first four or five yards of the fifty-yard dash. During this time, he is not in a state of equilibrium because of his positive acceleration (fig. 4.2). His position at this time is also one which could not be held in either a static or normal dynamic equilibrium. The center of gravity lies in front of the unilateral weight-bearing foot or base of support. However, his linear motion continues during this state of disequilibrium due to the fact that positive acceleration is occurring.

Courtesy Visual Track and Field Techniques, 292 So. LaCienaga Blvd., Beverly Hills, California 90211

Figure 4.2. Controlling disequilibrium through positive acceleration during the sprint start by Tom Jones, U.S.A. Olympic team member.

From this it can be observed that the lean of a runner during this type of acceleration is reciprocally related to the fact that he is accelerating. The lean position is a result of the acceleration and not the cause of acceleration, i.e., leaning forward does not automatically insure that a performer will accelerate. For example, during a 440-yard dash a performer cannot hope to lean forward throughout the entire race because he cannot positively accelerate over the entire distance. Furthermore, an exaggerated forward lean of the body throughout a race is not an efficient position from a myologic point of view. This arises from the fact that constant lumbar-thoracic flexion elicits an excessive amount of eccentric contraction within antigravity musculature. Therefore, energy consumption is directed toward counteracting the downward pull of gravity rather than moving the athlete linearly. The undesirability of a constant forward lean by a performer becomes more obvious as the distance of the race increases.

Adjustment of body movements to maintain equilibrium while accelerating also occurs during radial acceleration. When a runner is changing direction, acceleration is inward or toward the center of the curve of directional change. For example, this is observed when a base runner rounds third base trying to score from first base on an extra-base hit. Because of his extreme speed and the acute directional change at the base, it is necessary for the athlete to lean sharply inward in order to maintain equilibrium. This requires some spinal lateral flexion and rotation toward the center of the curve. Furthermore, the horizontal centripetal force necessary to provide this radial acceleration must be supplied by friction between the performer's shoes and the ground. To provide this extra horizontal force, design of baseball shoes includes the concept of cleats. These provide extremely high coefficients of friction as they dig into the earth during running.

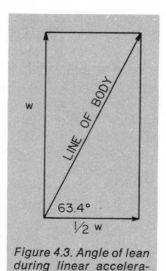

Figure 4.3. Angle of lean during linear acceleration.

Optimum angles of lean can be determined. For example, a sprinter accelerating at a rate of 16 ft/sec² uses horizontal force one-half his body weight. The most stable technique for him to supply this force to all parts of the body is to lean as shown in figure 4.3.

Likewise, a runner rounding third base at a speed and radius of curvature requiring a radial acceleration of 1 *g* (32 ft/sec²) must lean inward at a forty-five-degree angle (fig. 4.4).

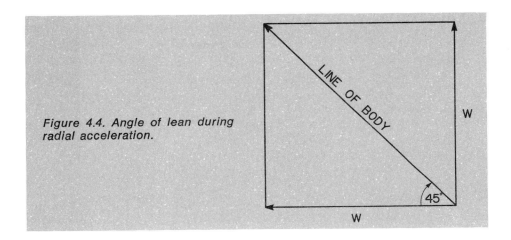

Figure 4.4. Angle of lean during radial acceleration.

TRAJECTORIES

One of the most common forces to be understood relative to its effect on motion is the force of gravity. Since almost all human body motion as well as motion of sport objects occurs relatively close to the ground, gravitational acceleration is considered a constant factor in biomechanic analysis. Every unsupported object is under the influence of this acceleration or the associated force called the weight of the object. Gravitational acceleration is always present and is directed downward regardless of the velocity of the body. When a body is moving straight upward, gravitational acceleration is against the direction of motion. Therefore, this causes speed of the body to decrease. When the actual velocity of the body is downward, acceleration is downward and, therefore, in the same direction of the velocity. This causes an increase in speed of the body or sport object. *Even at the top of a vertical flight path when an object has a velocity of zero, gravitational acceleration is constantly causing velocity to change and body motion to change direction and move downward.*

In considering the free-flight motion of an unsupported body or sport object, there are three important parameters: (1) maximum height reached during flight,

(2) total time of travel, and (3) maximum range or distance between the points where the body entered the air and returned to the ground.

The simplest form of motion in a gravitational field other than a falling object is vertical motion. A good example of this in a sport context is motion of a skilled rebound tumbler. In this case, most motion is either in the direction of or counter to the acceleration of gravity. Any marked deviation of this would result in a trajectory, causing the gymnast to land on the floor. There is a direct relationship between the initial velocity as the performer enters the air, maximum height the center of gravity will attain, and amount of time in the air before returning to the trampoline bed. These relationships are given by:

$$\text{Max. height} = \frac{(\text{Velocity})^2}{2g}$$

$$\text{Time} = \frac{2(\text{Velocity})}{g}$$

$$\text{Time} = \sqrt{\frac{8(\text{Max. height})}{g}}$$

These relationships hold in any sport maneuver where takeoff and landing occur at the same level.

To carry this one step further, suppose a coach using basic cinematographic techniques observes that a rebound tumbler reaches a maximum height where his center of mass has been lifted ten feet above the trampoline bed. From this information, how can the coach calculate initial and final velocities and the total amount of time the performer has in the air to execute the required skills?

$$10 = \frac{(\text{Velocity})^2}{64}$$

$$\text{Velocity} = \sqrt{640} \quad = 25.3 \text{ ft/sec}$$

$$\text{Time} = \sqrt{\frac{8 \times 10}{32}} = 1.6 \text{ seconds}$$

Since the upward and downward motions are symmetric, the velocity calculated in the example above represents both the upward speed leaving the trampoline bed and the downward speed striking the bed.

In most sport trajectories, however, motion is not purely vertical. Trajectories are a combination of vertical and horizontal motions. The important principle to be observed here is that in a very real sense these two directions of motion are independent. This makes the job of analysis somewhat easier since the conditions related to vertical motion can be used to determine time of flight, and horizontal velocity is used to determine distance the body or object travels. For example, a hurdler combines vertical and horizontal motions during his trajectory over the hurdle (fig. 4.5).

If it is assumed that the performer raises his center of gravity 18 inches (1.5 feet) while crossing a hurdle:

$$\text{Time} = \sqrt{\frac{8 \times 1.5}{32}} = 0.6 \text{ seconds}$$

$$1.5 = \frac{(\text{Vert. velocity})^2}{64}$$

$$\text{Vert. velocity} = \sqrt{96} = 9.8 \text{ ft/sec}$$

Thus, during takeoff the hurdler must give himself a vertical component of velocity of nearly 10 ft/sec. If his horizontal component of velocity is 22 ft/sec during flight, the total distance covered per hurdle is:

$$\text{Distance} = \text{Velocity} \times \text{Time} = 22 \times 0.6 = 13.2 \text{ feet}$$

It should be noticed in the case of hurdling that the desired result is accomplished by maintaining a maximum average horizontal velocity. If the hurdler actually jumps the hurdles, giving himself an excessive vertical component, he has a longer period of time in the air at a correspondingly lower horizontal velocity. Average horizontal velocity is decreased, and this means it will take the hurdler longer to run the entire race. Therefore, the stereotype of perfect form for hurdling involves the idea that a minimum amount of vertical motion of the hurdler's center of mass and maintenance of a steady maximum horizontal component should be attained during the trajectory over the hurdle. This is one reason the upper body is brought low (hip joint and lumbar spine flexions) as the legs are passing over the hurdle. The performer's center of gravity is maintained through these movements at a minimum height at the vertical peak of the trajectory.

Figure 4.5. Vertical and horizontal motions during a trajectory by Ralph Mann, U.S.A. Olympic team, over an intermediate hurdle.

Courtesy Visual Track and Field Techniques, 292 So. LaCienaga Blvd., Beverly Hills,Calif. 90211

Consider, for example, a performer whose form causes him to raise his center of gravity two feet and decrease his horizontal velocity to 19 ft/sec:

$$\text{Time of flight} = \sqrt{\frac{8 \times 2}{32}} = 0.7 \text{ seconds}$$

$$\text{Distance covered} = \text{Velocity} \times \text{Time} = 19 \times 0.7 = 13.3 \text{ ft}$$

As compared to the previous performer, this performer is taking 0.1 seconds longer to go essentially the same horizontal distance over the hurdle. Multiply this loss by the number of hurdles in a race and you have the difference between a winning effort and a poor showing.

It can be shown that under a condition of nearly constant horizontal velocity combined with a vertical motion, which first opposes gravity and then falls back in the same direction as gravity, the path followed by the body or sport object conforms to the geometrical shape known as a *parabola*. This is the origin of the term *parabolic trajectory* often used in describing sport motions. The term *trajectory* is a generalized term indicating the actual path followed by a freely moving nonsupported body. Such factors as drag due to air resistance and lift obtained in a flying object actually cause the trajectory to deviate from a true parabola. The true parabola is actually a mathematic construct and is probably most closely followed in sports by the paths of shots or hammers after they are put into the air. In these cases, the weights and inertia they have while traveling through the air are large when compared to any forces exerted by the air itself.

The actual shape of a parabola followed by an object moving through the air depends on (1) the velocity with which it leaves its base of support and (2) the angle at which it initially moves into the air. Projection into the air at a low angle gives a larger horizontal component of velocity but a smaller vertical component. Therefore, a low projection angle results in a correspondingly smaller time of flight. Projection at a high angle provides a large vertical component of velocity and a long time of flight, but there is a correspondingly lower horizontal velocity during this time.

Examples of the use of two angles of trajectory in a sport situation would be the spinless, low-velocity forehand shot on one hand and the contrasting lob shot in tennis on the other hand (fig. 4.6). Using the low trajectory, the amount of time necessary to reach the point where the ball contacts the court is at a minimum. This has the strategic offensive advantage of giving the opponent

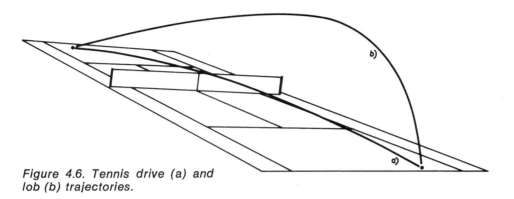

*Figure 4.6. Tennis drive (a) and
lob (b) trajectories.*

a minimum amount of time to react. When the lob shot is used, the amount
of time necessary to reach the contact point on the court becomes a maximum.
The offensive player hitting the lob shot provides himself with a maximum
amount of time to make a recovery of body position and establish a strategic
defensive position on the court.

The maximum range for a projected sport object striking the ground at
the same level from which it takes off exists at the compromise between these
"pure" horizontal and vertical factors or a projection angle of forty-five degrees.
The utilization of this optimum projection angle is relatively rare in sport or
dance motions since the body or sport object seldom completes the motion at
the same level from which it takes off. The equations applicable in these types of
calculations are as follows:

$$\text{Time of flight} = \frac{2(\text{Vertical velocity})}{g}$$

$$\text{Range} = \text{Horizontal velocity} \times \text{Time of flight}$$

To use trigonometric calculations:

$$\text{Vertical velocity} = \text{Initial velocity} \times \sin \Theta$$

$$\text{Horizontal velocity} = \text{Initial velocity} \times \cos \Theta$$

$$\text{Where } \Theta = \text{Angle with ground at takeoff}$$

Horizontal and vertical components of velocity applicable in these equations can be read directly from film by analyzing the horizontal and vertical motions indicated on the film. These observations would be made during an intermediate cinematographic analysis. The components can also be calculated by measurement of total speed and angle as shown in the film. However, this requires the use of trigonometric functions which are not included in this introductory text. If the tennis player strikes the ball at an angle of fifteen degrees above the horizontal and a speed of 60 ft/sec, then:

$$V \text{ (vertical)} = 15.5 \text{ ft/sec}$$

$$V \text{ (horizontal)} = 58 \text{ ft/sec}$$

$$\text{Max height} = \frac{(15.5)^2}{2 \times 32} = 3.75 \text{ ft}$$

$$\text{Time of flight} = \frac{2(15.5)}{32} = 0.97 \text{ sec}$$

$$\text{Range} = 58 \times 0.97 = 56.2 \text{ ft}$$

The ball would barely clear the net and strike the ground 56.2 feet away about one second after the stroke.

If, however, the player strikes the ball with the same speed and an initial angle of seventy-five degrees with the horizontal:

$$V \text{ (vertical)} = 58 \text{ ft/sec}$$

$$V \text{ (horizontal)} = 15.5 \text{ ft/sec}$$

$$\text{Max height} = \frac{(58)^2}{2 \times 32} = 52.5 \text{ ft}$$

$$\text{Time of flight} = \frac{2 \times 58}{32} = 3.62 \text{ seconds}$$

$$\text{Range} = 3.62 \times 15.5 = 56.1 \text{ ft}$$

The ball would strike nearly the same point as previously but 3.6 seconds after the stroke.

In the case where the landing point is not at the same height as the point at which the object enters the air, the angle of release for maximum range will not be forty-five degrees. In the case of the shot put, the optimum angle is a function of both velocity of release and the height at which the performer loses contact with the shot. Figures 4.7 and 4.8 illustrate typical values for these parameters for various classes of performers.

In general, the optimum angle decreases with a decrease in velocity or an increase in release height.

	Championship	College	High School	Junior High
Release height	8.5 feet	8.5 feet	8.0 feet	7.0 feet
Velocity	45 ft/sec	40 ft/sec	37 ft/sec	33 ft/sec

Figure 4.7. Release heights and velocities for shot-putting

	Championship	College	High School	Junior High
45°	70.55 ft	57.15 ft	49.5 ft	39.8 ft
44°	70.75	57.35	49.65	40.00
43°	70.90	57.50	49.78	40.10
42°	70.95	57.60	49.88	40.20
41°	70.95	57.65	49.92	40.22
40°	70.90	57.60	49.92	40.25
39°	70.70	57.55	49.88	40.22
38°	70.55	57.40	49.80	40.20

Figure 4.8. Range as a function of angle in shot-putting

The idea of a trajectory being a true mathematic parabola is based on the assumption that the only force acting on the subject in free flight is the force of gravity. Unfortunately, for almost all body and sport object motions in flight, there is an interaction with air, causing the trajectory to deviate from the true parabolic pattern. The air actually has two effects on the flights of bodies or objects: (1) *drag*, which is a force exactly opposite to the direction of motion and dependent on the shape of the object and amount of turbulence behind it, and (2) in some cases there is a *lift* due to a downward forcing of the air by the shape or angle of flight of the object. These two effects combine to give widely varying paths for different types of objects. Because of the importance of the interaction of bodies or objects with air, the next chapter will be devoted to the subject of aerodynamics.

An interesting and sometimes unnoticed example of trajectory motion occurs with the human body during jumping activities in sport and dance. In the high jump, long jump, triple jump, and dance leaps, the center of gravity of the performer is executing a near-parabolic trajectory during the time of free flight. In these cases, however, the motions of body parts in rotation or other motion about the center of gravity quite often masks the apparent path of the center of gravity. Observation of the trajectory of the center of gravity is also made difficult by motions of the limbs during these events. These limb motions tend to cause shifts in the actual position of the center of gravity but do not change the trajectory of the body's center of gravity previously established at takeoff.

In the Fosbury Flop style of high jumping, for example, the center of gravity would lie somewhere between the iliac crests during takeoff; but at the time the pelvic girdle is passing over the bar, the positions of the upper and lower limbs cause the center of gravity to lie somewhere below the body of the performer (fig. 4.9). While the rules specify that each part of the body must pass over the bar, it is at least theoretically possible for a performer to successfully execute a high jump with his center of gravity never reaching the height of the bar.

In the long jump, the performer must compromise between executing a high trajectory, which will give him a long time in the air, and maintaining a high horizontal speed, which will carry him linearly as far as possible during this flight time (fig. 4.10). It has been found that the conscious attempt at a high trajectory during long jumping has a tendency to decrease speed to such an extent that the total distance of the jump will be lessened. This leads to the technique of running off the takeoff board instead of jumping vertically (fig. 4.11).

Courtesy USC Athletic News Service

Figure 4.9. Shifting of the center of gravity during the Fosbury Flop as executed by Dean Owens, USC high jumper.

Figure 4.10. Long jump flight by Randy Williams, USC and U.S.A. Olympic team long jumper.

Figure 4.11. The long jump as performed by Johnny Johnson, U.S.A. Olympic team.

Courtesy Visual Track and Field Techniques, 292 So. LaCienaga
Blvd., Beverly Hills, Calif. 90211

Landing techniques included in the stereotype of perfect long jump form are designed to allow the center of gravity to drop as low as possible before any body part touches the pit, and the performer allows himself to move over that body part first touching the pit in order to obtain the maximum measured distance for the jump. The maintenance of a large horizontal velocity is also important in the landing because the body must be carried angularly over the point at which the feet hit, without falling backwards. Measurement is made from the takeoff board to the nearest point touched by a body part in the jumping area.

In the triple jump, the maintenance of horizontal velocity is even more important than in the long jump. The horizontal velocity in triple jumping must be carried through a series of motions. Thus, there are three separate trajectories, and the horizontal velocity must be maintained past the first two in order to obtain maximum distance. For this reason, it is found that the final takeoff angle for triple jumpers is generally several degrees lower than for long jumpers. Also, the most accepted form seems to be one in which the "step" portion of the performance covers a smaller distance than either the initial takeoff portion or the final jump. Normally in the execution of the event, the trajectory found in the final or "jump" portion of the triple jump has considerably more altitude than that found in either of the other two parts of the event. The difficulty of the triple jump lies in the fact that the three jumps are designed to interrupt the summation of linear forces and decrease the average horizontal velocity. Good triple jumpers overcome this biomechanic problem. This is an example in sport where rules of the event predetermine an inefficient series of motions and add to the difficulty of the event.

One final example related to body motions during an apparent jump is the situation of the steeplechaser in crossing one of the barriers. While these barriers may be hurdled, they are designed in such a way that the performer can place a foot on top, push off, and aid his subsequent motion (fig. 4.12). The motion of the center of mass in passing over the steeple will not be a true parabolic trajectory because he uses the steeple as a point to exert force with the foot at the midpoint of the maneuver. One would expect a plot of the trajectory of the center of gravity to have a parabolic rise followed by an additional rise again before falling on the far side of the steeple.

FORCES AND COUNTERFORCES

In a discussion of any motion involved in a sport, exercise, or dance context, the application of various forces and counterforces which occur within the human body is of great importance. As has been noted, almost all body movement must be described in terms of rotation about various joints. Any muscular action causing a motion of one part of the body also causes a compensatory motion elsewhere. This is made more complex by neurologic reflexive mechanisms which often combine certain types of motions with others at a subcon-

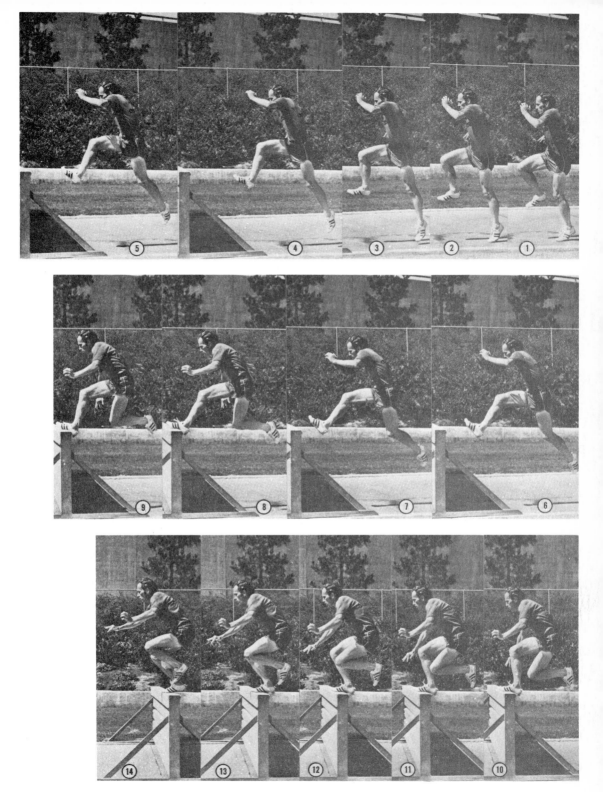

Figure 4.12. Steeplechase trajectory modification as demonstrated by Bill Reilly, U.S.A. Olympic team.

Courtesy Visual Track and Field Techniques, 292
So. LaCienaga Blvd., Beverly Hills, Calif.
90211

scious level. An example of this is the crossed-extensor reflex where the flexion of one arm tends to cause an automatic extension of the other. This complex force-counterforce reaction is also evident in learned skills such as walking and running, where there is a set of equal and opposite motions occurring in upper and lower limbs. Many sport and dance skills are actually learned complex sets of force-counterforce movements.

Force and counterforce in linear motion have an exact parallel in torque and countertorque of angular motion. For example, during ballistic actions muscles rotate the pelvic region and counterrotate the lumbar-thoracic spine concurrently during the preparatory phase of a throw or kick. This torque-countertorque effect is especially notable in those situations where a ballistic motion leading to generation of maximum force or velocity is of utmost importance.

This principle is also observed in many sport objects where an extreme acceleration in one direction is countered with an equal change of momentum in the opposite direction as in the "kick" of a rifle or shotgun in hunting or sport shooting. The effects of counterforce can often be lessened by use of a large body mass to receive it. For example, if one holds a shotgun during skeet shooting away from the shoulder when firing it, the relatively small mass of the gun will acquire a high velocity, and the impact of the butt of the shotgun at the shoulder will be quite painful. On the other hand, if the gun butt is pressed tightly against the shoulder before firing, the momentum of the "kick" is absorbed throughout the gun and the body of the hunter. The effects of counterforce, therefore, are much less noticeable.

A large number of learned motion techniques are designed to aid in absorption of excess velocity or momentum. For example, a long jumper in the landing phase neither lands completely extended at the knees, hips, and spinal column, nor does he allow all joints to move into extreme and damaging flexions. Full extension at major joints would involve excessive accelerations, large forces, and potential joint trauma. Upon landing, the performer controls the extent of flexions at the ankles, knees, hips, and spinal column by eccentric or lengthening contractions of the muscles associated with these areas. This eccentric contraction absorbs momentum and the energy associated with landing. The same stretched muscle groups contract concentrically immediately after landing to provide the rotation and extension necessary to rotate the long jumper over his base of support.

An interesting application of force and counterforce in ancient sports was the Greek Olympic form of the long jump. The performer came up to the takeoff point holding two hand weights or halteres. These were carried high and in front of him. When the jump was begun, the halteres were thrown sharply downward and backward. The force applied to these weights by the performer resulted in a counterforce which carried him farther in the jump. While this technique is no longer used in track-and-field events, it does come into play in an analogous fashion in competitive swimming where the basic idea is to shove the water backward in order to provide a forward thrust to the swimmer's body. This interaction will be discussed more fully in chapter six, which is concerned with hydrodynamics of water sports.

The absorption of these counterforces is much more difficult when the performer is not on the ground where a base of support can be established against the counterforce. For example, the jump pass in football is no longer considered good technique because the control of the passer's body motions is hampered to the point that distance and accuracy of the pass are lessened, i.e., forces are dissipated. The passer on the ground, on the other hand, utilizes the position of the rear foot to absorb the counterforce induced by the throwing of the ball. Therefore, there is a more effective arm movement, resulting in the probability of a more accurately thrown pass. In some sports, however, ballistic motions involving forces and counterforces without a base of support are a necessary maneuver. For example, a prime scoring technique in water polo is for the offensive player to come upward with his trunk and shoulders out of the water in full spinal extension. Through a series of torques causing rotation of the lumbar-thoracic spine, he makes a forceful shot toward the goal (fig. 4.13). Although the water has a certain viscous resistance, this is minimal and does not provide the necessary base of support for a full absorption of the counterforce. In any event, the skilled water polo player is able to impart enough velocity to the ball to be effective. Although the performer in this maneuver may lose balance, the fact that he is falling into water during his follow-through rather than onto ground minimizes the results of his disequilibrium.

The use of the foot to provide a stable absorption of the counterforce is important in the tennis serve. In order to provide an optimum trajectory over the net and into the serving court, the performer attempts to strike the ball as high off the ground as possible. However, if the player actually leaves the ground in attempting to reach the ball before striking it, the body reaction to the swing

Figure 4.13. Force applied against a minimal resistive counterforce during a water polo shot.

actually lessens the velocity of the racket head. This decreases speed and has an adverse effect on accuracy. Sometimes a performer is observed leaving the ground during the follow-through, but this has no effect on the speed of the ball.

Torque and countertorque are especially important since basic body movements are rotational in nature. An excellent example of the use of countertorque is found in the long jump style used by Bob Beamon, the present world record holder. One of the basic problems in long jumping is to keep the legs and feet as high in the air as possible during the latter part of the jump. In order to accomplish this, Beamon uses an extreme circumduction of the arms and lumbar-thoracic flexion. The erector spinae musculature plays the major role in the eccentric control of flexion within the lumbar-thoracic region in order to provide this rotation. The countertorque provided by this deep back musculature and gravitational pull facilitates raising the legs through an extreme hip flexion during the latter part of flight. This leg position allows the trajectory to continue to a point where the center of gravity is very close to the ground before any part of the body strikes the pit.

This extreme use of torque and countertorque has a second effect in the landing maneuver which Beamon is able to perform. Just prior to landing, he moves the hips and knees into a semiextended position. This forces the body upward and drives the heels downward into the pit. This extra lift gained from the heels is then used to carry the body over the landing position.

Another example of the use of torque and countertorque is in the balancing mechanism used by pole-vaulters and ski-jumpers while in flight. One of the problems generated by the new heights attained in pole-vaulting is simply landing in the proper position after completing the vault. For purposes of safety, the vaulter would like to land as flat as possible on the back of the rib cage, with the hips flexed. In order to achieve this position, the vaulter often will perform circumduction of both shoulder joints while in the air. This causes a rotational motion of the arms during the fall. The torque used to cause this rotation of the arms then develops a countertorque, rotating the body backward to achieve the proper landing position.

Likewise, in the sport of ski jumping one often sees circular or circumduction motion of the arms used to achieve balance in order to maintain the proper position before landing. In this case, the jumper goes into flight in roughly the position in which he would desire to land. However, if he has developed a small amount of angular momentum on leaving the ski jump, this tends to rotate him into an unfavorable position which could be disastrous and/or traumatic upon landing. Therefore, he uses circumduction of the arms simply to maintain the initial equilibrium position and keep his feet below him.

One last example of torque and countertorque lies in the optimum use of spine and shoulder motions during hurdling. As a hurdler approaches the hurdle, the motion of bringing the lead leg up and forward (hip flexion) involves a lateral rotation at the opposite hip just prior to the time the foot of the takeoff leg leaves the ground. This rotation, if not counteracted, could rotate the whole body through the transverse plane. Since this is an undesired motion, a countertorque is provided by a diagonal adduction of the shoulder joint on the side of the takeoff leg. This has the effect of driving that arm forward very rapidly through the high diagonal plane (diagonal adduction). Also, as the legs come up to pass over the hurdle, a flexion of the lumbar-thoracic spine combined with the shoulder-joint movements causes a rotation of the upper part of the body. This motion has the effect of minimizing the vertical lift of the center of gravity. (See fig. 9.1.)

COLLISION

The concept of a collision or impact between two bodies is a common occurrence in all types of sport and dance performances. From the point of view of biomechanics, impact may occur between two bodies, a body and sport object, an implement and object, or between a body or object and the ground or floor. As mentioned previously in the discussion on momentum and impulse, collisions may occur with high forces for very short time periods. Or, they may be sustained types of interactions with lower average forces occurring for longer periods of time. In either case, although the precise forces occurring at each instant during the collision cannot be analyzed, the change of momentum of each body can be observed to determine the total impulse of the collision.

Because of the difficulty of measuring forces occurring at each instant, the most efficient method of analyzing collision is in terms of the momenta of the bodies involved. If the total amount of momentum which each body carries into a collision can be measured, the total momentum of the system becomes a known factor. This, in turn, determines the momentum and direction the bodies will move after the collision. This principle in many types of human body or sport implement collisions leads to the importance of the follow-through in sustaining the contact of the collision and maximizing the impulse. The sustained block by the offensive football lineman is a classic example of an impact being sustained in order to continue building impulse. The proper technique for performing this maneuver is to make contact with the defensive lineman being blocked and continue this contact until such time as a force can no longer be supplied against him. This will often take an average of two to four seconds, or a major portion of the time involved to execute the play. Sustained contact is also necessary in those situations where spin is imparted to an object.

Energy Transfers During Collision

Since a collision always occurs between two bodies or objects moving on a course relative to each other, the initial energy of prime concern takes the form of kinetic energy. During the impact of collision, the change of shape or deformation of the bodies or objects produces a potential energy during the time of contact. Following the collision, as the bodies separate again relative to each other, there is a transformation back to kinetic energy. When considering the human body, sport implements, and objects, the transfer from initial to final kinetic energy is not perfectly efficient, i.e., during the deformation phase a certain amount of work goes into the form of heat or into a permanent deformation of the bodies. The loss of energy into heat is primarily due to internal friction within the bodies rather than by surface friction at their point of contact.

If the loss of energy during a collision is negligible or zero, the collision is described as being perfectly elastic. In a perfectly elastic collision, momentum is conserved. Furthermore, kinetic energy remains as kinetic energy. In any other collision, momentum will continue to be conserved, but part of the kinetic energy is transformed into heat. One of the examples nearest to a perfectly elastic collision in sport is the collision between two billiard balls. In this case, almost all total kinetic energy is conserved as kinetic energy after the collision. In the case of a head-on collision between spinless balls, the conservation of both momentum and kinetic energy during this collision means that the two balls must exchange velocities. Since one of the billiard balls is stationary before the head-on collision, the other ball will be motionless or have slight motion after the collision.

The other extreme in collisions is the type of impact which causes two colliding bodies to remain together. Scientifically, this is called a perfectly inelastic collision. Probably the most common example of a perfectly inelastic collision in sport occurs when a performer or sport object hits the ground and does not bounce. In this case, the body and ground represent the colliding bodies, and in essence they are "sticking together." An important factor in inelastic collisions is the amount of distortion occurring before the colliding bodies achieve the state of cohesion. Since the total relative momentum and relative kinetic energy must be absorbed during the time of collision, a very short period of active collision or small distortion leads to very large forces during the collision. This, for example, is the difference between hitting hard-packed ground and softer ground. The greater amount of elasticity means a smaller average force during the time the performer is stopping. Therefore, there is less chance for injury. This principle is used in the design of good wrestling mats. A more extreme example would be the situation of a slalom skier who misses a gate and falls into soft snow. He may travel a very great distance before finally coming to rest, and the smaller coefficient of friction within the snow makes this sliding type of fall much less dangerous to the skier than a similar fall of a motorcyclist on an asphalt or dirt track.

Another example of an inelastic collision with reference to horizontal motion is what takes place during a tackle on a football field. Both the runner and tackler have an initial momentum. As they collide and lock together, due to the arm action of the tackler, both of them move in a path determined by the sum of these momenta.

For example, assume that a 220-pound fullback moving at 25 ft/sec is met head on by a 180-pound defensive back moving at 15 ft/sec:

$$\text{Momentum (fullback)} = \frac{220}{32} \times 25 = 172 \text{ momentum units}$$

$$\text{Momentum (defensive back)} = \frac{180}{32} \times 15 = 84.4 \text{ momentum units}$$

Since the two are moving in opposite directions, the momentum after collision is the difference in their two individual momenta:

$$\text{Momentum (combined)} = 172 - 84.4 = 87.6 \text{ momentum units}$$

Therefore, at the instant of collision and before any momentum is transferred to the ground by other forces, the combination of fullback and tackler has 87.6 momentum units in the direction in which the fullback was originally moving. To find their velocity at this instant:

$$\text{Momentum} = 87.6 = \frac{180 + 220}{32} \times \text{Velocity}$$

$$\text{Velocity} = \frac{87.6 \times 32}{400} = 7 \text{ ft/sec}$$

During the immediate collision, the fullback is slowed from 25 ft/sec to 7 ft/sec, while the defensive back has his velocity reversed from 15 ft/sec to 7 ft/sec in the opposite direction. In this situation, the biomechanic advantage is given to the fullback.

In the previous chapter, *coefficient of restitution* was discussed with reference to elastic bodies. Coefficient of restitution is a term utilized in collision-type situations. *This coefficient is the measure of an object's kinetic energy after a collision, usually with a solid surface, compared to the amount of kinetic energy that it had prior to the collision.* This takes into account the amount of kinetic energy lost in the form of heat or deformation of the body.

Earlier it was calculated that the coefficient of restitution of an official handball was approximately 0.64. This means that on each vertical bounce sixty-four percent of the kinetic energy is retained, and thirty-six percent is converted into heat. In most sports where this quantity is specified, it is done in terms of the height of rebound after a specified drop. The gravitational potential energy before the drop is converted into kinetic energy before the collision. A certain percentage of this energy is maintained during the collision and is converted into potential energy again at the height of rebound.

Tennis rules specify a rebound of 53 to 58 inches for a tennis ball following a drop of 100 inches. This gives a coefficient of restitution of about 0.55, somewhat less than that of a handball. Lacrosse rules specify a rebound of 45 to 49 inches for the lacrosse ball after a drop of 72 inches. This results in a coefficient of restitution of about 0.65, the same as a handball.

The difference in coefficient of restitution becomes quite apparent in multiple-bounce situations. Since a certain percentage of energy is lost with each bounce, a succession of bounces dissipates the energy in a multiplicative fashion. That is, after the first bounce a handball has 64 percent of its original energy; after the second only 64 percent $\times$ 64 percent, or 41 percent, and so forth. Figure 4.14 compares a series of bounces of a lacrosse ball and a tennis ball to illustrate this effect.

	Coeff.	Drop	Height of Bounce (inches)				
			1st	2nd	3rd	4th	5th
Lacrosse	0.65	100 inches	65	42	27	18	11.5
Tennis	0.55	100 inches	55	30	16.5	9	5

Figure 4.14. Coefficient of restitution changes

In sports where multiple bounces are an integral part of rules and strategy, a higher coefficient of restitution is usually needed. Also, it should be pointed out that the coefficient of restitution is often a function of total distortion. A baseball may have a small coefficient of restitution for small forces but a much larger coefficient when struck by a bat or when striking the ground at high velocity.

The actual rebound velocity of a sport object may depend on the condition of both the object and the surface from which it is rebounding. For example, "dead spots" on gymnasia floors are rather common. Dribbling a basketball on such a floor becomes difficult because the ball simply does not bounce back effectively when it strikes a "dead spot." An even more critical situation in regard to basketball courts is the firmness with which backboards are supported. A variation in the "give" of the backboard can determine to a great extent whether rebounds fall close or away from the basket area. This affects both the positioning and the timing of rebounders. Knowledge of this reflection factor can add to the "home court advantage" in some cases.

The relationship between forces or energies involved in an elastic deformation and the actual distance of body deformation is called compressibility. An object with high compressibility will suffer large distortions with relatively moderate forces. On the other hand, an object with low compressibility shows very little "give" for extremely large forces. It should be emphasized here that virtually all sport objects are compressible to a certain extent. Probably the least compressible object in sport is the billiard ball.

Because all objects during collision are compressed somewhat and rebound to their original shape, there is a definite time associated with collision. A greater amount of compression results in a longer time of contact, and this contributes to a lower average force used to impart a given change of momentum.

In chapter three it was calculated that the change of momentum of a batted softball was approximately four momentum units. If the ball was new and quite hard, this change might be imparted by the bat in a period as short as $\frac{1}{100}$ second. In this case:

$$\text{Avg. force} \times \text{Time} = \text{Change of momentum}$$

$$\text{Average force} = \frac{4}{\frac{1}{100}} = 400 \text{ pounds}$$

If the ball were used enough to become soft, this time of contact with the bat might last as long as $\frac{1}{20}$ second,

$$\text{Average force} = \frac{4}{\frac{1}{20}} = 80 \text{ pounds}$$

A greater or lesser time of collision may strongly affect a performer's action in striking something with a sport implement, since the amount of contact time between the implement and the sport object determines, to a great extent, such factors as accuracy and amount of spin imparted to the object. This relationship between collision time and the resultant spin from that collision is presented later in this section.

Compressibility is a factor which may vary over a wide range in seemingly identical balls or other sport objects. It should not be assumed by a performer that a series of supposedly identical sport objects will behave the same under all situations. For example, even among a dozen high-grade softballs one may find small, but noticeable, variations in such factors as compressibility, weight, and surface-roughness characteristics. This lack of manufacturer's quality control has strong implications to the performances and strategies used during a contest, because each ball may have different interactions and motions during a collision or flight through the air. Highly skilled fast-pitch softball pitchers take full advantage of compressibility variations of softballs.

Glancing Collisions

A large number of collisions of interest in sport application are those where the collision is not "head on." In this type of collision, a sidewise motion is introduced to both objects simply due to the angle at which they hit. Since momentum is a vector quantity, it is conserved both in the initial line of motion and in the direction perpendicular to this initial line. This means that both the speed of the objects after collisions and the angles at which they rebound are determined by conservation of momentum.

If a billiard ball moving at 20 ft/sec strikes a second ball in such a way that it moves off at 14.14 ft/sec at an angle of 45 degrees to the path of the first ball, what is the subsequent motion of the first ball? The motion of 14.14 ft/sec

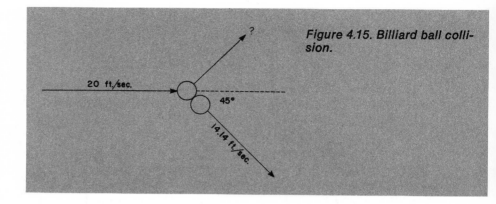

Figure 4.15. Billiard ball collision.

at 45 degrees represents components of 10 ft/sec in the original direction of motion and 10 ft/sec laterally perpendicular to this original direction (fig. 4.15).

To find the component of motion of the first ball in its original direction, use the conservation of momentum in that direction:

$$\text{Mass}_1 \times 20 = \Big(\text{Mass}_2 \times 10\Big) + \Big(\text{Mass}_1 \times \text{Velocity (parallel)}\Big)$$

Since the two masses are the same:

$$\text{Velocity (parallel)} = 20 - 10 = 10\,\text{ft/sec}$$

Since the original motion had no lateral component of momentum, the sum of the lateral components after the collision must be zero:

$$\Big(\text{Mass}_1 \times \text{Velocity (perpendicular)}\Big) - \Big(\text{Mass}_2 \times 10\Big) = \text{Zero}$$

$$\text{Velocity (perpendicular)} = 10\,\text{ft/sec}$$

The first ball would move with an equal and opposite lateral velocity to that of the second ball. The total motion of the first ball would be the sum of these two components, or a speed of 14.14 ft/sec at an angle of 45 degrees to the original direction (fig. 4.16).

The problems are slightly more complex if the two bodies do not have the same mass. If a bowling ball moving at 25 ft/sec strikes a pin and gives it a velocity of 28.3 ft/sec at an angle of 45 degrees, how much is the path of the ball deviated and how much does the ball slow down?

Consider an average 3.25-pound pin and a 13-pound ball. A velocity of 28.3 ft/sec at 45 degrees has components of 20 ft/sec parallel and 20 ft/sec perpendicular to the original motion (fig. 4.17).

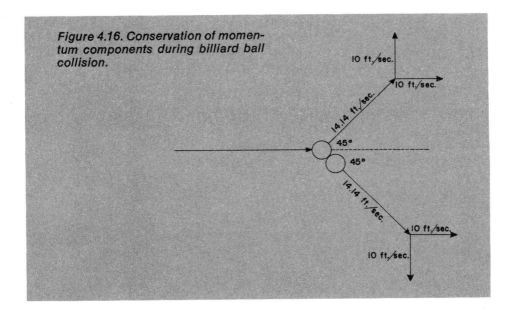

Figure 4.16. Conservation of momentum components during billiard ball collision.

10 ft./sec.

10 ft./sec.

14.14 ft./sec.

45°

45°

14.14 ft./sec.

10 ft./sec.

10 ft./sec.

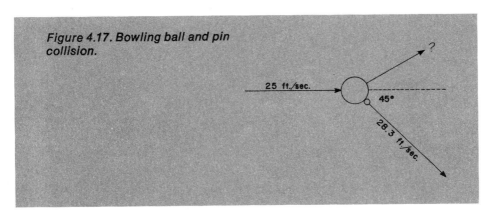

Figure 4.17. Bowling ball and pin collision.

25 ft./sec.

?

45°

28.3 ft./sec.

To find the velocity of the ball parallel to its original direction:

$$\frac{13}{32} \times 25 \text{ ft/sec} = \left(\frac{3.25}{32} \times 20 \text{ ft/sec}\right) + \left(\frac{13}{32} \times \text{Velocity (parallel)}\right)$$

$$\text{Velocity (parallel)} = \frac{(13 \times 25) - (3.25 \times 20)}{13} = 20 \text{ ft/sec}$$

The perpendicular velocity is given by:

$$\left(\frac{13}{32} \times \text{Velocity (perpendicular)}\right) - \left(\frac{3.25}{32} \times 20\right) = \text{Zero}$$

$$\text{Velocity (perpendicular)} = \frac{3.25 \times 20}{13} = 5 \text{ ft/sec}$$

Combining these two components provides a total motion of the ball of 20.6 ft/sec at an angle of 14 degrees from the original line of motion (fig. 4.18).

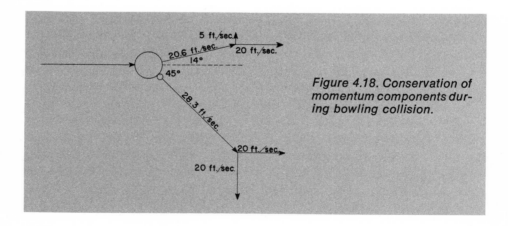

Figure 4.18. Conservation of momentum components during bowling collision.

The actual results of a glancing collision are highly dependent on a factor known as the impact parameter. *Impact parameter is a measure of the relationship between the direction of motion of colliding bodies and the line joining their center at the time of collision* (fig. 4.19).

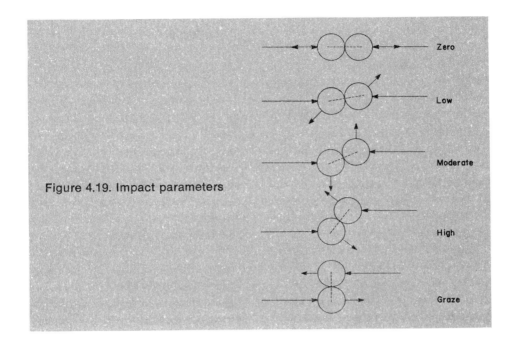

Figure 4.19. Impact parameters

The results of impacts between bodies of equal mass and speed at various impact parameters are:

Zero—pure rebound along the lines of approach
Low—primarily rebound but also with lateral motion
Moderate—primarily lateral motion; each body moves off at near a right angle
High—lateral motion but with each object having a component in the direction of the original motion
Graze—minimal change of motion on the part of either body

For cases where the objects have unequal masses and velocities or where surface friction is important, the changes of motion become more complex.

The foul ball in baseball or softball is a good example of a collision between a sport implement and a sport object with a high impact parameter. The contact between the ball and bat occurs at an off-center position as related to their relative lines of motion. Actually, in this case the curved surfaces of both the bat and the ball add to the effect of the impact parameter. Contact produces a motion of the ball perpendicular to its original line of flight. Instead of returning toward the playing field, the foul ball often goes high into the air and behind the batter.

Figure 4.20 provides the angles at which softballs leave the bat as a function of the impact parameter for a knuckle ball (spinless). It is assumed that the batter is swinging horizontally, the ball is moving upward at a four- to five-degree angle as it approaches, and there is no appreciable rebound of the bat. The parameter, *d*, represents the distance in inches below the center of the ball that the line of motion of the center of the bat passes.

	d (inches)	Angle Above Horizontal
Figure 4.20. Angles of projection as a result of impact parameters.	0.25	17°
	0.50	27°
	0.75	38°
	1.00	50°
	1.25	more than 60°

From this it can be observed that in order to successfully hit the ball, the batter must match the center of the bat barrel within the range from ¼ inch above the center of the ball—to hit at least a hard ground ball—to ¾ inch below the center of the ball—to hit anything other than a high fly ball. This range represents the allowable margin of error for hitting.

The glancing block between ice hockey players is another example of an impact parameter. As two players approach one another and bump shoulders, what happens is not an appreciable slowing of either player. However, the direction of each is deflected to one side of the original line of skating. This is much more exaggerated in ice hockey than it would be in a field sport played on grass because of the low friction between the performer and the ice surface.

Due to this fact, the ice hockey player moves with the lateral force occurring during the collision in order to maintain equilibrium.

A second effect of a glancing collision is the introduction of a spin into the objects involved in the collision. The fact that the direction of the line of centers at the point of collision is not the same as the direction of motion of the body means that the force can be broken into a component perpendicular to the surface, which causes a linear acceleration of the body, plus a force component parallel to the surface. The latter is the frictionally related component. The effect of this frictional force is to produce a torque around the center of gravity of the body, resulting in a spinning motion of one or both bodies. This spin factor is also observed in the example of the batted ball. A foul ball has a high spin component, and this must be considered by the player attempting to catch it.

Arm tackling in American football is another example of rotational motion introduced by an off-center collision. Arm tackling is considered a poor technique in American football. In this case, the tackler does not make a head-on collision with the ball carrier but, rather, hits him with one arm and shoulder. The result of this type of collision is often to spin both players, and the runner remains on his feet while the tackler loses contact and rotates around him. The momentum of the tackler often causes him to release the runner, and this leaves the ball carrier free to gain extra yardage during the play.

Many times in sport the body segment or limb motions before the collision and/or the position of the sport implement are used to impart an effective spin onto the object being hit. As an example, faces of various golf clubs are set at different angles, partially to give lift to the ball during the swing, but also to impart a backspin. Because of the slant of the striking surfaces of the irons, the relative velocity between the club face and the ball at the time of collision includes both a normal force component which drives the ball and a frictional component which imparts backspin to the ball. As will be discussed in the next chapter, this backspin is very important in giving an aerodynamic lift and greater range to the drive. Designs of club face and ball surfaces provide a maximum coefficient of friction between these two surfaces during the collision. The golfer is helped in his attempt to impart an optimum amount of spin to the ball.

In the sport of Ping-Pong, or table tennis, there is a very special relationship between the angle of the paddle and the direction of motion of the arm and hand at the time of contact with the ball. This implement-motion relationship is used to impart a wide variety of spins to the Ping-Pong ball. In order to produce high forward spin on the ball, a medial rotation of the shoulder joint is used during a forehand shot in order to bring the paddle up and over the ball during the time of contact. A good backhand shot is made by a diagonal adduction at the shoulder joint combined with an extension at the elbow. If no lateral rotation of the shoulder is made during this type of shot, the ball will have a backspin. The addition of a lateral rotation to the above motions produces a forward spin during a backhand slam.

Another important concept to be considered in collisions between sport implements and sport objects is the idea of the *center of percussion*—sometimes called the "sweet spot" on a bat or racket. This concept is strongly concerned with the relationship between the implement and the performer. In a swing of a bat or racket, the implement is acting as an extension of the performer's limbs. This provides extra leverage and has a multiplying relationship to the velocity of the implement. If there is an attempted rotation of the implement in the hands of the performer during collision, this leads to less than optimum results. When a ball is struck near the top or bottom of a racket, golf club, or bat, it tends to twist the handle in the grip of the performer. There is also the possibility, however, of a rotation of the implement around a transverse axis of the motion. In this case, the implement tries to pull out of or "jam" into the hand of the performer. Probably the most common example of this is hitting a baseball either on the end of the barrel or on the handle portion of the bat. In either case, there is a strong motion of the end of the bat which must be counteracted by the performer.

If a collision is made at the center of percussion, there is no attempt of the implement to rotate with respect to the performer. From a physics standpoint, the tightness of grip is not particularly important for hitting a ball properly at the center of percussion. However, a solid linkage between the implement and the performer is necessary in order to absorb the counterforce of the collision without excessive rebound. This is the reason grips must be maintained through the point of impact.

Since the very tip of a baseball bat is the part moving at the highest velocity, it might seem that this would be the best place to make contact with the ball. Empirically, however, most performers know this is not true. From an analytic point of view, the problem with contact at that point arises from the fact that the bat can rotate about a point along its own length, and this rotation will be in a direction opposite to the rotation of the swing. Impact on the end of the bat tries to rotate it in a direction which will allow the barrel to drop back and the handle of the bat to move forward more rapidly than its center of mass. This causes an extreme force between the handle and the hands—the so-called *sting of the bat.*

Because of the distribution of mass in the outer half of the bat, ball contact made near the center of gravity of the bat tends to produce a rotation in the opposite direction. This causes the handle of the bat to jam backwards into the hand. At a point outside the trademark and along the barrel of the bat, a collision does not tend to cause either of these rotations, but simply slows the lateral motion of the bat. This point is called the center of percussion.

The term "sweet spot" used as a synonym for the center of percussion is derived from the positive and subjective kinesthetic feeling experienced by the performer when a ball is struck at this point by the implement. It can be shown that a maximum transfer of momentum from the implement to the object occurs with this kind of collision. Therefore, this is a necessary condition for optimum performance. Interestingly, there is often a distinct auditory response to a collision at or near the center of percussion. This arises from the fact that a maximum amount of resonant vibrations occurs during a collision at or near the center of percussion. For example, a person with tennis experience, blindfolded and seated near a tennis court, would be able to tell from the sounds of the strokes whether the players were experts or beginners.

In a scientific sense, swinging a sport implement with the arms would be described as a *pendular motion.* Pendular action is usually thought of as being exerted only in a plane vertical to the earth. For example, arm motion through the anteroposterior plane during the release of a bowling ball is a pendular action. A pendular motion can also be executed in diagonal planes. Examples are observed in baseball, golf, tennis, and other sports involving ballistic activity.

Effect of Spin on Elastic Collisions

In the last section, the discussion centered around introduction of spin to a body or a sport object by collisions. What occurs during a collision of an object which is already spinning? In this case, as the surfaces come into contact, the perpendicular (normal) force is present, as well as motion along the surface due to the spin of the object. This tendency to move along the surface results in a frictional component of force which affects the subsequent motion of the object. *It is this frictional component of force which influences the rebound in the direction of the spin during the bounce of a spinning ball* (fig. 4.21).

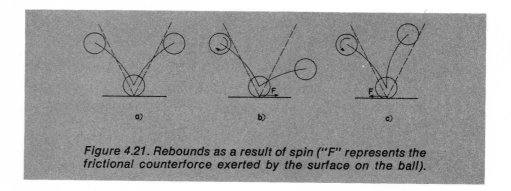

Figure 4.21. Rebounds as a result of spin ("F" represents the frictional counterforce exerted by the surface on the ball).

At times, exceptions may arise to this general principle. This occurs when the tangential component of linear motion is actually larger than the surface motion due to spin. In this case, the center of mass of the colliding object may actually override the surface and cancel out any effect of spin.

This effect is one that shows up in many instances during sport activities. Probably one of the most commonly observed is backspin put on a basketball during a shot. The performer applies backspin so the ball will rebound either off the backboard or rim with optimum probabilities of going into the basket. Striking the backboard, the spin of the ball provides a tangential force in the direction of the hoop itself. In a basketball shot, any component of rotation to the left or right of the ball's center of gravity has a tendency to cause the ball to spin around the rim, increasing the probability of its moving out of the basket.

The concept of backspin is also used in basketball in the bounce pass in order to make the ball easier for the receiver to handle. The backspin on the bounce reduces horizontal velocity; therefore, the ball tends to rebound upward in front of the receiver, allowing easier reception of the pass. Front spin imparted to the basketball during a bounce pass would provide a rebound trajectory of the ball which would be extremely difficult for the player to catch.

The concept of using spin to influence the angle of bounce is found in many court sports. A forward rotation gives a fast, low bounce, while a backspin tends to cause tangential velocities to decrease greatly. Also, in many sports the use of sidespin to cause a bounce off the original line of flight is used very frequently for strategic purposes. Handball is a classic example. In these cases, compositions of the court surfaces and striking object have considerable influence on the total effect of subsequent spin.

A good example of problems encountered in handling spin in a sport context is the possibilities which can occur during the "dig maneuver" in power volleyball (fig. 4.22). In this case, the defensive player receiving the downward and spinning shot, spike, or serve has the problems of playing the ball back into the air vertically and attempting to remove the spin. This must be accomplished so the second or setup shot can be executed most effectively. Since the dig is made with the surfaces of the forearms or radio-ulnar joint area, the effect of the rapidly spinning ball provides tangential forces, tending to pull the ball laterally rather than vertically. These factors, plus the uneven surface of the forearm rebound area, make the dig very difficult.

In considering the total effect of spin, the three most important factors are (1) total amount of spin, (2) coefficient of friction between surfaces, and (3) total time of contact between surfaces. For relatively soft sport objects, which would

Figure 4.22. Neutralizing spin during a volleyball dig.

have a long contact time during collision, the effect of spin tends to be greater than for very hard objects with short times of contact.

In the approach shot to the green in golf, the ball is given a high arching trajectory with a large amount of backspin. When the ball strikes the green, backspin causes a frictional counterforce, tending to cancel the horizontal component of velocity. If the green is hard, the time of contact during the first bounce may be as short as a few hundredths of a second. In this case, the total impulse (product of force and time) is insufficient to completely cancel the motion of the ball. Since much of the spin has been lost, subsequent bounces have less effect, and the ball "runs" across the green. If the green is soft, however, the time of contact may be as much as ten times longer. This leads to an impulse large enough to stop or reverse the horizontal velocity of the ball. In addition, a soft green absorbs much of the vertical motion so subsequent bounces on the grass phase out quickly.

When two sport objects collide, such as billiard balls on a billiard table, the spin of one of these objects exerts a tangential force which creates an opposite spin to the other object. Therefore, the spin in colliding objects often is transferred from one to the other, but always in the opposing direction. The use of spins acquired during collisions, both with other balls and with the side cushions, is often an advantage for the skilled player in the game of snooker.

OBSERVABLE AND NONOBSERVABLE QUANTITIES

It is necessary to point out that all physical quantities described in the two preceding chapters are not visually observable. Although each has a specific place in the organized description of mechanical motion and interaction, many must be calculated from simpler, more fundamental properties which can be observed either directly or from filmed records. The purpose of this section is to outline which properties can be observed visually and which must be calculated.

Position

The relative positions of two body parts can be observed directly during a performance. With experience it is even possible to do rough quantitative measurements noncinematographically on relatively slow motions. From filmed records, both relative and absolute observations of position can be made, and quantitative measurements can be made on film or on projected images or drawings made from film. Accuracy in these quantitative values often depends on such things as proper scaling, corrections for camera angle, and filming speeds.

Velocity

Relative velocities can be observed directly. By timing a motion over a fixed distance or by measuring the distance covered in a specific time, average velocity over a time interval can be quantitatively determined. From filmed records of a motion, velocities of various body parts over short intervals can be accurately measured. Ballistic motions require a high filming rate (frames per second) to freeze motion and give acceptably short intervals. Recorded events also allow separation of complex motion into its components.

Acceleration

Acceleration can be detected by direct observation of changing motion. However, any measurement or comparison of acceleration requires the use of film or an electrical accelerometer. From positional measurements on film, both velocity and acceleration can be calculated. This applies to single components as well as total motion.

Force

Only the *effects of forces* are directly observable during human body motion. From the observed changes of motion and a knowledge of the mass involved, force is calculated by Force = Mass × Acceleration. Various experimental techniques can be used to measure force by the distortion it causes in elastic objects or implements, but a calibration of the instrument is required to allow direct observation.

Mass

The mass of an object or body part is usually determined by weighing or balancing techniques. It is seldom determined by direct observation of motion changes. Mass may also be calculated by multiplying the density of the material involved by the volume of the object or body part. Calculation of the mass of body parts is difficult due to the necessity of determining the volume of each irregularly shaped body part. Studies useful to the determination of mass of body parts have been reported in the literature (W. T. Dempster).

Time Relationships and Synchronization

Relative timing of motions can be observed directly. However, this is much more accurate if recorded on film. Precise synchronization of complex motions is best determined by film analysis.

Pressure

Pressure can be observed directly by the distortions caused in elastic materials. Accurate determinations of pressure require instrumentation or precise measurements of distortion and calibration of elasticity.

Frictional Coefficients

Frictional coefficients can be observed qualitatively in terms of conditions necessary to produce slippage. Accurate determination requires measurement of force components perpendicular and parallel to the surface of contact.

Energy

Energy is seldom observed directly but is used as a calculated quantity. It is important because its conservation property can be used in considering transformations from one type of interaction to another. The three most important areas of mechanical energy to be considered in biomechanics are (1) kinetic energy—calculated as $\frac{1}{2}$(mass)(velocity)^2 of a body, (2) gravitational potential energy—calculated as the product of the weight of a body times its height above some arbitrary reference level, and (3) elastic potential energy—calculated from the force versus distortion characteristics of the body involved. In addition, the concept of energy production from biomechanic reactions is important in determining the possible mechanical energy production under a given set of conditions by a given set of muscles or muscle groups. *In this context, it is necessary to consider the concept of efficiency as the useful work output divided by the total energy input.*

Momentum

Momentum can be observed qualitatively in terms of sizes of bodies, body parts, or objects and their specific velocities. Momentum is more often calculated by multiplying a measured or calculated mass of a body or body part by its velocity. Like energy, calculations of momentum are useful in defining changes during transformations from one type of motion to another. Momentum calculations are most commonly involved in collision-type interactions.

Impulse

Impulse is almost always a calculated rather than an observed quantity as the product of force multiplied by the time of action of the force. It is useful since it represents the transfer of momentum during a collision.

Power

Power is observed only qualitatively even in cinematographic studies. It is calculated in either of two ways: (1) work done per unit time, or energy transfer divided by time, and (2) force multiplied by velocity.

Elastic Constants

Elastic constants can be observed qualitatively in terms of amounts of distortion present under application of forces and in terms of noticeable energy losses following collisions or other interactions. These are normally calculated for quantitative information but require specialized equations for each type of distortion. Elastic constants can be calculated in terms of force versus distortion or in terms of energy change versus distortion.

Angular Position, Velocity, and Acceleration

These are observed and calculated in much the same manner as their linear counterparts except they require more training to make valid judgments of angles and angular changes than to make similar judgments of relative positions. Comparisons of ballistic angular motions usually require the use of film records. Quantitative measurements require careful analysis of such records.

Moment of Inertia

Moment of inertia can be qualitatively observed in terms of general location of various portions of mass with respect to axis of rotation. Quantitative information can be obtained in two ways: (1) by dividing a known or calculated torque by the observed angular acceleration or (2) by summing each part of the mass multiplied by the square of its distance from the axis of rotation, $I = \text{Sum}(mr^2)$.

Radius of Gyration

Changes of radius of gyration can be observed qualitatively, but they are normally calculated as the square root of the quotient of the moment of inertia divided by the total mass.

Torque

Torque, like force, is observed only in terms of changes of angular motion which it produces. It can be calculated in two ways: (1) product of force multiplied by lever arm or (2) product of moment of inertia multiplied by angular acceleration.

Angular Momentum

Angular momentum can be observed in terms of the relative size of a body and speed of rotation. Observation is especially important with reference to the direction of axis of rotation. It is calculated as the product of the moment of inertia times angular velocity.

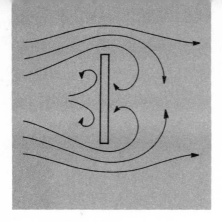

Chapter 5

Aerodynamics

In a wide variety of sport, the interaction of an object or body with air assumes a strong importance. The end result of many sport maneuvers is the placing of an object into free flight where for a period of time the forces of interaction with the air are the only forces, other than gravity, affecting motion of the object. In order to comprehend many aspects of airflow past an object, a few terms relevant to fluid dynamics must be understood.

The term "fluid" as used in biomechanics means any substance with relatively continuous properties which does not maintain a specific shape. As far as this text is concerned, this includes the study of sport object interactions with both air and water, i.e., air and water are both considered to be fluids. From a scientific standpoint, *interactions with air are studied under the title of aerodynamics or the dynamics of compressible fluids. Interactions with water, on the other hand, are the subject matter of hydrodynamics or the dynamics of incompressible fluids.* Hydrodynamics is presented in chapter six.

The major difference in the discussion of fluid mechanics from mechanics of bodies or objects is that many quantities have the property of being distributed. Instead of using the total mass of a fluid, it is expressed as the mass per unit volume or *density*. Instead of expressing the total weight of a fluid, the *weight density* or weight per unit volume is utilized. Often, instead of using the total force exerted by a fluid, the force per unit area or *pressure* is used. Likewise, in discussing energy, energy density is expressed as *energy per unit volume* or *energy per unit mass.*

From the viewpoint of sport analysis, the main concern does not involve motions of fluids. The primary consideration is the motions of objects or bodies through fluids. Therefore, only a limited part of the literature of fluid dynamics is considered.

One very important aspect of aerodynamics is the concept of laminar versus turbulent flow.

If a fluid is flowing perfectly and smoothly through a pipe or channel, certain characteristics of particle motion can be observed. Various parts of the fluid will all be moving in the same direction, so the total mass transfer is in a straight line. However, it is found that velocities of various parts of fluid are different. In the center of a pipe or channel, a high velocity will be noted while the friction within the fluid gradually slows until parts at the side are barely moving against their respective surfaces. It is this idea of sheets or lamina of flow which gives the name *laminar flow* to this kind of fluid motion.

In contrast *turbulent flow* does not have this simple motion associated with all particles. Some particles during turbulent flow are moving in other directions, creating eddies and whirlpools as well as a large amount of motion or kinetic energy, and this is not contributing to efficient transfer of mass during flow. As a result, in turbulent flow there is considerable motion and energy actually lost or dissipated as heat.

When transfer is made from motion of a fluid within the pipe or channel to motion of a body within fluid, it is found that both types of flow are possible involving sport objects. In laminar or streamline flow, the motion of the body is such that particles move in lines around the body and close together behind it with very little excess motion remaining to the particles. In the case of turbulent flow, however, the passage of a body through fluid creates excess motion of the particles, especially in the wake of a trajectory. The fact that this turbulence exists means that kinetic energy was given to the air by the object as it passed through. Thus, the force the object exerted in creating this turbulence means that air was exerting a counterforce on the object, and this tended to slow it down. Laminar flow causes a minimum loss of energy or amount of work performed by the object. The existence of any turbulence indicates that the object is performing work against opposing forces (figs. 5.1 and 5.2).

One other concept in fluid flow involves the idea of viscosity and surface friction. *Viscosity is the internal friction occurring within a fluid.* Owing to the

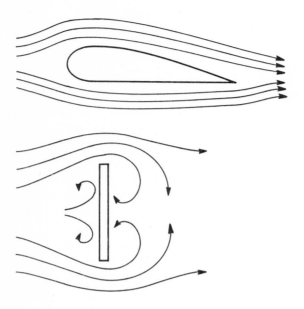

Figure 5.1. Laminar flow

Figure 5.2. Turbulent flow

fact that the various layers of fluid are moving with different velocities, they are, in effect, sliding over one another and creating frictional forces because of this sliding motion. The amount of energy lost to this viscous friction varies widely from one fluid to another. In most gases the viscosity is relatively low, although it accounts for an appreciable energy loss within a moving gas. In liquid the amount of viscosity varies over an extremely wide range from the alcohols, which have practically no viscosity, to materials like syrups with high viscosity where the major energy loss mechanism is in this interlayer conversion of mechanical energy into heat. Air and water tend to be intermediate in viscosity. The air man breathes is a normal gas, and water is a normal liquid from the point of view of viscosity.

Besides the internal friction described by viscosity, there is also friction existing between the surface of contact of a liquid or gas and an object immersed in it. This is due to the fact that the object in its motion tends to move parts of the liquid; therefore, forces are exerted on these liquid particles. The liquid then exerts a counterforce on the object. It should be emphasized that this is not a force due to a pressure difference because of the motion of the object through the air or a difference in the density of the air in front of the object. It is a force which the air exerts as it slides along the surface.

DRAG

"Drag" is the term used for that component of force of the air exactly opposite to the direction of motion of an object. In this sense, it is the portion of force resisting motion of the object moving through air. Drag is very sensitive to the relative velocity of the object to air; therefore, it becomes quite dependent on such parameters as wind or relative direction of movement.

The amount of drag a body will have in moving through the air is a complex function of its shape, surface, and actual velocity with respect to air itself. Because of the complexity of this function for most situations, the relationship is expressed simply in terms of a *drag coefficient.* Equations for drag force are written in the following form:

$$\text{Drag force} = (\text{Constant}) (\text{Area}) (\text{Drag coefficient}) (\text{Velocity})^2$$

Constant is determined by the density of air and the system of units used.
Area represents the cross-sectional area in the direction of motion.
Drag coefficient is determined by the shape of the body, its relative size, and its
speed.

As examples of calculation of the drag forces on three vastly different sport objects, consider the following:

1. When considering the cross-sectional area of a sport object in square inches and its velocity in ft/sec, the constant for this equation equals approximately 0.00001. For a sphere moving at nominal velocity, the drag coefficient equals approximately 0.7. Therefore, the drag force on the shot during the shot put would be:

$$\text{Drag force} = (0.00001) (19.6 \text{ sq. in.}) (0.7) (40 \text{ ft/sec})^2$$

$$= 0.22 \text{ pounds} = 3.5 \text{ ounces}$$

A 3.5-ounce force acting on a 16-pound shot will make no noticeable difference on the trajectory. Even a strong head wind, which increases the velocity of the shot relative to the air, should show little effect on the total distance.

2. The same calculation for a table tennis-ball slam gives the following results:

$$\text{Drag force} = (0.00001)\,(1.2\text{ sq. in.})\,(0.7)\,(60\text{ ft/sec})^2$$

$$= 0.03\text{ pound} = 0.5\text{ ounce}$$

This one-half-ounce drag force is five times the one-tenth-ounce weight of the ball. Therefore, the velocity of the slam slows very quickly to only a few feet per second where the drag force becomes small with respect to the weight of the ball.

3. A golf drive actually leaves the tee at such a high velocity that the drag coefficient is only about 0.2. The drag force can then be calculated:

$$\text{Drag force} = (0.00001)\,(2.06\text{ sq. in.})\,(0.2)\,(200\text{ ft/sec})^2$$

$$= 0.16\text{ pound} = 2.6\text{ ounces}$$

This is still appreciably greater than the 1.62-ounce weight of the ball, so the ball slows rapidly. As the ball slows down through a certain critical velocity, the drag coefficient increases rapidly to the 0.7 value. At this part of the flight, the drag force actually increases as the object slows down. This produces a marked change in the appearance of the flight. Precise calculations of drag forces on a golf drive are complicated still more by the fact that the spin of the ball causes changes in the effective drag coefficient.

For speeds with which most sport objects and performers move, the actual drag force tends to vary as the square of the velocity. This means that if velocity is doubled, force increases by a factor of four.

There has been considerable literature relating to the effect of wind on drag forces affecting the human body during sport events. For example, in all sprint and jumping events in track, there is a maximum allowable wind used in establishing new records. This concept implies that the wind will blow the runner along the track or assist the jumper through his motion. As noted earlier, a good sprinter can move nearly 30 mph, so a 10 mph tail wind hitting him from the back could not assist him. However, there is a beneficial factor to such a wind because the effect of the wind does reduce drag forces. Therefore, performance time would be aided.

When considering forces acting on bodies falling through air, there is an important concept known as *limiting velocity*. Since drag force of air is proportional to the square of the velocity, a falling body will accelerate until it reaches a velocity at which the drag force is equal to weight of the body. At that point, the net force acting downward on the body is zero, since the gravitational force is being exactly balanced by the upward force of the air. *This critical velocity beyond which acceleration does not occur is known as limiting velocity.* Limiting velocity is dependent on shape, size, and total weight of the falling body.

The whole purpose of using a parachute in sport parachuting is to achieve a configuration with such a high drag coefficient that its limiting velocity is only about 20 mph. This is the approximate velocity with which most sport parachutists strike the ground on landing. The limiting velocity for a human body during free fall from high altitudes in a tumbling condition is calculated as follows:

$$\text{Drag force} = (0.00001)\,(\text{Area})\,(\text{Drag coefficient})\,(\text{Velocity})^2$$

If it is assumed that the tumbling body approximates a sphere with a cross-sectional area of 500 square inches and that at the limiting velocity the drag force would balance the 200-pound weight of a man and equipment:

$$200 = (0.00001)\,(500)\,(0.7)\,(\text{Velocity})^2$$

$$\text{Velocity} = 239\,\text{ft/sec} = 163\,\text{mph}$$

This is approximately the limiting velocity observed in skydiving, but it will vary with size and weight of the sky diver, the wind conditions, as well as other factors.

If the performer goes into a position with limbs extended and abducted, the cross-sectional area is increased to approximately 1,200 square inches, and the shape factor increases the drag coefficient to about 1.0. Then:

$$200 = (0.00001)\,(1{,}200)\,(1.0)\,(\text{Velocity})^2$$

$$\text{Limiting velocity} = 129\,\text{ft/sec} = 88\,\text{mph}$$

In order to slow the limiting velocity to 20 mph for landing purposes:

$$200 = (0.00001)\,(\text{Area})\,(1.0)\,(29.3\,\text{ft/sec})^2$$

$$\text{Area} = 23{,}250\,\text{square inches} = 161\,\text{square feet}$$

The parachute would need an effective interacting area of about 160 square feet which would require a radius of about 7 feet. Actual design of the parachute changes the relation between the true radius and the effective area.

Skydiving groups utilize this concept in performing various maneuvers and patterns. A diver above the group can move into a flexed position at the lumbar-thoracic spine, hip, and knee joints. This will cause the diver to fall fast enough to rejoin the group. By abduction of the shoulder joints, hyperextension of the lumbar spine, abduction and extension of the hip joints, and extension of the knee joints, it is possible to control horizontal movements to achieve various configurations with the other divers. The latter position of the body increases the drag coefficient.

In sport applications outside of skydiving, seldom do sport objects fall far enough that limiting velocity becomes an important concept. Limiting velocity, for example, is not a factor in three-meter diving. However, in a large number of applications, a sport object will be projected with a velocity greater than its limiting velocity for air near the earth's surface.

LIFT

In addition to force offered directly counter to motion by the air, it is possible for an object to interact with air in such a way that a force perpendicular to the direction of motion will be achieved. *This component of force perpendicular to the direction of motion is called lift.* The term *flying* is reserved for those conditions in which lift exists. It is normally applied where the object is moving horizontally, and, therefore, the lift is against gravitational force. In the absence of lift, a sport object will follow a path through the air nearly corresponding to a parabolic trajectory. However, when an object is flying in the presence of lift forces, the trajectory will be greatly different from this parabola. Due to their weight, the shot and hammer do not fly, but follow parabolic trajectories. A discus, javelin, baseball, and golf ball actually can obtain lift forces from their interaction with air and have varying flight patterns. No specific name is given to flight trajectories, since these are highly variable and depend on such parameters as flight speed, amount of spin, or orientation of the object with respect to the direction of motion.

There are three different characteristics which produce an interaction with air to develop lift: (1) an airfoil shape, (2) a slanted angle of orientation with respect to the motion of the body, and (3) a rotation of the body. The effect in all three cases is to exert a force causing air to move downward. Since the object itself is exerting a downward force on air, it follows from the action-reaction principle that air is exerting an upward force on the object. In many cases, the analysis of lift is easier to understand by observing and thinking about what the object is doing to the air.

In the case of an airfoil shape, the lift is caused by what is scientifically known as the *Bernoulli Effect*. The Bernoulli equation is as follows:

Pressure at point 1 — Pressure at point 2 =

½ (Density) [(Velocity at point 2)² — (Velocity at point 1)²]

The Bernoulli Effect states that the transverse pressure exerted by air becomes lower as the velocity of air becomes higher. Since air flowing over an aircraft wing is moving faster than the air flowing under the wing due to its longer path, the pressure exerted on top of the wing is less than that on the bottom. Therefore, there is a net lift on the wing. Since air passing over a wing tends to be given a velocity downward, this means that the counterforce from this change then exerts a velocity upward on the wing itself. *Within the realm of sport, there are few cases where a purely airfoil lift is given to a sport object moving or flying through air.*

If an object moving through air is oriented in such a way that the front portion is slightly higher than the rear portion, the net effect will be to exert a downward force on the air. Since the object is forcing air downward, counterforce of the air exerts an upward force on the object. This is the aerodynamic situation observed in flights of the javelin, discus, arrows, or thrown or punted footballs. It should be noted that in all of these cases, the objects are given a spin around their longitudinal axes at the time of release in order to provide stability to maintain proper flight orientation with respect to air.

In the sport of ski jumping, the form used by modern performers provides lift by a combination of an airfoil described by the body and the slant effect of the skis. The body position over the skis actually presents a semi-airfoil shape to the air which the ski-jumper is moving through. In addition, the basic slant of the skis plus the body provides an additional lift.

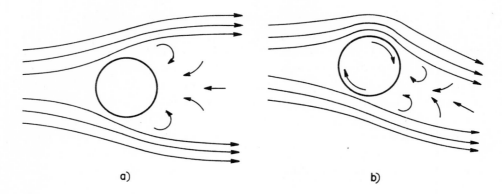

a)   b)

Figure 5.3. Lift as a function of spin: (a) flow without spin and (b) flow with spin.

The third type of interaction with air which can give lift is rotation of the moving object (fig. 5.3).

In this case, air behind a ball, for example, is forced in the direction of motion of the back of the ball. This means that the counterforce is then perpendicular to the direction of motion. In the case of a backspin, the force on the ball will tend to be upward. The trailing air will be moving in the direction of motion of the back portion of the ball. Force on the ball will be in the same direction as motion of the front portion of the ball. The actual value of the force is a complicated relationship between forward velocity, angular velocity, and frictional interaction between the air and the ball. This relationship is expressed as the *lift coefficient*.

The numerical calculation of lift is similar to the drag equation:

$$\text{Lift force} = (\text{Constant}) \, (\text{Effective area}) \, (\text{Lift coefficient}) \, (\text{Velocity})^2$$

Lift force depends, to some extent, on the square of the velocity. The lift coefficient is exceedingly difficult to calculate. It depends on such factors as shape, spin, surface roughness, and pattern of airflow around the object in flight. Exact calculations for examples from sport are beyond the scope of this text. In such actions as the flight of a discus or javelin, the lift force is appreciable, but not equal to the weight of the object. These objects have a much greater range than would be given by a parabolic trajectory. In the case of a golf drive or batted baseball, the lift force may actually exceed the weight of the object during the early part of the flight. This is shown by the fact that the initial trajectory of these sport objects often has a curvature upward. As the object rises, however, its velocity decreases, and the lift force becomes smaller than the weight. As a result, the final part of the trajectory curves downward and usually approaches the parabolic pattern.

It could be stated that almost all sport objects have a certain amount of flight, but it is only when the lift-to-weight ratio becomes relatively large that the effect of flying becomes apparent. As examples, a baseball hit with a small amount of spin would have a very low lift-to-weight ratio. Therefore, it would follow a parabolic trajectory and not meet the criteria of flight. A ball hit with extreme reverse spin, however, has a higher lift-to-weight ratio; consequently, it is actually projected into flight.

Both lift and drag forces on sport objects moving through air depend on the density of air as well as other parameters of the sport object. For air with high density, large values of drag and lift are obtained. Low densities of air produce correspondingly lower lift and drag forces. At high altitudes one would expect that trajectories which rely very little on lift would be increased in range. It would appear that drag forces would not counter the motion of the object to the same degree. However, those trajectories which depend on lift would tend to be diminished in high altitude. The available amount of lift force would be decreased with the decrease in density of air. Quite often the deadening effect of a high humidity is erroneously attributed to an increase in drag forces on the objects. Actually, high-humidity air is of lower density than dry air at the same pressure and temperature. In this case, the available lift is smaller than it would be on a dry day; therefore, the objects do not tend to fly as well.

The direction of lift force is always considered to be perpendicular to the line of flight of the object. This means that if the path of the object is highly slanted upward, there are lift force components upward and backward with respect to the horizontal motion of the object.

The effect of the lift can hold the object in the air and decrease forward horizontal motion of the object. Since the speed is also being decreased by a gain in altitude, a condition can be reached where the velocity drops very low. When this happens, lift essentially disappears. This is the situation known as *stalling*. In this case, the trajectory is one that has a sharp upward motion followed by a virtual stoppage of the object in air. It then falls with very little horizontal component of motion. This is seen at times when a sport object such as the javelin is released at an angle too high with respect to the ground. One sport skill which utilizes a form of stalling is the football punt. In order to gain maximum amount of time for downfield coverage by the punting team, the punter will attempt to "hang the ball in the air." This is accomplished by contacting the ball with the dorsum of the foot while the ankle is plantar-flexed (fig. 5.4). Flight angles and spin are both determined at contact. Actually, what is accomplished in this maneuver is to kick the ball on a high trajectory with an extreme slant, causing stalling at the peak of the trajectory. The fact that velocity decreases almost to zero during the upper portion of flight gives the football a maximum amount of time in the air.

If the spin of a round ball moving through air is not a perfect backspin, the direction of the lift force will not be entirely vertical. For example, a spin about a vertical axis causes a lift horizontal to the left or right. This results in a

Courtesy USC Athletic News Service—Robert Parker

Figure 5.4. Punt trajectory is determined by motion of the ankle at point of impact. Plantar flexion of the right ankle demonstrated by Dave Boulware, USC punter, is essential.

curved path of the ball during flight. This is the basic spin used by baseball and softball pitchers who throw curves.

In order to impart this horizontal spin, the right-handed baseball pitcher throwing through the high diagonal plane utilizes a combination of lateral rotation of the shoulder joint, elbow extension, supination and ulnar flexion, together with an off-center finger pressure as the ball leaves the middle finger. For the right-handed pitcher, this imparts a clockwise spin, causing the ball to curve away from a right-handed batter. For the left-handed pitcher, the opposite direction of spin imparted at release gives the opposite motion of the curve. *The direction of curvature of the ball is in the same direction as the motion imparted to the front of the ball by the spin.* A complicated relationship between velocity of the ball and the rate of spin accounts for the change-of-pace, slider, and slow curve thrown by many pitchers.

A fast-ball pitcher with an extreme backspin will sometimes gain enough lift to cause an upward curvature of the trajectory as the ball reaches the plate. This is the so-called "hop." In softball, it is quite easy to give an extreme forward spin to a ball, resulting in the pitch known as the "downer" or "drop." In all these maneuvers, the proper relationship between the orientation of the seams and axis of spin provides an optimum effect both in stabilizing the ball and in maximizing interaction with air.

A body in flight due to its lack of contact with the ground and availability of frictional forces is not in a position where stability can be maintained easily. A small lack of balance between forces either due to air or internal body motions can cause drastic changes in either direction of flight or orientation of the body. Unbalanced pressures due to the motion of air cause torques about the center of mass and may also change flight direction. Examples of this lack of stability are observed in the responses of sport objects to sudden gusts of wind alternating with low-pressure areas during a long flight. A discus or javelin quite often will oscillate when a wind gust hits. Throwing a football accurately on an open field in gusty wind is difficult. This is especially true if the object itself does not have considerable spin to maintain a strong angular momentum. Probably the best-known example of erratic motions for a nonspinning object is the behavior of the knuckle ball in baseball and softball. Very slight changes in pressure either from the characteristic of air into which the nonspinning ball is moving or in turbulence forming behind the ball are capable of causing sudden deviations from the path of motion. Similar types of flight deviations may be caused by the application of spit or Vaseline to a ball.

Because of the size and construction of the human body plus the low density of air, in almost all sport actions the forces coming from air are incapable of greatly changing the motion of a performer while he is not in contact with the ground. The exception to this rule would be in the case of skydiving where the relative velocity between the performer and the air is three to five times greater than that found in any other sport event. This means that forces acting on a sky diver are ten to thirty times greater than those found working against an athlete diving from a ten-meter platform. Movements of the platform diver are not designed to interact with air in order to elicit changes in position or velocity. However, the diver will conserve angular momentum to provide specific body orientations and rotations. The center of mass of the platform diver would follow a parabolic trajectory predetermined by the forces exerted against the platform by the diver.

Chapter 6

Hydrodynamics

There are many sport actions and events associated with water. As variations on the concept of swimming, there are sports and activities such as water polo, synchronized swimming, and underwater diving and swimming, either free or with self-contained underwater breathing apparatus (SCUBA). Performers using a small amount of equipment perform such events as the various types of surfing and water-skiing. Also, there are many sport events associated with the use of boats. In the man-powered category, there are sculling, canoeing, and kayaking. Interaction of air with water leads to sailing and yachting. Beyond this, there are the motorized sports ranging from small-craft competition to high-speed hydroplane racing. The latter type of sport also involves the use of forces from air and water.

COMPARATIVE AND CONTRASTING ELEMENTS OF HYDRODYNAMICS AND AERODYNAMICS

The term "hydrodynamics" is defined as a study of mechanical properties of incompressible fluids of which water is the most notable example. While both air and water are technically considered fluids, there are certain differences in their properties which become extremely important when considering their application on sport action. The chief difference is density. While average density of air at sea level is 0.075 pounds per cubic foot, it is found that average density of water is about 62½ pounds per cubic foot. This combined with the incompressibility of water leads to a far different ability in obtaining forces and counterforces as a performer interacts with water as contrasted with air.

In the preceding chapter, it was pointed out that a performer is incapable of moving sufficient air fast enough to create forces comparable with his own body weight. In contrast to this, a performer in water can easily create forces against water of the same magnitude as the body weight because of the size of the limbs and the velocity with which the limbs can be moved. This means that limb or body-segment motions are perfectly capable of moving the position of the center of gravity of a performer in water. As one example, a seemingly unimportant motion such as cervical hyperextension by a beginning swimmer attempting to breathe during the front crawl causes a drastic change in the orientation of the body. As a result, this increases drag and decreases the ability to maintain a forward thrust in the water. As an example of the contrast between drag forces in water and air, consider the case of the hand being brought through the water in the front-crawl stroke. The drag force would be calculated as follows:

Drag force = (Constant) (Area) (Drag coefficient) (Velocity)^2

Constant for density of water = 0.014.

Area of the average hand in the anatomic position is equal to approximately 35 square inches

Drag coefficient for the extended hand is equal to about 1

Maximum velocity with respect to water is equal to about 7 ft/sec

Drag force = (0.014) (35) (1) (7)^2 = 24 pounds

This would seem to represent about the maximum force which a swimmer could obtain during a stroke. The average force is much smaller because of the small fraction of the time during which the hand is moved at maximum velocity. The obtainable force is also highly dependent on the size of the hand and its position. Cupping the hand not only reduces the effective area but also reduces turbulence and may drop the drag coefficient by as much as half. It is estimated from some studies that in order to maintain a body speed of five to seven feet per second through the water, a swimmer must maintain an average thrust of about ten pounds.

THRUST

Because forces obtainable in the direction of motion of a body moving through water are large enough to cause appreciable changes of velocity, thrust is an important concept in hydrodynamics. Thrust is the opposite of drag. *Thrust represents a force component in the direction of motion, while drag represents a force component against the direction of motion.* The term *propulsive force* is used by many swimming coaches as a synonym for thrust.

In the various aquatic activities involving swimming, the techniques and maneuvers used by performers are those designed to be most efficient in providing forward thrust. The arm movement provides a high drag coefficient, while the trunk is oriented to minimize drag. This results in the body being moved linearly. A large amount of water is being displaced, but with a relatively low velocity. The shoulder-arm motions of the front crawl, as an example, are designed to "plant" the hand and forearm. The diagonal adduction seen in the pull of the arm through water subsequently moves the body over the "plant" position. In this context, the body is analogous to a racing shell, and there is similarity between the arm action of the swimmer and the oar action by the oarsman. Carrying this analogy one step further, there is a definite parallel between the oarlock and the enarthrodial or ball-and-socket arrangement of the shoulder joint. Both are triaxial in nature.

An important function of arm motion while swimming is to maintain body orientation and equilibrium during the execution of the stroke (fig. 6.1). For

Figure 6.1. Arm action of Tom McBreen, USC swimmer, helps maintain body orientation and equilibrium.

Courtesy USC Athletic News Service

an efficient motion through the water, rotation of the body about its longitudinal axis must be minimized. This type of motion tends to increase drag, and it represents a type of completely wasted energy. Equilibrium functions and thrust provided by arm and leg motions are commonly called "stroke mechanics" by swimming coaches.

Leg motions in swimming strokes do contribute to equilibrium but are primarily designed to provide extra thrust. Both the flutter and whip kicks are designed to provide a scissor-type action which forces water along the legs and back past the feet (figs. 6.2 and 6.3). In both kicks, the most efficient action comes

Figure 6.2. Flutter kick for propulsive force during the back crawl

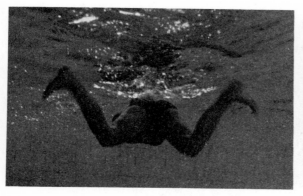 

Figure 6.3. Whip kick action to produce thrust

with the knees and ankles dynamically stabilized. The major internal force is provided by muscular actions occurring at the hip joints. *Dynamic stability implies a cooperative contraction of all muscles associated with the joint without a true fixation of the joint involved.* This arrangement allows a limited amount of motion to occur within the joint while it remains stable. This condition is referred to in the literature as the Lomac Paradox.

It is actually the laminar flow along the lower limb, beginning near the pelvic girdle and extending to the feet, which causes resultant water motion and counterforce against the body during the flutter kick. The fact that a transverse motion of water is induced and turbulence results from the kick means that this is not a maximally efficient method of achieving thrust. By his anatomic configuration and physiologic mechanisms, man is not adapted to efficiently moving through water.

The motion by which man most nearly imitates fish and aquatic mammals is the dolphin kick used with the butterfly swimming stroke (fig. 6.4). In this motion, the primary propulsive movement is a lumbar-thoracic flexion-extension-hyperextension. The hips, knees, and ankles remain dynamically stabilized. This provides a sinuous motion of the lower half of the body which traps water and propels it backward by laminar flow. This is the same motion which many fish use in their swimming technique through a different plane of motion. Unfortunately, the musculature and skeletal structure associated with this motion in man is not developed to the point that it can be continued for long periods of time.

Figure 6.4. Dolphin kick during the butterfly stroke

Much of the same concept of obtaining thrust is found in various sports where implements are used in order to propel oneself through the water. In the sport of crew, for example, the idea is to plant the oars in the water, and the pulling motion of the rowers forces the shell forward in the water (fig. 6.5). The limited amount of motion of the oars requires great precision in the timing, stroke length, and stroke power to maintain a straight course. The design of the oar and shell is such that the oar has a large drag coefficient, while the shell has a small drag coefficient. As a consequence, when the oar is planted in the water, its linear motion is minimal, but the motion of the shell across the top of the water is maximal in terms of stroke force.

The same general motion with the paddles is used in canoeing and kayaking, but with a much wider variety of strokes. Again, the basic idea is to plant the paddle with high drag coefficient and then exert a force to cause as much forward motion of the boat as possible. Since the strokes must be applied off-center to the boat, they actually constitute a torque, and any single stroke has a tendency to turn the canoe or kayak off the line of motion. Therefore, it becomes imperative to apply a balancing torque from each side or to use a

Figure 6.5. Thrust

Courtesy USC Athletic News Service

feathering of the stroke in such a way as to counteract the generated torque. In kayaking with the double-bladed paddle, the lower body motion of the performer is often used to exert torques and actually turn or maneuver the craft.

In motorized craft, thrust is obtained by propelling smaller amounts of water backward at higher velocities. In this case, interaction of water with the propeller exerts a force backward on the water. This action, in turn, results in a counterforce forward on the boat. This same principle actually can be used with air-driven boats, but it requires motion of very large volumes of air. Extremely large propellers are utilized on these boats as compared to water-driven craft. One of the newer concepts used in power boat design involves taking water into tubes and thrusting it backward from the boat at extremely high velocities. This provides a water jet for forward propulsion.

DRAG

As in the discussion on interaction with air, the term *drag* is used for those forces occurring directly in opposition to the direction of motion. Drag is the force with which water resists motion of the performer or object. Drag forces are divided into laminar or frictional drag and viscous or turbulent drag.

Frictional drag occurs because of the actual slipping motion between the body moving through water and the water itself. In this frictional component, the performer tends to move water in the direction of motion. Therefore, the counterforce exerted by water on the performer is opposing his motion. In minimizing this type of drag force, many performers have used various oils on the skin or have shaved hair from the torso, arms, and legs. Theoretically, this may be effective to minimize drag and assist the performer psychologically, but shaving is only a minor factor in the resistance of water to motion through it.

The major source of resistance to a body moving through water lies in the viscous or turbulent drag. In the same way that higher density of water allows larger thrust to be developed by body motion in water than in air, turbulent motion within water represents a correspondingly larger energy loss than comparable turbulent motions in air. Higher density means that water carries more energy with it, and performers moving through it are doing more work and meeting more opposing force than they would while moving through air. As noted earlier, the design of the human body does not allow efficient operation within a water medium. All motions involved in swimming actually result in rather large amounts of energy being carried off in the water due to turbulent eddying motions following the swimmer.

In order to minimize the effect of water on the performer, it is necessary that the longitudinal axis of the swimmer be maintained as nearly as possible in the direction of motion. A twist to one side or slanting the body in the water leads to a much greater surface presented in the direction of motion; therefore, much larger turbulent action follows the swimmer. Because of the necessity for keeping the cervical spine hyperextended and the body at an oblique angle during the playing of water polo, the swimming in this sport is far less efficient than that in competitive swimming. The water polo performer has a far greater output of energy in moving the same distance through the water than a competitive swimmer executing the front-crawl stroke over the same distance.

An especially important source of viscous drag in motion through water occurs at the surface between water and air. Because of the high surface tension of water, forces exerted parallel to a surface tend to move water into wave formations which move away, carrying energy with them. This wave effect formed by moving through water is responsible for the wake seen behind swimmers, boats, and other objects moving at the surface. The energy loss at this point is so drastic that frictional force tends to develop as the cube of the velocity rather than the square as is common in most fluid motion. In order to double the velocity of an object moving along the surface of water with waves, eight times as much power must be expended. For this reason, swimming motions producing the least amount of waves at the surface are those which will be most efficient in moving a body through water.

In swimming in a competitive pool, the wave motion at the surface introduces other problems. A competitive pool is normally overfilled beyond the gutter level to reduce the reflected wave motion, but considerable choppiness at the surface remains during a race. The leading performers tend to swim in much smoother water than those following by a body length, or more, behind. Therefore, in swimming events there is a biomechanic as well as a psychologic advantage in staying ahead of the competition. The wave problem becomes especially significant for trailing swimmers at the end of the pool where flip turns are being made. The leading swimmer, as he makes the flip turn, creates a wave of water which washes back directly into the face of those who are swimming behind the leader. This wave force increases their drag coefficients and makes the maintenance of stroke form more difficult.

In sports where a high velocity can be attained with respect to water, the technique known as *planing* tends to reduce these surface losses. In the sport of water-skiing, for example, before a skier is able to "get up on the skis," he is literally plowing through water and is exerting a large drag on the boat attempting to pull him. However, once he assumes a standing position, only a small part of the surface area of the ski is in actual contact with the top of the water. At that time, the drag coefficient is reduced tremendously. The actual surface area in contact with the water during planing may be quite small. As an example, the trick skis used for high maneuverability are rather short in length, and the ultimate trick in skiing is to eliminate the skis altogether and plane simply on the soles of the feet. In order to successfully perform this maneuver, however, the velocity of the tow boat and the skier behind it must be exceptionally high. In performing turning maneuvers during water-skiing, it is necessary to interact strongly with the water so the resultant drag will supply centripetal force necessary for curved motion (fig. 6.6).

Figure 6.6. Increasing drag to provide radial acceleration. Note the lean of the skier to provide equilibrium between weight and centripetal force.

BUOYANCY

Another important effect in considering an interaction with water is the phenomenon known as *buoyancy*. When the forces acting on a body submerged in water are considered, it is found that these forces have a tendency to exert a force upward against the force of gravity operating on the same body. *This upward force is known as buoyant force.* The magnitude of buoyant force is enough to support the water in a given space if the object were not there. *From this it can be stated that buoyant force is equal to the weight of water displaced by the object.* The effect of this buoyant force is to apparently decrease the gravitational action on the body being considered.

Since the human body contains a high percentage of water, buoyant and gravitational forces very nearly counteract one another for performers in water. Since the density of adipose tissue or fat is less than that of water, it is the percentage of adipose tissue within the body which generally determines the imbalance between buoyancy and gravitational force. For the average person, the balance is in favor of buoyancy, i.e., in a relaxed position most people tend to float. For a small percentage of people, however, the percentage of lean body mass is high enough that in a relaxed position they will actually sink. The latter condition is extremely rare in women since the average mature woman has a higher percentage of adipose tissue than the average adult male. The better long-distance swimmers in open waters tend to have relatively high percentages of body fat. This adds buoyancy and reduces heat dissipation.

This effective balance between upward buoyant force and downward gravitational force gives an apparent weightlessness for many performers in water. It is this condition which allows the slow maneuvers and rotations observed in the sport of synchronized swimming. In competitive swimming, the weightlessness shows up in the fact that strokes and kicks are designed to give horizontal forces rather than vertical forces necessary to support the body.

Since ocean water has a higher density than fresh water due to its dissolved salt content, buoyant forces in the ocean are about five percent greater than for an equivalent body in fresh water. For this reason, a swimmer or floater in ocean water tends to ride with a larger percentage of the body above the surface than the same performer in fresh water. This is one reason that major long-distance swimming records have been established in salt water rather than in fresh water. In these long-distance swimming records in salt water, a woman would theoretically have an advantage over a male swimmer.

Since the average density of the human body at maximum inhalation is about 0.98 that of water, the submersion of 98 percent of the body will displace a weight of fresh water sufficient to counter the weight of the person. Under these conditions the person can float in a relaxed state with 2 percent of the body above water. In sea water, the relative density would be $0.98/1.03 = 0.95$. This means that equilibrium would require only 95 percent submersion, leaving about 5 percent of the body above the surface. It should be emphasized that the relative percentages of muscle, bone, and adipose tissue cause the average density to vary several percent. Some people with lean body mass will actually sink when relaxed in fresh water, and most people cannot float in fresh water without having the lungs expanded. In ocean water, on the other hand, few people are able to sink even in a fully exhaled condition.

The density of the water in the Great Salt Lake is greater than 1.15 relative to fresh water. A person can float relaxed in that lake with nearly one-fifth of the body above the surface. When upright, this allows the head and shoulders to remain out of the water; when on the back, the head, hands, and feet can all be above the surface at the same time.

An increase of the density of water also causes craft such as sculls, kayaks, and canoes to have a smaller portion of their volume underwater during a race. The major contribution of this occurrence is to reduce the total drag on the craft and allow a slightly higher speed to be maintained for the same thrust effort.

COMBINED WATER AND AIR INTERACTION

Certain sport applications, examples are sailing and surfing, involve an interaction with both air and water. The resultant motion of the performer and craft is the result of a large number of forces interacting partially to aid and also to counteract one another. In sailing, for example, the primary force used to drive the boat is the force of the moving air or wind. The setting of the sail is designed to choose a component of this force moving more or less in the direction the sailor wishes to travel. The angle of the keel and the rudder is set to select a counterforce from the water to allow the combination of wind force on the sail and counterforce in the water to provide the desired motion.

Figure 6.7 indicates a typical situation in small-craft sailing. With the craft pointed at an angle thirty degrees into the wind, the sails are close-hauled to give a force of about 180 pounds in a direction fifteen degrees forward of a line drawn amidships. This force will then have components of 46.6 pounds in the direction of motion and 174 pounds in a sideways direction. Because of the design of the hull and keel, the drag coefficient is high for such sidewise motion, and the 174-pound force causes a drift in that direction of only 0.75 ft/sec. In contrast, the design of the boat is such that the 46.6-pound component will not be countered by drag until the boat achieves a velocity of 8.33 ft/sec (5 knots) in the forward direction. These two components of velocity add to give a total motion of five knots in a direction only five degrees away from the direction the boat is pointed. As a result, the boat achieves a five-knot speed in a direction twenty-five degrees into the wind.

It should be emphasized that this is only a set of typical numbers and that the actual motion depends on a great number of factors of design, wind velocity,

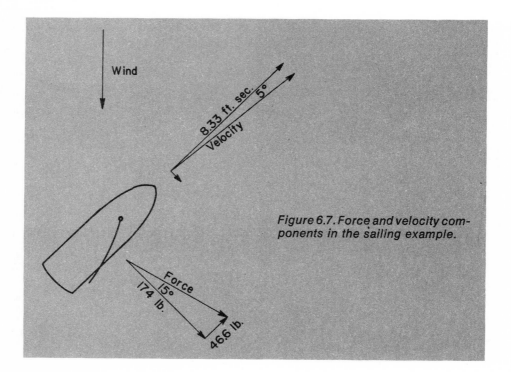

Figure 6.7. Force and velocity components in the sailing example.

and water conditions. The angles at which the sails can be set are limited to those which do not cause stalling. These, in turn, restrict the most efficient angles at which the boat can be pointed. The wave conditions and angle of tilt of the boat cause great variation in the drag coefficients and in the final result of the wind force. The expert sailor must learn to match the known performance characteristics of the craft with the existing weather and sea conditions in order to achieve optimum results with minimum risk of capsizing or stalling.

One concept of interest in sailing is the difference between sailing downwind versus sailing crosswind. In sailing downwind, the maximum possible velocity of the boat is slightly below the velocity of wind. As the craft approaches wind velocity, the relative velocity between boat and air becomes so small that the force is balanced out by the drag of the boat moving through water. On the other hand, when sailing crosswind it is often possible for the boat to reach velocities greater than the velocity of the prevailing wind. This is due to the fact that as the boat moves crosswind, the downwind component of the velocity with respect to the sail remains a constant regardless of how fast the boat is moving.

The ultimate in the use of the aforementioned concept in sport lies in the techniques used in iceboating where a wind of 10-15 mph is capable of propelling the iceboat at speeds near 100 mph. The iceboat actually has an advantage over a sailboat because forward frictional forces in iceboating are almost zero regardless of the velocity, and sidewise drag or frictional forces are nearly infinite, i.e., there is very little resistance to forward motion, and it is almost an impossibility to slide the iceboat sideways. In the case of a boat moving through water, however, there are drag forces which increase as the cube of the forward velocity. The fact that the keel does not exert a perfect drag means that there is a sidewise or leeward drift downwind against the action of the keel.

If the craft in figure 6.7 were an iceboat instead of a sailboat, the 174-pound component of force would be countered by a sidewise force of the runners against the ice, with no component of motion in that direction. Also, the forward velocity might reach 75 ft/sec before the 46.6-pound component were overcome by the drag due to the air. The iceboat would be moving at 75 ft/sec (51 miles per hour) in the same direction it was pointed. Again, wind conditions and stability limit the possible sail settings, and the condition of the ice causes great variation in possible performance alternatives.

Another problem with relation to forces affecting a sailboat is the fact that the air force is occurring above the surface of water, while the keel force is exerted below the surface. This means that the boat is always acting under the influence of a torque about its longitudinal axis. Improper setting of sails, especially with the small centerboard craft, can very quickly allow this torque to tip the boat. During racing of small craft, the person on board, in order to allow the choosing of a large component force from the wind without tipping the boat, at times will hike out to the side as far as possible to provide a gravitational countertorque (fig.6.8).

Force due to air on a sail is a combination of a high-pressure region behind the sail due to an actual deflection of wind, the so-called "jet effect," and a low-pressure area created in front of the sail by the passage of wind around a shape resembling an airplane wing. This is another example of the Bernoulli Effect. The total surface area and shape factors of the sail are used to give maximum components in the desired direction with minimum resistive effects in the various forms of drag. The importance of the Bernoulli portion of the force on the sail is illustrated in what happens when a sail stalls. Tilting a sail at too small an angle with respect to wind tends to lose the wing shape. The sailcloth then forms a series of ripples. At this point, the effective force on the sail drops nearly

Figure 6.8. Providing a gravitational countertorque during sailing

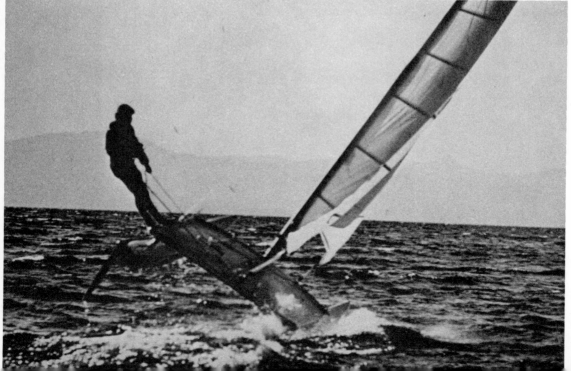

to zero. Maneuvers must be made to once again fill the sail with air before effective motion can be resumed. The possibility of stalling is greatly enhanced if the wind is gusty rather than steady. Therefore, for the same average wind speed, a steady wind drives a boat much more efficiently than a gusty one.

In the sport of surfing, the components resulting in the eventual motion arise from an interaction of gravitational and water motion forces. The wave on which the surfer is riding consists of water moving primarily upward toward the surfboard. While it appears that the wave is rushing toward the shore, the exchange of water composing the wave means that the water is moving upward (fig. 6.9). The surfer, therefore, is sliding downhill, using gravity on a water surface moving upward with enough velocity that his total distance above the ground remains nearly a constant. Skilled performers maintain this balance by various techniques of sliding diagonally along the wave, lifting or dropping the nose of the surfboard, or by maneuvers involving a shift of their own weight on the board.

Stabilization with respect to direction is usually provided by the drag of a very small keel located near the tail of the surfboard. One good illustration of

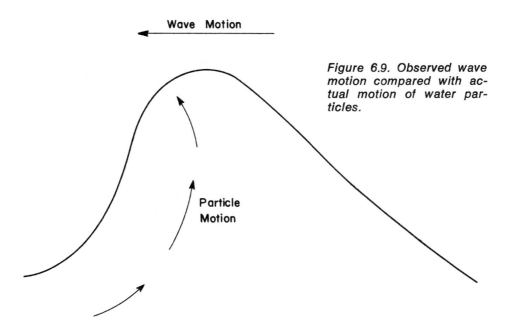

Wave Motion

Particle Motion

Figure 6.9. Observed wave motion compared with actual motion of water particles.

the upward velocity of the water on which the surfer is riding is a surfer's "wipe-out." After the performer leaves the board, the board is normally thrown high in the air by the upward action of the water.

As the surfboard is moving at a relatively high velocity with respect to air, there are drag forces between the surfer's body and air. His arm and upper-body motions are designed to counteract this force as well as to maintain equilibrium during the various maneuvers on top of the board.

The velocity of a surfer with respect to water can be increased by moving the center of gravity forward on the board. This causes the board to tilt more nearly parallel with the surface of the wave. The surfer then gains speed as he literally "moves downhill." He moves toward the shoreline by taking a diagonal path along the front surface of the breaking wave. Near the end of the ride, he will normally shift weight farther back on the board, causing the nose of the board to rise. This increases the drag coefficient and causes him to move up and over the back of the breaking wave (fig. 6.10).

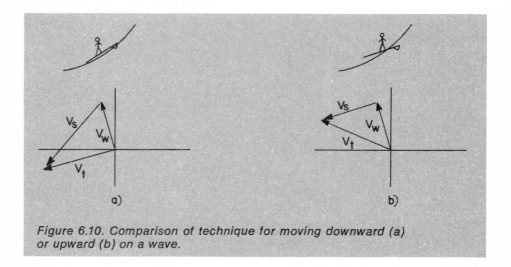

Figure 6.10. Comparison of technique for moving downward (a) or upward (b) on a wave.

Chapter 7

Principles of Biomechanics

In the preceding chapters of this section on the physics of sport, a basic mathematic-physics approach is utilized to present the principles of biomechanics. As indicated in chapter two, there are students who do not relate to concepts too well when numbers are used as symbols primarily to present ideas. That is to say, numbers have a tendency to place some students in a state of "symbol shock." When a person is in this condition, communication of ideas is exceedingly difficult. In such cases, other symbols are often substituted to transmit or communicate ideas.

The purpose of this chapter is to restate many of the principles discussed in chapters three through six, but the principles will be described with words used as symbols to communicate the basic principles of biomechanics to the reader. The principles are stated briefly, and each is preceded by a short "recall phrase" which should assist the reader in remembering the principle once it has been comprehended beyond the rote memory level. This type of comprehension is greatly enhanced by a thorough understanding of material already presented in chapters three through six.

An understanding of these biomechanic principles is necessary for the physical educator to adequately conduct noncinematographic and basic cinematographic analyses. These are the most common forms of biomechanic analysis techniques, and the following are the most commonly confronted principles in the areas of exercise, sport, and dance. These are the principles, for example, which performers most commonly utilize, effectively or ineffectively, while performing in athletics. Therefore, numerous examples from athletics are presented to clarify the implications to performances when these principles of biomechanics are utilized either effectively or ineffectively.

VELOCITY

Specific Velocity

Most sport actions involve the optimization of velocity of a specific body part, sport instrument, or sport object.

What this statement implies is that in any given sport action there is a particular part of the motion which is seeking to be optimized. Any extraneous motion which does not lead to a maximum value of this specific velocity represents a lost or impeding effort on the part of the athlete. One of the characteristics which separates the beginning performer from the championship-class performer is the appearance of extraneous motions which do not add to the specific velocity of the desired object or limb. It is imperative for the professional physical educator to recognize which are the important velocities in a given event or performance and to aid the performer in maximizing these velocities. For example, in the javelin throw the specific velocity of the throwing limb is the critical factor in the distance which will ultimately be traveled by the javelin itself. All motions starting with the toes and ending with the fingers must be used in such a way as to maximize throwing-limb velocity. Any motion tending to diminish this velocity results in a loss of the ultimate horizontal distance achieved by the javelin.

Summation of Velocities

All velocities are measured relative to other objects or body parts.

In almost all sport motions, the final motion of a limb or sport instrument or object is the result of the summation of several of these relative velocities. In many sport actions, a whole body motion is added to the velocity of a body part relative to the whole body in order to produce the final specific velocity desired. As an example, in the basketball jump shot the velocity of the performer going into the air is the result of the summation of an ankle plantar flexion, knee extension, and hip extension (fig. 7.1). The maximum height obtained is directly dependent on the summation of these three velocities. The jump shooter who fails to utilize the best possible summation of these velocities will not be able consistently to clear the defensive player with his shot.

Courtesy USC Athletic News Service

Figure 7.1. Summation of lower limb joint velocities to achieve maximum height for the jump shot by Bruce Clark, USC forward.

Sequential Velocity

The maximizing of a specific velocity is derived by the proper application of the time at which each component velocity reaches its greatest contribution in sequence to the final performance.

Many times the optimum results will come from the application of joint movements critically timed to the nearest thousandth of a second. These motions may occur simultaneously or sequentially, and more often occur in an overlapping type of sequence. For example, in the *long* jump shot in basketball, the motion of the arm and shoulder and especially the forceful extension of the elbow must be started at the proper time of the flight upward in order to get the ball released at or slightly after the peak of the jump (fig. 7.1). This will lead to optimizing the final key movement of the wrist joint (flexion) at the highest possible position and with the best force against the ball. Any defect in the previous sequence of motion will lead to a loss in accuracy, height of release, or velocity in this final wrist action.

Angular Velocity

Because of the configuration of the human body, almost all sport actions are the result of angular velocities about joints by limbs or body segments.

Even in such apparently linear motions as running or sprinting, the primary actions are angular velocities about the ankles, knees, and hips. As a performer begins to recognize the combination of flexions, extensions, and rotations at the joints, he can better correlate the desired results with the kinesthetic sense of motion. Many times the maximizing of specific velocity is actually dependent upon maximal angular velocity or rotation of body levers at joints. As an example, the discus thrower tries to obtain a maximum angular velocity at the shoulder in terms of diagonal adduction at that joint (fig. 7.2).

Radius of Movement

Linear velocities normally result from an angular motion multiplied by a radius of movement or distance from the axis of rotation.

Continuing with the discus example above, the maximum range of the discus requires a maximum linear velocity at the time of release. This linear

Courtesy Visual Track and Field Techniques, 292 So.
LaCienaga Blvd., Beverly Hills, Calif. 90211

Figure 7.2. The point of maximum angular velocity of the throwing limb of Ludvik Danek, Czechoslovakian discus thrower.

velocity results from angular velocity at the shoulder mentioned previously, multiplied by the radius of movement which is maximized by this full extension at the elbow and wrist joints. This maximum radius of movement combined with maximum angular velocity provides an optimum linear velocity to the discus and the greatest potential range of flight.

ACCELERATION

Positive Acceleration

An increase in speed of an object results from an acceleration in the same direction as the velocity.

Negative Acceleration

A decrease in speed of an object or body part results from an acceleration in the opposite direction from the velocity.

Change of Direction

A change of direction of motion results from an acceleration perpendicular to the direction of velocity.

The ability to distinguish the relationship between direction of acceleration and its effect on total motion is one of the most important in applied biomechanics. These differences are exemplified in the movement of a basketball guard working against the various players on the defensive team. In the fast break he may increase his speed very rapidly. At times he may stop or slow down quite suddenly to allow a defensive man to pass by, and at other times he may suddenly change direction in order to throw an opposing player off-balance.

At times the unwanted existence of a negative acceleration may lead to a diminishing of athletic performance. For example, a long jumper who either adjusts his stride near the end of the run or who plants the foot very strongly in leaving the board tends to negatively accelerate with respect to horizontal motion. This results in traveling forward more slowly through his trajectory. The total result of this negative acceleration is decreased total distance for the long jump.

It should be emphasized that the use of acceleration to decrease or modify motion is often fully as important as a maximizing of speed. In the case of a pulling guard preparing to run interference in American football, the initial acceleration will be utilized to provide maximum velocity for him to get into a position where the play is developing. After reaching this position, however, it is often important that he slow down in order to be in the most effective position to block the defensive man approaching the ball carrier. Too large a velocity at this point will often carry him past the position where the block should be made.

Sequential Acceleration

Most movements of body parts or sport implements are the result of a timed sequence of individual accelerations.

The importance of combining a properly timed sequence of velocities in order to obtain a maximized specific velocity has been emphasized. Likewise, in the development of the stereotype of perfect form for many sport actions, the proper sequencing of change of velocity or acceleration is highly important. Again, this is the starting or stopping of accelerations relative to one another within a few thousandths of a second of time. An example of such a sequential acceleration occurs in the sport of baseball when a player is trying to stretch a single into a double. As he approaches first base, it is necessary for him to decrease velocity with a negative acceleration in order to minimize the radius of curvature. Once the turn is made, velocity must be increased toward second base. It has been found that the optimum sequencing of these accelerations can be performed if the player attempts to hit the corner of the bag with his left foot on rounding first base. An example of an improper sequence occurs when players attempt to jump to reach the first-base bag on a close play. The very act of planting the foot to jump decreases horizontal velocity. This means that the actual time necessary to reach the base is longer than if the athlete had simply run across the bag (fig. 7.3).

Gravitational Acceleration

Most sport actions are influenced by constant gravitational acceleration.

Since most human body actions take place at or near the surface of the earth, the downward attraction of gravity is a constant factor which must always be considered. The concept of weight is the force associated with this acceleration. The motion of any body in flight will follow a trajectory determined primarily by this gravitational acceleration. Muscular forces used in all jumping

Figure 7.3. Proper sequencing of accelerations while running to first base—Rod Towe, SMS baseball player.

events are designed to counteract this acceleration of gravity in order to maintain optimum times or distances in the air. In interaction with fluids, the effects of buoyancy or of lift force in flight are necessary forces in order to counteract the relationship of gravitational acceleration. Knowledge of gravitational accelerations can lead to optimum angles of projection in such events as the discus, javelin, and shot put. On the other hand, too much concern for overcoming gravitational acceleration can be detrimental to a performance. For example, a long jumper may sacrifice considerable horizontal velocity in a firm planting of the foot in order to obtain maximum lift at takeoff from the board. This negative horizontal acceleration results in a loss of total linear distance for the jump.

FORCE

Force-Acceleration Relationship

Every acceleration is associated with an unbalanced external force acting on the object. Acceleration is in the same direction as the force and is proportional to the force.

This principle relates the observed phenomena of accelerations and velocity with the kinesthetically felt phenomena of forces. In the analysis of sport skills, it is important to be able to communicate the movements as observed, either noncinematographically or cinematographically, in terms of forces kinesthetically felt by the performer. In limb actions requiring considerable ranges of motion, the performer is unable to visually determine limb positions, velocities, and accelerations. Therefore, the performer is dependent on the sensory inputs developed by the proprioceptors located in muscles, tendons, and joints. For example, in the butterfly stroke in swimming the concurrent circumduction of both shoulder joints carries the arms well past the limit of visual contact, so a part of training in this event must be a development of the proper kinesthetic feeling which accompanies the optimum range of motion of the arms.

One reason for the extreme importance of this principle is that the direction of applied force is a performer-controlled variable of the action. *In order to produce optimum motion in the performance, force must be applied in the intended direction.* To return to the example of the butterfly stroke, circumductions at both shoulder joints must be concurrent and symmetrical in order to get the best motion through the water, i.e., the forces must be applied with the same strength in the same direction with both arms at the same time. Failure to do this leads to extraneous body motion and to a variable path direction in the water. This leads to a longer time for the greater total distance traversed during the race.

Force-Time Relationship

Total effect of force on motion of a body is the product of the magnitude of force and time over which it operates.

This principle is important in producing maximum motion or maximal changes of motion. It is not only important to reach optimum forces, but it is also necessary to hold them for the longest time possible. Physiologically, there is a muscle length-force ratio. *The force exerted by a muscle is proportional to its length.* It is found that there is a reciprocal relationship between this principle and the increased range of motion in a given joint. The increased range of motion not only leads to the potential of greater internal force being generated by the muscle groups most involved, but it also allows this force to be exerted over a greater time span. For example, during the preparatory diagonal abduction at the shoulder joint by a baseball pitcher, the diagonal adductors which will be used immediately following diagonal abduction are placed on great stretch if the pitcher has gone through a complete range of motion for diagonal abduction. This increase in range of motion for diagonal abduction means that he will have a greater range or movement time for the subsequent diagonal adduction prior to release of the ball. This is where the critical reciprocal relationship lies between the muscle length-force ratio principle and the force-time relationship principle of biomechanics. Anything less than a full range of motion will lead to a subsequent decrease in the release velocity of the ball. This interrelationship between the force-time product of biomechanics and the stretch principle from anatomic kinesiology is of utmost importance in all ballistic actions.

Force-Counterforce

Whenever an object or body part exerts a force on another object or body part, it in turn receives a force equal in magnitude and opposite in direction.

This principle applies in the case where a performer is exerting forces against an instrument or object or against another performer or where one part of the body is being used to exert forces against another segment. This application of force and counterforce is a basic ingredient of combative sports such as boxing, wrestling, or judo. In wrestling, for example, when one performer exerts a large force against his opponent, he must be prepared either through his body position and balance or his contact with the mat to receive and nullify the effects of the equal and opposite counterforce exerted on him (fig. 7.4).

In weight lifting, force the lifter is producing against the weight in order to raise it above his head produces a counterforce against muscles of his body. This counterforce must be controlled while moving the weights to the floor in

Figure 7.4. Force-counterforce by wrestlers during a match

order to maintain equilibrium. In an unsuccessful lift, often the lifter will attempt to push the weights forward. This results in a counterforce which moves his body backward, and sometimes results in a fall or backward roll by the athlete.

Internal Forces

In the action of one body part against another, the effects of both force and counterforce will be apparent in motions of the body.

The principle of internal forces is of utmost importance in regard to relative positions and velocities of body parts during athletic performances. Every muscle has two attachments to enable it to pull (contract) on levers. Therefore, in biomechanics one must consider muscular contractions from both force and counterforce points of view. These need to be especially noticed when dealing with a body in flight where it is impossible to negate effects of counterforces by contact with the ground. As an example of the use of forces and counterforces during flight, consider the competitive diver who is capable of transferring from a twisting motion to a tumbling motion by making the desired arm motions. In this case, forces used to move arms also provide the desired change of motion of the body by their counterforces.

The principle of internal forces is also important when external forces are being used to help propel the body. As an example, during running the actual external force used to propel the runner is the counterforce of the ground against the feet. However, a complex and sophisticated set of internal forces are used by the experienced runner in order to make the most efficient use of these forces by eliminating extraneous body motions and controlling equilibrium. In essence, the skill of running includes the utilization of internal forces to allow the most efficient use of external forces through an optimum series of alternate equilibrium losses and gains. This timing is especially critical in distance races, since muscles require "relaxation time" between contractions necessary for ballistic motions of lower limbs.

Concentric-Eccentric Forces

In the human body, muscular forces can be used both to cause motion against gravity (concentric contraction) and to control motion with gravity or by receiving external forces (eccentric contraction).

Concentric or shortening contraction of a muscle group is the *causative force* for all body motions against gravity. This action is used to produce greater motion or to add kinetic energy to the moving body. Eccentric or lengthening contractions, on the other hand, provide the *controlling force* for a body moving with gravity or receiving other external forces. These are used for a decrease of total motion or an absorption of kinetic energy. Eccentric control of a joint in motion is used both to control range of motion and to limit speed of motion. In this sense, eccentric control is very much a built-in safety mechanism of the body. As an example, in the sit-up exercise involving lumbar flexion, the abdominal muscles are the muscles most involved. They contract concentrically during the first ninety degrees of the exercise. As the trunk is lowered during lumbar extension with gravity, the abdominal muscles are contracting eccentrically in order to control both the extent of motion and speed. While in the position of ninety degrees of lumbar flexion, the force of gravity by itself would be capable of causing a return to the supine position through lumbar extension. This action without the control of eccentric contraction by the abdominals could cause injury in some cases.

Summation of Forces

Effect of more than one force acting on a body can be found by the summing of forces, taking into account the direction of each.

This vector or directional addition of forces is apparent in situations where both a gravitational acceleration and another desired acceleration are present. The combination of vertical and horizontal components of necessary force leads to a lean for a runner who is accelerating or a bank for a runner who is changing direction. This principle is also used in cycling, auto racing, and such activities as bobsledding or luging (fig. 7.5). In these activities, the performer has the option of controlling centripetal forces by staying low on the bank and playing it relatively safe or maintaining a high speed and going to the upper parts of the bank. While the performer moving higher on the bank travels a small distance farther, the higher average velocity actually leads to a minimum time around the curve. In these examples, the combination of the force of gravity downward with the force of the earth or ice upward and inward produces a net result of an inward centripetal force, giving the desired acceleration for change of direction.

Figure 7.5. Control of centripetal force on an inclined surface during cycling by Mark Logan.

The term *summation of forces* is also applied to the sequencing of internal forces in order to provide an optimum motion for the performer or athlete. Any time this sequence is interrupted, even for a period of a few microseconds, it may lead to a less efficient total motion for the athlete. This would produce diminishing results for the performance. This is particularly true in ballistic skills.

Equilibrium

Equilibrium of a body or object is obtained when each force acting on the body is balanced by an equal but oppositely directed force or force component.

The condition of equilibrium in a body is a situation where motion of the body remains unchanged, i.e., a stationary body remains stationary or a moving body continues moving at the same velocity in a straight line. The condition of zero acceleration implies a net zero force. This does not mean that there is not a force acting on the body but, rather, that each force is being balanced by another equal but oppositely directed force as illustrated by the gymnast in static equilibrium on parallel bars (fig. 7.6). Another example of this situation is the sailing of a boat crosswind at a constant velocity. In this case, the cross com-

Courtesy USC Athletic News Service

Figure 7.6. Static equilibrium during a parallel bar routine by John Kolb, USC gymnast.

ponent of wind is balanced by an equal but opposite force of water against the keel of the boat. Meanwhile the forward component of wind is balancing the drag of water. This maintains a constant linear velocity for the boat. It is necessary for the sailor to maintain the proper sail setting in terms of both angle and tension in order to keep these forces in balance and to continue moving in the straight line down the course.

Pressure

Since it is pressure and not total force which often causes pain or tissue damage, application of force should be spread over as wide an area of the body or body part as possible.

Pressure is a term used to denote force per unit area. High pressure can result either from an extremely large force or from a small or moderate force localized to a small area of the body. It is therefore a good rule to spread forces as widely as possible in order to prevent tissue damage. A classic example of this principle in sport lies in the falling techniques used in judo. The judoka lands on the mat with as much body surface area as possible to dissipate the force. A properly executed baseball slide utilizes the same principle (fig. 7.7). This is

Courtesy SMS Public Information Office

Figure 7.7. Dissipation of force to minimize pressure during a slide by Bill Helfrecht, SMS all-American baseball player.

also the reason that a small rubber tip is placed on the foil in fencing. Although small in surface area, this increases the area of the foil and prevents actual stabbing or penetration. This is an important principle to be considered by manufacturers of athletic equipment. For example, baseball gloves, football pads, and other items of this type need to be designed to dissipate forces over as large an area as possible. Changes in design of the catcher's mitt, as one example, have increased during the past few years and have provided a greater surface area over which the force of the pitch is absorbed.

Weight and Mass

Weight is the downward force of gravity acting on a body. Mass represents the total amount of matter in a body and its inertia to changes of motion in any direction.

There is often considerable confusion and uncertainty regarding use of the terms *weight* and *mass*. *The term "weight" actually refers to a force, the force with which the earth attracts the body (pounds). The term "mass" is used in measuring the amount of force in mass units necessary to cause a change of motion of a body, i.e., the larger the mass, the larger the amount of force necessary to cause the same change.* While these terms are greatly different in meaning, the differentiation is not exceptionally important in sport actions since they normally take place at the surface of the earth where weight and mass will always have the same proportionality, i.e., an object which weighs more than another object will always have a greater mass. However, as previously discussed, it is necessary when making numerical calculations to put both weight and mass in their proper units. In gravitational fields other than those found at the surface of the earth, the mass-weight relationship may change drastically.

Center of Gravity

External forces alter the basic position of the center of gravity of a body, while internal forces alter the position of various body parts with reference to that center of gravity.

The center of gravity of a body is a theoretical point at which the weight of the body could be located to produce the observed biomechanic effects during motion and balance. For the human body in the anatomic position, the center of gravity is located near the umbilical region. However, as the limbs are moved through various planes at shoulder and hip joints or during spinal column motions, the center of gravity may move outside the region occupied by body parts. This is the situation occurring during the high jump, long jump, and pole vault.

It is important in the analysis of motion of a performer to consider both motion of the center of gravity and motion of various body parts with reference to the center of gravity of the body. For example, the experienced hurdler uses his hip, shoulder, and lumbar motions to keep the center of gravity as low as possible during the flight phase so it moves with as little vertical motion as possible. On the other hand, the inexperienced hurdler, especially one who "jumps" the hurdles, has a large amount of vertical motion of the center of gravity. This necessarily means a slower average linear velocity, and a longer time is required to complete the hurdle race. During events where a performer is in the air, it is the center of gravity which executes the gravitational parabolic trajectory, while the internal forces (muscle contractions) control orientation and rotation about the center of gravity.

Frictional Forces

Magnitude of the frictional force parallel to the surface of contact depends on materials and smoothness of surfaces and on the force pressing surfaces together.

One of the most important forces found in all sport activities is friction force. It is through the action of friction on the surface of the ground that all running and jumping events acquire their horizontal velocity. Friction is also the main factor to consider when analyzing grips on sport implements. Negative aspects of frictional losses tend to be emphasized. There are many examples in sport where frictional force needs to be maximized to achieve an optimum performance. Since the available force of friction depends on the force pressing the surfaces together, there is an optimum angle at which a force should be exerted against a surface in order to obtain the greatest component of thrust parallel to that surface. If, for example, a runner plantar-flexes slightly and pushes against the ground with too shallow an angle, the component of force holding the foot to the ground is not great enough to allow a large value of friction. The foot will slip, and summated motion will be interrupted. On the other hand, if a runner plantar-flexes too much during the downward-thrust motion of the lower limb, then he simply does not develop a large enough horizontal component of force to give him the needed acceleration.

The principles involving friction are of special importance to people who design equipment and facilities for use in sport. Both the material used and the surface condition can be varied in order to increase or decrease available frictional forces. As one example, where the frictional coefficient is especially important, problems of the owner or manager of a bowling alley can be considered. In the first place, the material for surfacing the lane has to be one which provides a relatively low coefficient of friction between the ball and the floor and allows a high coefficient of friction between the bowler's shoes and the floor. Secondly, it is extremely important with experienced bowlers that the lane be consistent both from one side to the other within a single lane and as one moves from one lane to another. If one lane tends to have a high coefficient of friction while another has a low coefficient, the bowler cannot adjust his lift on the ball in order to give the proper curve for obtaining strikes. It might appear to the spectator that the bowler is being inconsistent, while the inconsistency would actually lie in the differences of the frictional coefficients of the lanes.

Centripetal-Centrifugal Forces

Change in direction of motion of a moving body requires a force directed inward toward the center of curvature of the path.

Since a change of direction of a moving body actually represents an acceleration, there must be a force associated with this acceleration which depends on the mass of the body and on the velocity with which it is moving. *This inward force is known as centripetal force and increases as the mass of the body increases and as the square of the velocity.* A body moving twice as fast requires four times as much centripetal force. *The equal and opposite reaction to the object or body providing centripetal force is known as centrifugal force.* These forces become important where a ballistic rotary motion of a sport implement is involved such as tennis, baseball, jailai, hammer and discus throwing, and golf. It should be recognized that these forces are present so the performer can counter them in order to maintain body stability during rotary ballistic motions. In this context, the foot placement is of extreme importance in providing the countering force against the ground to maintain body stability.

TORQUE

Lever Arm

Rotational effect of a force is directly proportional to its distance from the axis of rotation.

It needs to be recognized that effects of forces not only provide motion of the center of gravity of a body, but also cause rotations of a body about some axis. Muscle attachments at major joints of the human body are arranged to give a multiplication of the range of motion or velocity of motion rather than to multiply force exerted by muscles. The purpose of many sport implements is to increase this leverage still further. For example, the velocity with which a person can strike a handball can be increased by the addition of a racket as used in the game of squash.

Moment of Inertia

The inertia with respect to rotation of a body depends on the total mass involved and the average distance of this mass from the axis of rotation.

In order to provide a rapid rotation of a body or implement, it should be held with the limbs or portions of the implement as close to the axis of rotation as possible. This allows the torque generated either by the feet against the ground or by action of internal forces within the body to produce a maximum acceleration and velocity of rotation. As an example, the experienced discus thrower keeps the hand holding the discus located very near the lumbar spine as the rate of body spin in the circle is increased. After the body has attained maximum rotational velocity, the discus is moved away from the body. If the discus thrower were to keep the arms and discus away from the longitudinal axis of the body at all times, a smaller rotational velocity of the body would result, producing a smaller linear velocity at the time of release of the discus. The end result would be a smaller distance of flight.

Torque-Countertorque

Any time one body exerts a torque on another body or body part, it receives an equal and opposite countertorque.

This principle applies to rotational motion in the same way that the force-counterforce principle applies to translational or linear motion. A good example of this lies in the kinesiologic construct known as the Serape Effect (fig. 7.8). During high-velocity ballistic throwing or striking actions as observed in discus and javelin throwing, as two examples, the torque exerted on the rib cage in order

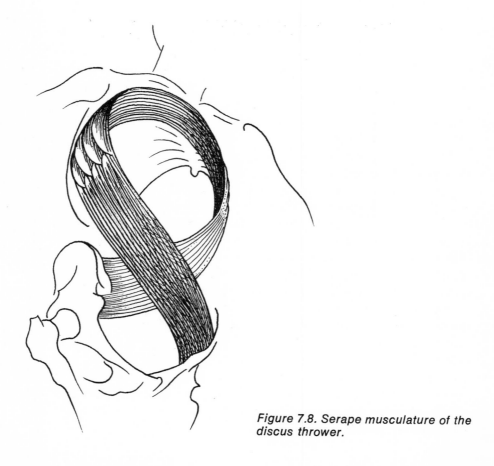

Figure 7.8. Serape musculature of the discus thrower.

to provide rotation of the upper body results in a countertorque being exerted on the pelvic girdle. This can be seen very clearly in figure 3.2. It is for this reason that transverse rotation of the pelvic girdle immediately preceding ballistic action of a limb is of utmost importance. If the pelvic girdle is moving in the direction of this ballistic motion, angular velocity which it is able to give the rib cage is greater. This ensures a higher velocity for the ultimate ballistic motion. If the pelvic girdle is stationary at the beginning of the ballistic motion, it will recoil and will provide a smaller ultimate velocity to upper portions of the body.

Equilibrium or Balance

Rotational equilibrium of a body requires that each torque acting on the body must be effectively cancelled by an equal and opposite countertorque.

This principle deals with the effect of externally applied torques. The concept of balance in sport actions corresponds to the maintenance of a rotational equilibrium. Normally, this means an equilibrium with zero rotational velocity. This requires that any torque exerted on the body part, generally due to the effect of gravity acting on an extended limb or other body, must be counteracted by an equal and opposite torque against the base of support. In the maintenance of equilibrium, it is important that the center of mass of the body be kept above the area known as the base of support. The width of a stance is extremely important in establishing a large base of support and allowing the effect of forces at the feet to have large lever arms in the exerting of torque to recover or maintain equilibrium. In some sport action, this width of stance is not allowed due to either the rules, skill execution, or the equipment used. For example, for a gymnast performing on the balance beam, the limited width of the beam at times negates the possibility of establishing a wide base of support. In this case, internal muscular forces must be used in the establishment and maintenance of equilibrium. A loss of equilibrium is normally overcome only by making some type of compensating body movement.

It should be pointed out that even when equilibrium is lost, there is a certain amount of time before the rotational motion is enough to cause a complete fall. Even during this period of disequilibrium a skilled athlete is often able to perform, complete the attempted sport action, and recover equilibrium. For example, a skilled basketball player can often make a leap off-balance to make a shot. He will use follow-through motions from the shot and other compensatory limb actions to regain equilibrium without falling (fig. 7.9). The unskilled athlete, on the other hand, does not possess this ability to recover, and an extreme disequilibrium will almost always result in a fall. For this reason, he

Courtesy USC Athletic News Service

Figure 7.9. Controlled motion in a state of disequilibrium by Paul Westphal, USC basketball guard.

constantly strives to maintain himself in a state of near-equilibrium. When this is done, a performer misses the opportunity to complete successful sport actions.

ENERGY

Force-Distance Relationships

The transfer of energy from one body or body part to another is accomplished by means of a force acting through a distance of motion.

While the most common method of describing motion is in terms of forces and accelerations, this description can also be made in terms of energy transfers. The transfer of energy from an athlete to a sport object or implement, for example, is accomplished by the exertion of a force through a distance of motion of that object or implement. Maximum transfer of energy requires the most efficient use of force-production motions in the body and the maximum range of motion at the point of contact with the instrument or object. This maximizing of the range of force action in a throwing skill is exemplified in the body and limb actions observed during a javelin throw. If the thrower does not go through an extreme range of body motions before release of the javelin, the result will be a lower release velocity and a shorter distance for the throw.

Kinetic Energy

Change of speed of an object requires a force acting through a distance since kinetic energy is dependent on the square of speed.

To increase or decrease speed of a body part, instrument, or object, work must be performed or absorbed in the process. As indicated in earlier chapters, the term used for energy associated with motion is *kinetic energy*. This depends on the mass of the object and its speed. One area where applications of this principle are of vital importance is in the stopping of objects in motion. Simply due to their motion, they have a large amount of energy. The performer must absorb this energy in bringing the object to rest. As an example of this, consider the dismount move at the end of a gymnastic routine. The performer coming off the final movement from the parallel bars, uneven parallel bars, horizontal bar, or rings has a considerable amount of kinetic energy. As he comes in contact with the mat, he must absorb kinetic energy and control his motion by eccentric contraction of the muscle groups within the lower limbs associated with major joints. The extent to which he does this without having extraneous movements is an important part of judging the performance.

Potential Energy

When work is performed while distorting the shape of an object or lifting it against gravity, it is stored in the object as potential energy.

The term *potential energy* is one which is given to an object's ability to perform work due to either its position above some base surface or to an elastic distortion of the object itself. As the object or body returns to its base level or as the distortion disappears, this energy is then converted into some other form. As an example, the sport of competitive diving is highly dependent on the storing of potential energy in the board during the final approach step on the board itself. If the diver fails to store an optimum amount of energy at this point, it cannot be returned to him in the form of kinetic energy as he leaves the springboard. Therefore, the diver will have less total time in the air in which to complete the maneuvers and make a successful entry into the water. The manufacturers of diving boards attempt to design them so the competitive diver can store a maximum amount of potential energy more easily, and the adjustable fulcrum allows each diver to adapt the leverage to his own style and weight.

Energy Transformation

Almost all human body motions represent a series of transformations from one form of energy to another, and the stereotype of perfect form is usually that one in which energy transformations are carried out most smoothly and efficiently.

It is necessary in the transfer of energy from one form to another to do this with greatest efficiency, since a lower efficiency means a loss of total energy by the performer during performance of the event. In the case of ballistic and antigravity events, which are controlled by the final energy available to the body or object, this loss of energy necessarily means a lesser performance. The smoothness of transfer is important in order not to dissipate energy into extraneous motions. One characteristic observable in a beginner who is still learning a sport skill is the presence of extraneous motions. As a result, the beginner may actually expend more energy during the performance of a particular athletic movement than the skilled performer, but with lesser results.

In the human body, the best transfer of energy occurs from large muscle groups in the direction of smaller muscle groups. The stereotype of perfect form for most athletic performances involves an initial motion with the large muscle groups, followed by the sequences of motion controlled by smaller muscle groups within the body. This proper sequence of motion is often referred to as the "kinetic chain" associated with performance.

Energy Expenditure

Each human body has rates at which energy can be supplied to muscle fibers. These rates regulate the possible muscular performances over extended periods of time dependent upon the cardiovascular efficiency of the individual.

During an athletic performance involving reciprocal movements, a given set of muscles or muscle groups are not constantly undergoing contraction, i.e., following an expenditure of energy during contraction, there is a cessation of contraction within muscle, but motion continues due to momentum. This alternate contraction-cessation process is repeated during each limb motion in a running action, as one example. If on the average the energy being expended by a muscle group is greater than the rate at which it can be replenished by the oxygen consumption and other factors within the body, the condition known as fatigue will set in. In such activities as middle- or long-distance running, it is the rate at which muscles can be replenished with energy that determines the average velocity with which the race can be run. Such things as the training effect tend to increase the rate of delivery of oxygen and, therefore, energy to the muscle group. This increases the average velocity and permits a given distance to be run in a shorter time, i.e., the potential energy expenditure is increased by means of the training effect. On the other hand, any motion involving excess tension or excess muscular contraction uses energy inefficiently and decreases the total amount of energy available for the running action. Coaches often refer to this excess tension in terms of the runner being tight. Indicators are a clenched jaw and excess flexion at the hands or elbow. This extra energy expenditure necessarily means that average velocity during a race must be lower. Therefore, total time necessary for a given distance will be longer.

POWER

Force-Velocity Relationship

Maximum force applied during a ballistic motion may be limited by the rate at which power can be developed within a muscle group.

Scientifically, *power* is defined as work performed per unit time, or the product of force times velocity. Since this is a limiting factor in many human body performances, it follows that at times maximum force can be administered only at the sacrifice of a maximum velocity of motion. This limitation can often be overcome by the use of a greater range of motion, providing for a higher limb velocity in many throwing or other ballistic motions as discussed earlier under the force-distance relationship.

Length of Application

Short-interval ballistic actions deliver high power, while long-interval continued actions deliver large amounts of energy.

The power which can be delivered by a muscle group is highly dependent on the time the action must be continued. In situations requiring a very short but intense effort, the quantity delivered is power. An example of this would be the situation discussed earlier in weight lifting where a man was capable of exerting up to seven horsepower during the snatch lift. The time interval involved in actions of this type would be measured in seconds or fractions of a second. Other examples of these power-delivering moves would be such things as the explosive charge of a football lineman from his stance at the beginning of a play, the jump of a rebounder in basketball, or the starting motions in either swimming or track (fig. 7.10). In most of these applications, the need for high power comes from the necessity to overcome inertia.

On the other hand, when an action requires delivery of large amounts of energy, the need is for a less-intense continuous action but of longer duration.

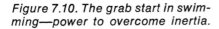

Figure 7.10. The grab start in swimming—power to overcome inertia.

For example, in an event such as the rope climb, which was an NCAA gymnastic event, the total energy necessary was far more than could be delivered in a single burst. Therefore, this required a sustained effort in order to reach the top of the rope. A 160-pound man climbing the twenty-foot rope in a time of three seconds would represent an average power output of about two horsepower. On the other hand, for greatly extended periods of time such as long-distance running, the average athlete can only perform at about three-quarters horsepower.

LINEAR MOMENTUM

Inertia

The total amount of movement carried into a situation by a body or object depends on the mass of the body or object and on its velocity.

The term *momentum* or *quantity of movement* is used to describe the product of the mass of a body or object and its velocity. As discussed earlier in the concept of force, external forces provide changes of momentum of a body. In order to give the same inertial results in a sport or athletic performance, a smaller body requires a higher velocity than a larger body. In the impact sports such as American football or ice hockey, a larger, more massive man can achieve the same type of blocking results while moving at a lower velocity than a smaller or less massive man.

It should be noted here that the term *inertia* refers to a resistance to change of motion, i.e., a stationary body can have inertia against being set in motion in any given direction. Or, a body already in motion has inertia against being stopped or diverted in its motion. The stances commonly observed in various sports are designed to allow the performer to efficiently overcome static inertia to begin a sport motion. Within the stances, the muscles are placed on stretch in order to quickly apply the large forces necessary to overcome inertia and place the body in motion.

Action-Reaction

In any two-body interaction, total change of momentum of the bodies are equal but opposite in direction.

This principle is simply another facet of the force-counterforce principle discussed earlier. Since the result of an external force is to cause a change of momentum of a body, then the result of the counterforce will be to provide an equal and opposite change of momentum. Again, in this principle the concept that bodies of large mass will acquire smaller changes of velocity in any given interaction than bodies of smaller mass becomes important. Anytime there is a collision or impact between two performers in a sport, the smaller man will have a larger change in his velocity than the larger man.

Conservation of Linear Momentum

A moving body tends to maintain its same state of motion except when acted on by an external force.

This conservation of linear momentum is most apparent when an object is not in contact with the ground to enable the external forces to be applied as readily. A body or object in air will maintain the same horizontal momentum and will gain a downward vertical momentum due to gravity unless it can strongly interact with another body or object or with air. For example, a place-kick after leaving the foot of the kicker will follow its prescribed trajectory through the air, involving conservation of this momentum unless it is touched by an opposing player. Such action would provide an external force and deflect its horizontal momentum into a new direction.

Much of the techniques of footwork are designed to enable the performer to obtain external forces from the ground in order to provide necessary changes of momentum for actions. The experienced athlete will often make a certain action or performance "look easy" because he has acquired the necessary footwork to adjust his linear momentum to perform the necessary skill; whereas the beginning athlete without this ability seems to be fighting against his own momentum or to be in a state of disequilibrium.

ANGULAR MOMENTUM

Linear-Angular Interrelationship

Most efficient sport movements should be viewed in terms of a linear motion of the center of gravity of the body combined with angular rotations of the various body parts about this center of gravity (fig. 7.11).

Courtesy SMS Public Information Office

Figure 7.11. Combination of linear motion and angular rotations by a hitter, Dan Cook, SMS baseball player.

All motions relating to positions of various body parts or orientations of the body itself can be viewed in terms of angular motion about the center of gravity. These motions are controlled primarily by internal body forces as described earlier in this chapter. A total angular rotation, however, requires an external torque normally acquired through torques due to forces from some base of support. An important aspect in the analysis or observation of a human body movement is the orientation of various body parts with respect to some axis of rotation.

An example of linear and angular motion of body parts combined to give an optimum result occurs during the throwing action through the high diagonal plane of the shoulder as observed in an outfielder's throw in baseball or the quarterback's pass in football. The linear velocity in this case is being supplied primarily by a diagonal adduction at the shoulder joint. A critical addition to this motion is the medial rotation of the shoulder joint just prior to release of the ball. This action not only adds linear velocity, but also helps impart the critical spin to the ball. In some unskilled performers, this rotation occurs as a part of the follow-through *after release* rather than while the hand is still holding the ball so the force transfer can be made. In this case, while the final motion may look the same, the rotational component of motion has not added to the motion of the ball since it occurred following release. In the analysis of ballistic movements, it is very difficult to observe this critical timing of medial rotation of the throw without the use of motion-picture film.

Action-Reaction

Any time one body or object changes the angular momentum of another body or object, it in turn receives an equal but opposite reactive change.

This concept of action and reaction has been discussed under the principles involving forces, torques, centrifugal and centripetal forces, and linear momentum. In this situation it again is simply the idea that one motion of this type tends to offset another. This factor is exceedingly important with respect to angular momentum because of its use by the body to maintain an equilibrium position in many sport actions. This principle of biomechanics is a fundamental basis in many of the reflexive movements observed in human body motions.

Conservation of Angular Momentum

A rotating body tends to maintain the same quantity of angular momentum unless it is acted on by an outside torque.

This principle with respect to angular momentum has certain connotations which do not occur in linear momentum. Since angular momentum depends not only on the total mass of the body, but on its extension with respect to the axis of rotation, the actual rotational velocity of a body may be adjusted by conserving angular momentum. If the body mass is brought closer to the axis of rotation by a series of flexions, the total moment of inertia will be decreased since the average radius from the axis to a body component is less. The conservation of angular momentum principle then specifies that the angular velocity will increase. On the other hand, if the body is extended so the mass is located farther from the axis of rotation, conservation of angular momentum will cause a decrease in rotational velocity. As an example of this effect, during a tennis serve or overhand smash involving diagonal adduction (rotary action) of the racket limb through the high diagonal plane, a flexion of the elbow decreases the average radius, and this increases the velocities of the racket at impact and the tennis ball during flight (fig. 7.12). A similar effect occurs in the case of the

Courtesy USC Athletic News Service

Figure 7.12. Conserving angular momentum within the racket limb prior to impact increases limb velocity.

knee flexion used in sprinting. In order to allow the legs to be brought forward with a higher rotational velocity at the hip, sprinters utilize extreme knee flexions while running.

Effects of conservation of angular momentum are often apparent in whole body motions as well as limb motions. For example, a diver leaving the board with a twisting action has a much higher angular velocity during the twist phase while rotating about the longitudinal axis of the body. The degree of difficulty of a dive is judged on the basis of the ability to generate and conserve angular momentum. For example, a dive in a full layout position is much more difficult than the same dive performed in a pike or tuck position because of the larger total angular momentum required to make a set number of rotations during the time of flight in the layout position.

COLLISIONS

Impact Time

The magnitude of forces involved in an impact varies inversely with the amount of time of contact between the two colliding bodies.

When two bodies collide, producing a change of momentum for both, the product of force and time is called the impulse of collision (fig. 7.13). This im-

Courtesy SMS Public Information Office

Figure 7.13. Impulse of collision between two wrestlers.

pulse will vary over a small margin for most collisions as a function of whether it is a short- or long-time action. Therefore, for very short-time actions, the total forces involved must reach much higher levels of magnitude. To minimize the possibilities of injury during a collision either with another body or with the ground, impact time should be spread as far as possible to keep forces at a minimum. As an example, the football player is taught to land on the ground using a shoulder roll, in which case his motion is dissipated over a longer time than if he were to simply land on the acromion process of the shoulder. The latter impact would probably result in a dislocation of the acromioclavicular joint and/or sternoclavicular joint.

Rebound Angles

For an object bouncing off a surface with no spin, the angle of rebound will be symmetrical with the angle of incidence.

During a collision from a surface where spin is not involved, the component of momentum parallel to the surface will remain approximately the same, and only the component perpendicular to the surface will be reversed. An example of this type of collision is the placing of the ball against the backboard in basketball on a driving layup. Since spin is not involved at this point, the angle at which the ball rebounds toward the hoop will be symmetric with the angle at which the player projects the ball toward the backboard. When possible, the approach angle of the drive for this shot should be at about forty-five degrees toward the basket.

Courtesy USC Athletic News Service

If the object bouncing from the surface has a spin, frictional forces come into play and modify the motion of the object parallel to the surface. This is the case in most rebounds of tennis balls from the racket surface (fig. 7.14). Another example of this

Figure 7.14. Rebound angle of the tennis ball from the racket face during a backhand drive by George Taylor, USC tennis player.

would be the layup where the player passes under the basket, shoots the ball, and uses spin to bring it back into the basket. The control of a collision involving spin presents new factors of difficulty. Collisions with a nonspinning object should be used, when possible, in preference to those that are spinning.

Elastic-Inelastic

Two bodies colliding are said to rebound elastically if they separate and maintain the same total kinetic energy which was carried into the collision.

A collision is said to be perfectly inelastic if the colliding bodies stick together. Actually, most actions fall somewhere between perfectly elastic and inelastic in their structure.

Coefficient of Restitution

Coefficient of restitution is a measure of the total amount of kinetic energy carried away from a collision divided by the amount of kinetic energy going into the collision.

The collision of a number-one wood with a golf ball during a drive off the tee serves as a good example of this principle. The swing and the elasticity in the shaft of the wood are used to impart a maximum kinetic energy to the club head before collision. During collision, this kinetic energy is transferred into a deforming potential energy of the club head and ball. As the ball rebounds from the collision, this potential energy is retransformed into kinetic energy primarily within the ball itself. The coefficient of restitution in this case is a measure of kinetic energy of the ball after collision compared to the kinetic energy which the club carries into the collision. A less efficient energy transformation occurs when a field hockey ball is struck during a drive. This is due primarily to the materials and weights of the sport implement, the stick, and the sport object, the field hockey ball (fig. 7.15).

It is the purpose of equipment manufacturers to make balls or surfaces with as high a coefficient of restitution as possible in order to make maximum energy transfers during the sport action. This must be accomplished within the rules set forth for the various sports.

Figure 7.15. Energy transformation during a field hockey drive.

Impact Parameter

Subsequent motion of two bodies after a collision depends to a large extent on the angle between their relative velocity and the line joining their centers.

The concept of impact parameter is discussed with the use of such terms as *head-on collisions* and *glancing collisions*. In the case of a head-on collision where the line joining centers of two bodies is in the same directions as their relative velocity, there is a maximum transfer of energy from one body to another. In a case where the collision is slightly off-center, there is less transfer of energy but more scatter in the directions of motion of the bodies following the collision. In the case of maximum impact parameter, or what is called a glancing collision, little energy is transferred from one body to another, and only small changes in direction of motion are noted.

In many sport applications such as a hit in baseball, a slap shot in hockey, or a shot in field hockey, optimum conditions occur with the smallest possible impact parameter, i.e., maximum velocity will be imparted to the ball or puck by as nearly as possible a head-on collision. A slight deviation from the head-on collision tends to give the sport object a high velocity, but in the wrong direction.

A large deviation or a glancing collision tends to prove ineffective in causing a change of motion of the object.

There are situations, on the other hand, where the ability to deliver a precise but glancing type of collision becomes important. For example, some batters in baseball become masters at protecting the plate by fouling off pitches until they get the pitch they want or they work the pitcher for a walk. In these glancing-type collisions where the impact parameter is not zero, whether the objects rebound elastically or stick together in inelastic collision, a large amount of spin will normally be introduced into the motion of the sport object. This is commonly observed in good punting techniques in both soccer and American football. As the ball is released from the hand before the kick, it has no spin, and the proper kicking technique has just enough impact parameter to direct the ball with a high velocity and optimum spin.

Effect of Spin

When two bodies, either one or both of which are rotating, suffer a collision, the effect of spin is to transfer rotation from one to the other and provide a frictional force which causes a rebound in other than a normally elastic direction.

As noted earlier, when a nonspinning object strikes a surface, the angle of reflection tends to be equal to the angle of inflection. This again is the same as saying that the horizontal velocity or horizontal component of momentum is maintained in such a collision. The effect of spin is to provide a frictional force with the surface which either adds to the horizontal component of motion or subtracts from it. For example, a tennis ball striking the court surface with backspin tends to lose its horizontal velocity and rises vertically. A tennis ball with a large forward spin tends to take a very low, fast rebound as the frictional force due to spin adds to the horizontal component of velocity. Often, such a collision will result in a change of spin, causing a different modification of subsequent rebounds. For example, in the sport of handball, a lateral spin on the ball driven into a side wall will either add to its forward velocity or subtract from it, depending on whether the spin can be considered forward with respect to the wall or backward with respect to the wall. However, in the case where the spin diminishes the speed of the ball, this spin is generally reversed by contact with the wall so the subsequent contact with the front wall results in a different type of rebound than would be expected from spin which the performer originally placed on the ball. In all cases in court sports where spin is imparted to a ball before a rebound from a wall, a floor, or even the ground as in the case of a baseball, a skilled performer needs to understand not only the original trajectory and direction of motion of the ball, but also needs to be able to "read spin" before and after each rebound in order to successfully predict the motion of the ball following future rebounds. The ability to "read spin" both in direction and magnitude on a ball also becomes important when considering that this determines motion of the ball in the air regarding whether it will rise, drop, or curve in various directions. This ability to "read spin" is one of the most important skills of the experienced and well-coached athlete.

AERODYNAMICS

Drag

Resistance of air to motion of an object through it depends both on the shape of the object and on the relative velocity between the object and air.

The term *drag* is used for that component of force due to air directly resisting motion of an object or body through it. This force becomes more important as the velocity is increased, since for most shapes and velocities the force varies as the square of velocity. For a given velocity, force depends on the amount of streamlining effected by the shape and cross-sectional area in the direction of motion. The human body in a crouched or forward-lean position meets with a much smaller drag force at a given velocity than when standing erect with limbs extended. For example, the long jumper who maintains equilibrium while abducting both shoulder joints may be sacrificing distance due to an increase of the drag coefficient afforded by this position.

It should be noted here that the counterforce to drag—the force of the object on the air—produces a forward motion of air behind the moving object or body. This forward-moving package of air, sometimes called the slipstream, can be beneficial to a performer who can use it to decrease his own drag resistance. For example, in the sport of cycling, riders tend to maintain a minimum distance behind the leader in order to utilize the slipstream of air created as he overcomes drag resistance. This principle is particularly noted in the teamwork used in team-pursuit cycling as one man will take the lead for a short period of time and then drop back behind his teammates. Each person spends a certain part of the race time countering a maximum drag and creating a slipstream for his teammates to "rest."

Yaw

When objects move through air, it is important that they have a minimum amount of sidewise rotational motion, otherwise known as yaw, during the flight.

This question of orientational stability during flight is exceedingly important, since an object which begins with this problem usually will not counteract it during flight. An object which begins with an excessive rotational motion or a wobble will continue to do so throughout the flight. The effect of this is to interact with air in such a way as to increase the drag coefficient by losing the natural streamlining which comes from the aerodynamic design of an object such as a football or arrow. An example of this problem would be the archer who places too much pressure on the nock of the arrow where it contacts the string at the time of release. This causes a yaw as the arrow clears the bow. The effect of this motion decreases horizontal velocity by an extreme amount and causes the arrow to fall far below the intended target.

Lift

When a body or object interacts with air in such a way that air is forced downward, counterforce due to the air exerts a force upward which helps the body overcome gravity.

The concept of lift or flight is often given a mysterious connotation involving various shapes, spins, or other aspects of motion. The important idea in obtaining lift from a motion through the air is simply to interact in such a way as to push the air downward. This may be done in terms of an aerodynamic shape, or it may be accomplished simply in terms of the angle of attack as, for example, with the flight of the discus or javelin.

One of the commonly observed techniques of lift in sport is that due to the spin of an object. In a well-hit golf ball or baseball or a well-kicked soccer ball, the backward spin of the ball as it travels through the air brings air behind it downward. The resulting force upward then causes the ball to fly much farther than it would in a simple parabolic trajectory. This same effect is also responsible for the curve, rise, and drop balls thrown by a softball pitcher. A modern example of the use of lift is in the fast-growing exercise of kiting. This is often seen in association with water-skiing where a performer will use a large kite and the proper angle of attack in order to give a lift greater than the weight of his body and kite. This causes him actually to fly at the end of the towrope. In this case, the boat doing the towing is providing the energy to maintain a wind velocity, and the performer can adjust the lift or interaction with air by the angle at which he holds the kite.

Trajectory Patterns in Flight

A body interacting with air will not follow a simple parabolic trajectory due to the force of gravity.

Only by understanding the effect that air is having on an object can a performer expect to predict the angle of approach or distance which such a body will traverse before coming back to earth.

One of the most important techniques for a performer is learning to judge the motion of flying objects. For the performer attempting to obtain maximum distance with the javelin or discus in a field event, the ability to read the effects of wind on a given day and adjust the throwing style and angles becomes of utmost importance. Failure to take advantage or to compensate for head winds, tail winds, or crosswinds will result in a less than optimum performance. In some events, for example, the shot put, the interaction possible with air is so small compared with other forces involved that it may be disregarded, and the trajectory will follow a classical parabolic pattern.

Imparting spin to a sport object in order to affect its flight pattern or trajectory is an integral aspect of many sport skills. In sports ranging from tennis, handball, and table tennis to the large field sports such as baseball and soccer, the actual flight of the object during a given contest will often be drastically affected by the spins involved. The flight pattern will deviate from the normal parabolic trajectory in the direction of the spin. A ball with backspin will tend to be lifted and carry farther and stay in the air longer than a ball with forward spin. In the latter case, the front part of the ball is moving downward. For example, baseball coaches should teach all players at all positions to throw the ball by gripping across seams and imparting a backspin at release. This grip with respect to the seams insures a maximum interaction with air, and the backspin gives maximum lift to overcome gravity as long as possible. It is also important that the performer be able to "read" the spin of an incoming sport object in order to interact with it in an optimum manner. For example, a tennis player needs to be able to detect spin of all serves and ground strokes coming toward him in order to tell not only what their flight trajectories will be and thus where they will bounce, but also the effect the spin will have on the bounce. If the tennis player fails to observe this spin or observes it too slowly, he will not be able to get the proper foot and body positions to hit a well-placed return shot.

In considering the range which will be obtained by an object in flight, the angle at which it is projected from the ground is of extreme importance. In the case of an object which has no lift, this angle should be forty-five degrees for an object released near the ground. Release of the object significantly higher than the ground, as in the shot put, or deviation of the trajectory due to spin of the object, as in a golf drive, requires that the angle of projection be less than forty-five degrees in order to obtain maximum distance. In other cases, such as the long jump, the angle is determined, not by that which gives an optimum possible flight pattern, but rather by the limitations of the human anatomic structure which will allow speed to be maintained only for relatively low angles of takeoff. Still another example occurs in the sport of football, where at times the purpose of a punt is not to obtain a maximum range, but rather to obtain a maximum time in the air to allow coverage. In this case, an extremely high angle of projection becomes important.

Flight Stability

An object not in contact with the ground is susceptible to various types of instability of motion, especially with respect to orientation.

Since an object in flight is capable of interacting only with the air, the stability during the initial phase of flight is especially important. An object launched into the air with yaw or a tendency to turn in an unwanted direction has little capability of stopping this motion while in flight. Stability during flight is aided, at times, by the design of the sport object. Examples are raised seams on various balls and fletching on arrows. At other times, stability is obtained through the conservation of the direction of angular momentum by causing the object to spin, and this is the case in flight of the discus, arrow, and javelin. An object without rotation will have a much more erratic flight pattern, especially if interacted by a side wind or other nonsymmetrical force. In order to make optimum use of this principle, a spinning object needs to be placed into the air without any yaw. It is for this reason that the technique of release of a sport object is such an important part of many sport skills.

For a performer in the air, stability is often maintained by using internal forces. These muscle contractions cause adjustments of arm positions, and slight deviations from stability of the body can be controlled. In extreme cases where disequilibrium is apt to occur, the countertorque to the rotational tendency is obtained by circumduction of one or both arms. This technique can be used either to absorb excess rotation or to create rotation needed as in the case of the pole-vaulter during the landing phase after passing over the bar.

In those situations where the performer desires to enter the air with an angular momentum in the form of a twisting or tumbling motion, as in diving or rebound tumbling, it is necessary that these motions be started while still in contact with the board or trampoline. Once in the air, any twist of one portion of the body is counteracted by an equal but opposing twist of some other portion of the body. For example, if a performer enters the air with no spin and attempts to change his position by a forceful diagonal adduction of the right shoulder, his body will turn to the right around the longitudinal axis. However, when he has reached the limit of his range of motion, both the adduction of the arm and rotation of the body will cease. He can change position but cannot introduce a total spinning motion. These extraneous actions of the limb will not change the flight pattern or trajectory.

HYDRODYNAMICS

Drag

Due to density and viscosity of water, objects passing through it are retarded greatly by drag force.

Drag force is that component of force directly opposite the direction of motion. In water, these forces are anywhere from 10 to 100 times greater than those encountered in air at low velocities. For all activities involving motion through water, streamlining of shape and orientation of the object with reference to direction of motion become extremely important. For example, in the case of competitive swimming strokes it is a necessity to minimize, as much as possible, lateral plane movements such as shoulder and hip abductions. These add to the cross section presented to the water in the direction of motion and decrease the streamlining and greatly increase drag. Any motion causing the body to lie obliquely rather than horizontally in the water has the same effect.

The design of objects such as kayaks, sculls, or sailboats becomes of vital importance in minimizing drag forces which will be met while moving through water. Literally millions of dollars are expended for engineering and designing hulls of yachts to be used in the sport of yacht racing.

In any situation where there is turbulence in the water, the drag problem is greatly compounded. Since turbulence represents water moving in many different directions, this means that there is no possibility of meeting the water always in the most streamlined position. In the sport of competitive white-water kayaking, the problem is made still greater by the fact that the kayaker must, at times, pass through the gates with, against, or across the flow of the stream. The stream itself shows turbulence and eddies due to the various obstructions present in the stream.

Buoyancy

Objects in water are buoyed upward in such a way that the effect of gravity is partially or completely cancelled.

Motions necessary in water sports are somewhat different from those in sports performed on land because the buoyant effect of water cancels the need for antigravity muscular actions. There are exceptions to this rule. For example, the water polo shot is definitely an antigravity motion due to the vertical force component required of the athlete. However, in most swimming events, and in such sports as kayaking or canoeing, the primary forces necessary are almost completely horizontal. While the competitive swimmer may not be completely buoyant due to the fact that he has a high percentage of lean body mass, nevertheless the total vertical force which he must use to remain at the surface of the water is at most only a few pounds. His execution of stroke mechanics is developed to the point that this lack of buoyancy is negated.

Thrust

The density of water allows major thrust forces to be developed through standard limb motions associated with swimming.

In contrast with human body motions in air, motion of limbs through water interacts with a mass of water representing a large fraction of the mass of the human body. Therefore, forces against these masses can be large enough in size that the counterforce of water provides noticeable acceleration to the body. These forces are known as thrust obtainable in water.

The strategy of strokes in competitive swimming is to obtain a maximum amount of thrust while keeping the body in such a position as to have a minimum amount of drag. In this way, the highest average velocity can be maintained through the water. For this reason, any motion involved in swimming which either decreases the thrust interaction with the water or increases drag will lead to less than optimum results. For example, in the kicking process for the front crawl and back crawl, a kick which brings the foot out of the water represents a loss of thrust during the part of the motion while the foot is not in the water. On the other hand, a kick which goes too deep in the water increases the drag, thereby decreasing the ultimate speed. It is also important that in considering the total time of a stroke, time in which thrust is developed becomes as large a fraction as possible as compared to time when the swimmer is simply gliding through water. This glide portion is an almost unnoticeable part of the stroke in competitive swimming but may become a much more important part in such activities as recreational swimming or lifesaving. In a lifesaving situation, the conservation of energy is more important than ultimate speed. Therefore, use of such strokes as the side and breast strokes becomes important.

part three

techniques of biomechanic analysis

Chapter 8

Noncinematographic and Basic Cinematographic Analyses

Cinematography is the study of human performance through the use of motion-picture film. The human eye is incapable of stopping ballistic motion of performers. In order to have a permanent record of a given performance and to study the component parts of performances, the use of film helps objectify the otherwise subjective elements of viewing while preserving the performances in a relatively permanent state.

Out of necessity, the teacher-coach in the daily performance of his or her duties must utilize noncinematographic techniques when attempting to improve performances of students or student-athletes. The physical educator must have a professional or disciplined system to observe performances of students when film is not available. The reason for this lies in the fact that a considerable amount of precision is lost while doing a noncinematographic analysis of a performer. If the physical educator does not have a systematic approach to analysis without film, very little objectivity or precision will be obtained; therefore, the quality of the subsequent teaching will be diminished considerably. "Seeing in depth" without the use of film is essential to teaching-coaching because this analytic technique is used the vast majority of time in physical education. The physical educator must train himself to see what is actually taking place as opposed to what he thinks is occurring within the student or student-athlete who is performing.

The procedure for doing basic cinematographic analysis is essentially the same as the procedure utilized in noncinematographic analysis. The main difference lies in the fact that the analysis is done from film instead of from observation of the performer on the field or elsewhere. In this context, any type of motion picture can be utilized for analytic purposes. This includes the game film commonly taken at football games, basketball games, track-and-field events, and so forth. Game films are often overlooked for their value in terms of biomechanic analysis. Although game films do not meet the critical criteria of biomechanic research film, they can be utilized extensively for biomechanic observations.

NONCINEMATOGRAPHIC ANALYSIS

The beginning point for observing performers without the aid of film is to observe the same skill executed a number of times. Too often, extensive teaching or coaching suggestions are made after the coach has observed the performer executing a skill on a once-only basis. It is entirely possible that a coach may not see a consistent or major performance problem while observing the performance one time only. A coaching suggestion in this context may only serve to compound the performance problem; therefore, the performer should be observed many times prior to making any type of teaching suggestion. This situation is analogous to a physician making a diagnosis and prescribing medication. A physician usually does not prescribe medication until he has completed a "total workup" of the patient's symptoms. To prescribe medication on the basis of one symptom related by the patient would be poor professional practice. The same thing can be said of physical educators who make performance recommendations based on minimal observations of performers.

To continue with the analogy—like the physician who makes numerous analyses of the patient's various systems, the physical educator must have a systematic approach to viewing performers. One way of doing this is through observations of moving body segments at joints. It is very difficult to visualize cause-and-effect relationships when viewing the overall performance. In other words, it is absolutely unrealistic to attempt to generalize about specific motion of a given body part when the observation includes the total performance only.

The sport fan looks at the total performance, while the trained physical educator looks at body segments moving in relation to each other. Moreover, the observation of various moving body segments must be made in a systematic manner.

In order to improve performances, the physical educator must ask and answer questions based on biomechanic principles. These principles are presented in chapters three through seven. The type of questions asked by the physical educator is dependent upon the individual skill under analysis. For example, a coach analyzing a discus thrower would ask entirely different questions than the choreographer doing an analysis of a dancer's leap. This is one reason why there is no one recommended procedure for undertaking an analysis without the use of film. Each person must develop his own system for controlling observations of the performances under his or her direction.

In order to assist the reader toward a greater comprehension of biomechanic analytic techniques, several examples of noncinematographic and basic cinematographic analyses will be presented in this chapter. Each analysis should be read slowly with frequent reference to the figure. Four noncinematographic analyses are presented, including a sprint start, shot put, high jump, and hurdling. Three examples of basic cinematographic analyses are presented, including the hurdles, high jump, and javelin throw. In order to clearly demonstrate differences between the three levels of biomechanic analyses, the hurdles analysis will be continued through the intermediate level in chapter nine. This will enable the reader to compare and contrast the differences in the three analytic techniques. In addition, an intermediate cinematographic analysis of the discus throw is presented in chapter nine. While all of the analyses included as examples are from the area of track and field, they do include basic athletic components of running, jumping, and throwing common to many sport skills.

Figure 8.1 includes a sequence of the sprint start. The following is an example of how a noncinematographic analysis would be made by utilizing what is known as **a segmental analysis.** The first thing which should be accomplished by the coach is to **observe the total performance** of the performer a sufficient number of times until a general feeling for the execution of the performance is obtained. By doing this, the coach should gain some insight into the potential general outcome of the skill, as well as the overall timing or interrelated aspects of the body parts by the performer. Also, this gives the physical educator an opportunity to compare the observed performance with what he believes constitutes the stereotype of perfect form for the sprint start.

Figure 8.1. The sprint start of Tom Jones, U.S.A. Olympic team. Preparatory phase: frames 3-4. Movement phase: frames 5-13. Follow-through: frames 14-20.

Virtually all sport skills can be divided into logical sequences. These sequences or phases are called (1) the preparatory phase, (2) a movement phase, and (3) follow-through and/or recovery phase. The latter, in many cases, actually assists the performer in the execution of the skill which follows. Or, the recovery may actually be a portion of the preparatory phase for the subsequent skill or movements to be executed.

In the example of the sprint start, the preparatory phase would start in frame three and end in frame four. The movement phase would begin in frame five and end in frame thirteen. Frames fourteen through twenty would be follow-through for the sprint start. At that point, the athlete is actually in the acceleration of the sprint itself and has successfully executed the sprint start. To point out the observation difficulties from a noncinematographic standpoint, it must be kept in mind that the coach would be observing frames three through twenty in a matter of one-half second. That, in itself, is a strong argument for the use of film in coaching.

The **pelvic area and rib cage** segments of the body are good to observe simply because they are relatively slow-movement areas and are pertinent orientation points for analytic purposes. The performer should be observed from more than one angle. For example, in the case of the sprint start the coach should observe the athlete from posterior, anterior, and lateral views.

Questions the track-and-field coach might ask himself and attempt to answer while observing the pelvic girdle and rib cage of the athlete during the sprint start are, How high is the center of mass above the base of support throughout the entire skill? Are there any extraneous rotations of the spinal column and pelvic girdle through the transverse plane? Is there an undesired hyperextension of the lumbar spine during the sprint start? Does the path of the pelvic girdle deviate from a straight line at any time during the skill? In the illustration shown, the performer exemplifies ideal pelvic, spinal column, and rib cage position in frames twelve and thirteen. From frame five, or the start of the movement phase, the lumbar spine moves from flexion to extension in frame thirteen. This is accomplished without any extraneous transverse rotations. There are, however, slight lateral rotations of the pelvic girdle when the athlete is in a unilateral weight-bearing position. This is accomplished without excessive movement while the pelvic girdle, lumbar spine, and thoracic spine remain dynamically stabilized. If the pelvic girdle, for example, were not dynamically stable at this time, force executed through the blocks would not be effective in driving the center of mass linearly.

The **base of support** should be observed from lateral and posterior views by the coach. The posterior view, which is not shown in the illustration, is very advantageous from the standpoint of seeing undesired transverse plane movements of the lower limbs. During the preparatory phase of the sprint start, the athlete actually is in a four-point stance. Are the hands and right foot bearing most of the weight? Is the block setting for the feet adequate to provide optimum force and range of motion within the ankle, knee, and hip joints at the start of the movement phase? During the recovery phase, are the changing bases of support following movement through anteroposterior planes of motion? Is there a prolonged period of time when both feet are off the ground before the recovery process begins? Are the feet too wide apart or too close together throughout the performance? The answers to these questions relative to this performance actually determine the degree of efficiency the athlete has in transferring internal forces from muscular contractions into accelerating forces for the center of mass. If the coach observes considerable extraneous motion within the bases of support during the sprint start, the athlete will not be effective in transferring these forces.

Another important body segment to observe during any athletic performance is the **head and cervical spine.** The most important question the coach should ask himself regarding the positions of the head and cervical spine during the sprint start is, How soon does the cervical-spine movement occur which allows the athlete to actually look down the track toward the finish line? Any hyperextension of the cervical spine will cause a corresponding reaction in the lumbar spine. These two major movements have a tendency to extend the trunk and greatly increase the resistive or drag force caused by air. Cervical hyperextension also tends to raise the body to the point where the horizontal force component is diminished during the acceleration phase. Both factors contribute to a decreased velocity. In the example, the cervical spine and head are stabilized in an extended position in all three phases of the skill. This is a highly desirable technique.

Arms and hands are vital segments to observe specifically during noncinematographic analyses. During the sprint start, the arms must provide a powerful counterforce from the end of the movement phase to the start of the recovery phase. In order to be in this position, the arms must be moved to a position as high as possible during the power phase of the sprint start, while the left foot in the example is pushing back against the blocks. The diagonal movements of both upper limbs are made in such a way as to provide an optimum state of equilibrium. It must be remembered that during the sprint start the sprinter is actually in a dynamic state of disequilibrium. He is protected from falling only because he is undergoing extreme acceleration. Movement of the arms through the diagonal plane during the movement phase is extremely important relative to the principle of equilibrium. Movement through the diagonal plane provides a greater moment of inertia than movements at the shoulder joints through anteroposterior planes. Movements of the hands and fingers are of interest. Are the fingers flexed or extended? If the sprinter has a flexed hand or fist, this is an indication of considerable amounts of extraneous internal tensions which will ultimately inhibit or decrease linear velocity. In the example, actions of the arms are excellent.

Legs of the athlete must also be observed critically during noncinematographic analysis. Specifically, the actions of the ankles, knees, and hip joints must be viewed to determine their overall contributions to the skill. Are the flexions in these joints adequate to provide an optimum range of motion and subsequent force? Are there any transverse rotations at the knee and hip joints which might inhibit performance? Are the extensor movements performed throughout their complete range of motion prior to the time the sprinter leaves the blocks? Are the knee flexions adequate to provide optimum angular velocity through conservation of angular momentum?

The culmination of noncinematographic analysis of a sprint start should be in the recovery phase of the runner as he starts into the second aspect of this skill: the actual sprint. Many of the same questions asked above, and others, are relevant during the acceleration phase of the sprint through the finish line.

From a noncinematographic standpoint, it must be remembered that the shot-put sequence shown in figure 8.2 takes approximately two seconds. Frames one through eleven constitute the preparatory phase of the shot put. This is usually a slow, deliberate type of motion requiring approximately one second of time. During the preparatory phase, velocities of various body segments are relatively unimportant. The performer is more concerned with basic body equilibrium and placing muscles on stretch, particularly within the knee extensors, for the subsequent internal force necessary during the critical movement phase. The movement phase occurs between frames twelve and thirty-two. The important follow-through phase occurs from frame thirty-three through frame thirty-nine.

The greatest velocity is attained by the performer during the movement phase. From a noncinematographic standpoint, it is very difficult to perceive all basic movements during the movement phase because the performer moves through this phase in approximately one second of time. Therefore, it is essential that the physical educator take it upon himself to watch the important movements within the various large body segments several times from at least three angles.

From the standpoint of biomechanics, it is imperative that the shot-putter release the shot at its maximum velocity, maximum altitude, and at a release angle of slightly less than forty-five degrees. Anything which would interfere with any of these biomechanic objectives should be observed by the coach and ultimately eliminated by skill adjustment of the athlete.

During the preparatory phase, the **pelvic girdle and lumbar spine** are being moved with gravity and maintained over the supporting leg, keeping the athlete in a state of equilibrium. In frames seven through twelve, the center of mass is actually being lowered eccentrically, and this places the knee extensors of the right leg on stretch for forceful concentric contraction at a critical point during the movement phase. This lower center of mass is accomplished by the flexion with gravity by the right hip and knee joints. Is the lowering of the center of mass consistent with placing the critical muscles of the knee and hip extensors on stretch? The pelvis remains dynamically stabilized from frame twelve until frame twenty. In order for maximum internal force to be generated, the coach watching the shot-putter's pelvic girdle and rib cage should determine whether or not there is a torque-countertorque effect at this moment in the shot-putting performance. In other words, does the pelvic girdle rotate to the left—left transverse pelvic girdle rotation—while the rib cage remains relatively stable at this point during the performance. The subsequent movement of the lumbar spine and rib cage would be left rotation through the transverse plane. The major torque force would be supplied by the previous rotation of the pelvic girdle which would have placed the critical muscles on stretch. In the example, the torque-countertorque between these areas is not great enough to place critical muscles on stretch. From frame twenty-five through frame thirty-nine, the lumbar-thoracic spine is simply continuing to rotate to the left through the transverse plane as the athlete releases the shot, follows through, and recovers, maintaining his equilibrium within the ring During these rotations of the pelvis and lumbar-thoracic spine, there is a sequential elevation of the center of mass through the time the shot is released. In frame thirty-two where the shot is released, it should be noted that the center of mass is at its highest point and is lowered slightly thereafter.

In putting of the shot, the sequence of movement for the **base of support** shifts from (1) a complete unilateral weight-bearing position, (2) to a bilateral weight-bearing position, and (3) returns to a unilateral weight-bearing position. The velocity across the ring is of extreme importance in terms of ultimate velocity and distance obtained by the shot itself. During the preparatory phase, does the initial unilateral base of support shift in either direction? During this phase, all adjustments of weight and other body segments should be centered above the unilateral weight-bearing right foot in this example. It should

Figure 8.2. The shot put as performed by Randy Matson, U.S.A. world record holder. Preparatory phase: frames 1–11. Movement phase: frames 12–32. Follow-through: frames 33–39.

be noted that the base of support does not move until the performer has completed the preparatory phase and starts into the movement phase. At this time, the athlete is starting his movement and showing a strong linear acceleration. The left foot has no supportive function until the performer has moved his body laterally across the ring. Is there a shifting of weight from the base of support synchronized with the timing of the torque-countertorque effect seen in the pelvic girdle and rib cage? Is the left foot placed in a position advantageous for torque of the pelvic girdle and lumbar-thoracic spine? Does the actual placement of the left foot in the ring interrupt linear motion or the summation of motions? Are plantar flexions observed in both ankle joints immediately prior to release? If not, this would detract from the summation of motion. Are the motions of the base of support adequate to make maximum use of the diameter of the ring? What is the status of the base of support at the time the shot is released? Does the center of mass come back over the unilateral base of support during the follow-through and recovery phase? This is absolutely essential to maintain functional rotation for dynamic equilibrium.

The **head and cervical spine** of the shot-putter should remain in a relatively stable and extended position virtually throughout the complete performance. When the coach is viewing this performance from the lateral view, he should see a cervical hyperextension—frame twenty-seven—synchronized with the weight shift to the left leg and the forceful start of left lumbar-thoracic rotations. This movement of the cervical spine allows the shot to follow its linear path uninterrupted. Excessive cervical rotations would cause undesired compensatory rotations elsewhere in the spinal column.

The coach should observe the performer posteriorly several times while viewing **arm and hand actions.** One noncinematographic observation should be of the path the shot is actually following as the performer moves linearly and rotationally across the ring through the point of release. There should be no lateral movement or vertical undulations of the shot as the performer goes through the basic motions of putting the shot. Such excessive movements as these would contribute to excessive disequilibrium and many extraneous compensatory movements on the part of the athlete. When the skill is observed from the lateral view, the left arm should be viewed for its contributions to maintaining equilibrium during the preparatory phase and early part of the movement phase. During the latter part of the movement phase, what is the contribution of the left arm to the torque processes taking place in the lumbar-thoracic spine? Does the movement of the left arm "lead the spinal column rotations"? Does the action of the left arm contribute to the flexor-extensor reflex mechanism and equilibrium during release and ultimate follow-through? If not, the athlete most likely will "scratch." Is the shot held on the distal end of the arm lever? If not, the decrease in the length of the lever will negate the ultimate concentric contractions and movement capacities of the wrist-finger flexors at release.

The coach should specifically watch for finger abduction and wrist flexion by the athlete immediately after the shot is released. If the wrist remains in hyperextension or extension, this will indicate that a maximum velocity of the putting limb has not been attained at the time the shot was released. Another point in regard to maintaining the shot near the ends of the fingers at the time of release is that three to four more inches of altitude are attained at the time of release which would result in roughly an equal increase in horizontal distance. In regard to the arm holding the shot, does it maintain its relative position throughout the preparation and movement phases until the transverse rotations of the lumbar-thoracic spine have virtually been completed? If the shot is moved away from the position relatively close to the neck, this will increase the length of the lever and cause a decrease in rotational velocity, which, of course, is not desired at this point of the put. Does the right shoulder become diagonally adducted immediately prior to the forceful elbow extension which precedes release? What is the action of the right arm during release and follow-through?

Actions of the **knees and hips** are critical in shot-putting. Are the right knee and hip joints being flexed with gravity to optimum angles for placing critical muscles on stretch? This should be observed during the latter part of the preparatory phase. If these muscles are not placed on stretch, the subsequent kinetic chain of events will not have an optimum level of force. During forceful knee extension as the performer is moving linearly across the ring, do the left knee and hip move into virtual extension? At the time of spinal column rotation, are both knees flexed with gravity and in a position to ultimately exert forceful concentric contractions for knee extension? If the knees are not flexed at this point, they will be unable to contribute to the rotary movements and vertical lift necessary in putting the shot. At the time of release, is the left knee totally extended? If not, this may contribute to an inadequate angle or altitude of release which potentially would lead to a diminished horizontal distance.

The first two examples of noncinematographic analysis included a basic linear motion and a motion involving a short linear acceleration combined with rotational accelerations of the body mass. The following example of a high jumper using the Fosbury Flop style of jumping was selected because it involves a very strong vertical force component. The kinetic energy of the high jumper is transformed into potential energy through work accomplished against the gravitational field. The concept of segmental analyses in a noncinematographic sense is very important in looking at the high jumper, because, literally, it is the movement of body segments in a sequential framework over the bar which composes the major portion of the skill aspect of high jumping.

In the high-jumping sequence shown in figure 8.3, frames one through fifteen constitute the preparatory phase for the high jump, and frames sixteen through thirty-eight are the movement phase of this skill. The follow-through aspect of high jumping is relatively unimportant because, as shown in frames thirty-nine and forty, once the body has cleared the bar it literally becomes a falling body, and the only concern for the athlete and coach is that the landing in the high-jump pit is one where the athlete does not incapacitate himself.

In viewing the **pelvic girdle and lumbar-thoracic spine** during the preparatory phase, the coach needs to observe the nature of horizontal motion of the center of mass. This should be a relatively smooth linear acceleration without any excessive deceleration prior to final placement of the left foot at the time of vertical lift. As the performer nears the final stride, the center of mass will be lowered in order to make internal bodily adjustments for the final vertical motion of takeoff. If lowering of the center of mass is exaggerated, this will negate the potential internal force component of the subsequent contraction of muscles most involved, in addition to causing diminishing linear momentum. Both of these factors, obviously, would have a negative influence on the height subsequently attained in the jump. It should be emphasized that some high jumpers do raise the center of mass significantly at frames thirteen and fourteen. If this is done, it actually starts the vertical lift transformation and uses some of the force generated from the right foot exerting pressure back against the ground. In our example, this is not a significant aspect of this jumper's skill.

In observing the pelvic girdle and lumbar-thoracic spine during the movement phase, the coach should be aware of the transverse rotations of the lumbar-thoracic spine immediately following the time when the athlete becomes airborne. Is there a left transverse rotation of the lumbar-thoracic spine? Does the pelvic girdle remain dynamically stabilized during this transverse rotation? These rotary aspects of this skill move the shoulders into a position so they lie horizontal to the high-jump bar. As the athlete is moving vertically, is there a pronounced hyperextension of the lumbar spine? This internal force component caused by the spine extensors actually causes a counterforce in the thoracic spine and ultimately a lifting of the pelvic girdle. In order to observe this phenomenon from a noncinematographic standpoint, the coach should position himself at the end of the high-jump bar opposite from the takeoff point of the athlete. Once the athlete is directly above the bar in a position of lumbar hyperextension, is there a return to lumbar extension? If so, this initiates an action-reaction between the lumbar spine and both hip joints. It is imperative that both hip joints be slightly flexed in order to facilitate bar clearance prior to the follow-through aspect of the jump. Many times jumpers will fail

Figure 8.3. The Fosbury Flop as performed by Kestutis Sapka, USSR. Preparatory phase: frames 1–15. Movement phase: frames 16–38. Follow-through: frames 39–40.

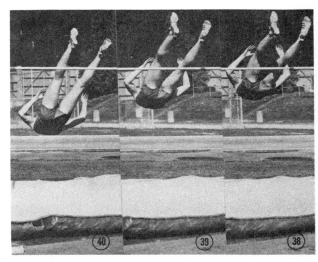

Courtesy Visual Track and Field Techniques, 292 So. LaCienaga
Blvd., Beverly Hills, Calif. 90211

at this point in the jump because they maintain the lumbar spine in hyperextension throughout the remainder of the jump. During the follow-through phase of the high jump, most high jumpers will move into a flexed position of the lumbar-thoracic spine in order to present a broad surface to the landing pit. This is good technique because it dissipates a large percentage of force over as wide a surface area as possible instead of over a small body area where injury might occur.

The **base of support** observations should focus primarily around the latter aspect of the preparatory phase and the initial portion of the movement phase or lift-off. The critical leg to watch in this example is the left leg. At the conclusion of the preparatory phase, is the base of support in the last stride adequate to place the left foot at an appropriate angle for optimum plantar flexion in the ankle immediately prior to vertical lift-off? If the final stride prior to lift-off is too long, the effect will be a negation of horizontal momentum. On the other hand, if the final stride is too short, there will not be an optimum range of motion to transfer horizontal momentum into vertical components of momentum. Obviously, during the airborne portion of the movement phase there is no base of support.

There should be no excessive **movements of the head and cervical spine** throughout any phase of high jumping. During the preparatory phase, are the head and cervical spine maintained in a relatively stable and extended position? During the movement phase, does the cervical spine rotate or laterally flex? There is a very human tendency during the Fosbury Flop for an athlete to want to "look where he's going." This usually takes the form of cervical rotation to the right or lateral flexion to the right as in the case of our example. If cervical rotation occurs, this is usually at the expense of a counterrotation elsewhere in the spinal column. This has a tendency to upset the horizontal position needed to adequately clear the bar. In terms of biomechanics, a track-and-field coach might well teach the athlete performing the Fosbury Flop to hyperextend the cervical spine at the same time the lumbar spine is hyperextending during the flight aspects of the movement phase. The combined hyperextensions of the lumbar and cervical spinal regions would have a positive effect in the counterforce which would be evident in the "lifting" of the pelvic region. This is a rather commonly observed series of spinal column movements in such activities as diving, rebound tumbling, and tumbling. Therefore, it might be good teaching practice to ensure that a high jumper who executes the Fosbury Flop has considerable training in the area of gymnastics.

Actions of the arms during noncinematographic analysis of high jumping should center around two important aspects of the performance: (1) What do the arms contribute to vertical lift? and (2) What do the arms contribute in terms of body equilibrium during the airborne phase? As noted in our example, both arms of the athlete are moved from extreme hyperextension into a forceful flexion at the time of vertical lift. This is an absolute necessity to add to the vertical momentum already being generated elsewhere in the body. During the movement phase, actions of both arms contribute significantly to spinal column rotations and then stabilize for a brief period of time to contribute to body equilibrium as the performer is moving parallel and perpendicular to the bar. It must be remembered that motion of the high jumper includes a velocity component both along and across the bar.

Noncinematographic observations of the legs should be for specific joints within both legs during the three phases of the performance. During the preparatory phase following the initial run, are the series of flexions at hip and knee joints occurring with gravity at angles which will not interrupt the summation of forces and cause a negative acceleration? Will the flexions in the left knee and hip joints at the end of the preparatory phase during the stride provide an optimum range of motion and a vertical lift? At the end of the preparatory phase and start of the movement phase, is the velocity of the limb during the movement from right hip extension to right hip flexion great enough to contribute significantly to vertical lift? Is the range of motion great enough for right hip flexion at this point to add to vertical lift? Is the right hip extension-flexion pattern at the time of lift-off synchronized with flexion movements in the shoulder joints? Does the knee go through a complete range of motion for knee extension at the time of vertical lift? During the airborne phase, does the right hip joint move into an extended position? The fact that hip extension occurs at this time contributes immeasurably to rotations observed concurrently within the spinal column, and it also places the legs in a symmetrical position for the final portion of movement over the bar. As the pelvic girdle or center of mass crosses over the bar, do the hip joints move into flexion and do the knee joints move into extension? If these movements do not occur, the performer is in extreme danger of knocking the bar from the stands by hitting the bar with his heels or some part of the legs.

The example of the hurdler shown in figure 8.4 differs from previous examples because in this case the athlete is trying to obtain an optimum vertical lift component while maintaining a relatively high linear or horizontal velocity.

Figure 8.4. The high hurdling form of Willie Davenport, U.S.A. Olympic team. **Preparatory phase:** *Lift-off: frames 5-11. Flight phase: frames 12–28. Recovery: frames 29–32.*

This combination of factors makes hurdling as a skill infinitely different from the track start, shot put, or high jump skills.

The preparatory phase for hurdling is actually the movement of the athlete in his running between the hurdles, which does not involve any projection into the air. The movement phase for hurdling can arbitrarily be divided into two aspects: (1) lift-off and (2) flight pattern or trajectory. The recovery occurs when the performer touches the track after clearing the hurdle and leads effectively into the subsequent running pattern toward the next hurdle. In our example, the preparatory phase is from frame one through frame four. The lift-off phase is from frame five through frame eleven, and the flight phase is from frame twelve through frame twenty-eight. Frames twenty-nine through thirty-two show the recovery aspect of the skill. Hurdling, unlike our preceding three examples, requires considerable effort on the part of the performer to control counteracting ballistic movements of the upper and lower limbs during the act of hurdling which will not interrupt his summation of forces and decrease horizontal velocity.

Observations of the **pelvic girdle and lumbar-thoracic spine** are of immense importance in hurdling. In making noncinematographic observations of the pelvic region, the coach should observe a relatively smooth transition from linear motion into a low parabolic trajectory of the pelvic girdle as the athlete clears the hurdle. If there is a sudden vertical lift of the pelvic region during the lift-off and flight phases, this will indicate horizontal motion being converted into undesired vertical motion. Obviously, this would decrease the horizontal velocity and increase the amount of time to traverse the 120 yards.

During the preparatory, movement, and recovery phases, are there any rotational components through the transverse plane of the lumbar-thoracic spine? If so, the athlete would most likely have some severe equilibrium problems during both the flight phase and the recovery. Does the athlete flex the lumbar-thoracic spine during the airborne or flight phase? If this is not done, there would be a greater surface area of the body presented to the air which would create a greater resistance or drag and decrease horizontal velocity. Also, if the lumbar-thoracic spine is not flexed at this point of the skill, the center of gravity would be excessively lifted during flight. This would not be a desired action in hurdling, although it would be desirable in high jumping. At the time the athlete lands after clearing the hurdle, is the lumbar-thoracic spine moving into an extended position? This is highly desirable from the standpoint of maintaining a dynamic equilibrium, and it provides the performer with a relatively good position to move linearly down the track toward the next hurdle.

If the length of the running stride of the performer is adequate for his sprinting style, the two major checkpoints for **base of support observations** in hurdling are made at lift-off in the flight phase and immediately upon landing during the recovery phase. In both cases, the athlete is in a unilateral weight-bearing position. At the time of takeoff, does the ankle of the supporting leg move through a complete range of motion for plantar flexion? This is a very important move in helping to determine the actual angle of projection. Upon landing, do the landing ankle and foot reach the ground in a position of slight plantar flexion? This is an essential movement, because a considerable amount of force must be absorbed as the ankle moves from plantar flexion back into the normal anatomic position. At this point, a good hurdler should have virtually full extension in both knee and hip joints. If the base of support foot were in the normal anatomic, weight-bearing position at the time contact was made with the track, excessive forces would be transferred through the ankle, knee, and hip joints into the pelvis and spinal column. As a result, there would be some likelihood of trauma occurring. Another observation which can be made noncinematographically by the coach is to check on foot position during the running portion of the skill, as well as during takeoff and landing. Does the athlete "toe in" or "toe out"? Both of these movements, which could occur either at the knee joint or hip joint, are contraindicated. These rotary movements, which occur elsewhere but are observed in the foot, will cause excessive lateral forces which interfere with linear or desired motion.

There should be absolutely no motion within the **cervical spine and head** during hurdling. Although there are rather extreme or ballistic actions occurring within hip and shoulder joints, musculature around the cervical spine should keep this area stabilized. If the coach observes lateral plane or transverse rotations within the cervical spine, they will usually indicate that there are undesired rotations elsewhere in the spinal column.

The importance of the **arm movements** during hurdling is often overlooked. Arm movements contribute minimally to vertical lift, but their main purpose in hurdling is to counterbalance the ballistic actions necessary within hip joints. This means that the action of the arms helps maintain rotational equilibrium during the process of hurdling. Just prior to the time the athlete reaches the hurdle, does the left arm diagonally adduct at the same time the right hip joint is moving into full flexion? This is a very important torque-countertorque aspect of hurdling. During the latter part of the flight phase, does the left shoulder move back into diagonal abduction as the left leg is being diagonally adducted at the left hip joint? Again, this is a torque-countertorque series of movements between the two body segments vitally important for maintaining dynamic equilibrium. During the flight phase, does the right shoulder joint remain in an extended position while the elbow is flexed almost to the mid-position? At the beginning of the recovery phase, are the arms in good position for linear movement to the next hurdle? If arm adjustments have to be made at this point, it probably indicates that the athlete has landed in a position of disequilibrium.

Leg action is of vital importance in hurdling. One of the first movements which should be critically observed noncinematographically by the coach is the degree of flexion in the right knee joint immediately following the preparatory phase and during the first portion of the so-called lift phase. At this point, does the right knee flex through a great enough range of motion to effectively conserve angular momentum in the right lower limb? This knee action contributes significantly to the ultimate lifting force of the body in hurdle clearance. Also, this conservation of angular momentum contributes significantly to the velocity of the right leg moving from extension at the right hip joint into extreme flexion of the right hip joint. This must be a high-velocity, ballistic action of the right hip joint in order to effectively lift the body into the proper trajectory for hurdle clearance. Does the right knee joint remain relatively extended throughout the flight and landing phases? Upon landing, does the right knee remain extended or flexed? Many inexperienced hurdlers will utilize knee and hip flexions upon landing to absorb shock instead of making the shock-absorption adjustment within the ankle movement. Upon contact with the ground, the extended right leg serves as a lever for subsequent linear motion. In regard to observations of the left leg, are the left hip and knee joints completely extended at takeoff? This extension in the left hip is important in view of the fact that this allows for a maximum range of motion at takeoff. Are excessive left knee and hip flexions seen immediately prior to takeoff? If so, this is a good indication that the athlete is trying to jump instead of hurdle. During the flight phase, does the left hip joint move from extension into diagonal adduction as he crosses over the hurdle? This diagonal movement at the left hip joint, plus concurrent flexion of the left knee, is the optimum series of motions needed to clear the left leg efficiently over the hurdle. At the point of impact with the ground, is the left hip joint moved into a position of full flexion? Is the left knee fully flexed at the point of impact? These two motions within the left knee and left hip joint are essential to provide a smooth transition from an effective rotary force component to linear force desired in running, i.e., subsequent motions within both lower limbs at this point should be primarily through the anteroposterior plane. If the coach observes any rotations through the transverse plane in hip and knee joints during the running phase or lift-off phase, these would be undesired motions. These motions would interrupt the kinetic chain and cause an inefficient "flow of motion" for the hurdler.

BASIC CINEMATOGRAPHIC ANALYSIS

As stated previously, the only difference between noncinematographic and basic cinematographic analyses is the fact that the coach can study the performance at his leisure by viewing film. There is no time pressure to make decisions in a rapid fashion while doing basic cinematographic analysis. The film can and should be viewed a number of times at various projector speeds, and then critical aspects of the performance should be viewed frame by frame. This procedure can objectify many of the observations of the coach who has viewed the performance noncinematographically. In other words, basic cinematographic analyses are really an extension of multiple observations made without the advantage of utilizing film.

During practice sessions and games, the coach has the opportunity to observe the same performance by an athlete many times. Through this accumulation of observations of the same performance, the coach has an opportunity to discover positive and negative "motion tendencies" of the performer. This series of multiple observations during noncinematographic analysis is a positive aspect of this analytic procedure. In contrast, the coach observing a film loop of a performer, for example, is given the opportunity to view only one performance. The performance on film may or may not be indicative of the athlete's most commonly used performance style. This aspect of basic cinematographic analysis is a disadvantage in comparison with noncinematographic analysis. However, the performance on film can be observed more critically and sequentially without any pressure of time on the coach. This is a definite advantage of basic cinematographic over noncinematographic analysis. Due to the advantages and disadvantages of these two analytic styles or techniques, it is rather obvious that for better coaching the two types of analyses should be used concurrently to objectify the nature of movements by performers.

Film for purposes of basic cinematographic analysis should be taken during athletic contests. This principle should be followed as much as possible in order to determine true movement trends. If film is to be taken of a given skill during a practice session, the coach should do everything in his power to place the athlete under "gamelike conditions." If not, the athlete is very likely to act out what he considers to be the stereotype of perfect form. From an analytic standpoint, this type of performance on film is not indicative of what the athlete would actually do in a game situation. Another factor to consider in filming practice situations is that some athletes simply do not practice in the same way they perform, no matter how much extrinsic motivation is applied by the coach.

For purposes of basic cinematographic analysis, filming speeds of 32 frames/second or 64 frames/second are recommended. The determining factor for filming speed is the nature of the skill being filmed. For a fast ballistic type of action such as a golf swing, the filming speed should be 64 frames/second. This degree of filming speed will be fast enough to determine with some degree of accuracy only what is happening in regard to motion within the golfer. It will not clearly define what is happening during the angular motion of the golf club. For most gross body actions, 32 frames/second is entirely adequate. For example, 32 frames/second would be adequate for looking at such activities as hurdling, wrestling, movement of football players, and basketball shooting. From the viewpoint of expense, there may be times in motion description of gross body movements where 16 frames/second would be adequate for basic cinematographic analysis. In most school situations, this most certainly would be one of the determining factors for filming.

The development of the new portable videotape units has brought this medium to great usage in many school systems for recording athletic events. Videotape has the advantage of nearly instant playback so the performer can observe himself immediately following the performance and then attempt to correct the performance in a subsequent trial. The disadvantage with most systems which are presently being used in educational institutions is that they are difficult to use in a frame-by-frame analysis. However, television can be used in many cases to objectify the noncinematographic analysis which has been made previously, since the coach can view the same actions several times. In some ways the advantages of videotape lend themselves to use during practice sessions much more than the use of a camera and film. The videotape can often be used for a positive reinforcement of a skill improvement. From the economic point of view, the fact that videotape can be reused many times makes it an important tool for analysis.

In viewing a performance at the basic cinematographic level, it is still necessary to use a segmental approach to the analysis. The frames in which specific body-segment motions are important can be isolated by the coach and studied specifically with reference to that body segment. One advantage in the cinematographic record is that it is possible to observe synchronization of various body-segment movements much more specifically than is possible in a noncinematographic observation. To return to figure 8.4 of the hurdler, the first observations should be of the **pelvic girdle and lumbar-thoracic spine.** The two motions which need to be observed most closely in the analysis of the frames during this action are the transverse rotation of these segments of the body and the angle of lean for the lumbar-thoracic flexion during passage over the hurdle.

The observation of transverse rotation can be carried out by scanning the frames and observing specific points on the athlete's jersey. It will be observed in the presently considered figure that there is a slight left rotation in frames one through five which is a normal part of the running sequence between hurdles. Starting at frame six, the lumbar-thoracic region is returned to the midposition facing down the track and will be observed to remain within a few degrees of that position throughout the entire takeoff phase and flight over the hurdle. No further rotation occurs during these phases. In the observation of a film of an unskilled performer, rotations do occur due to improper motions of arms or legs. The rotations provide excessive torque on the lumbar-thoracic region, and the extraneous motions will be quite evident by observing these points on the athlete's jersey. Such motions represent an actual disequilibrium during the flight phase and indicate energy outputs or energy losses which are not productive to the motion of the athlete moving down the track.

Flexion of the lumbar spine during the flight phase can be observed in frames fourteen through twenty. The purpose of this flexion is twofold: (1) to reduce the height to which the center of mass must be lifted in the passage of the various body segments over the hurdle and (2) to provide a more streamlined effect and thus reduce the drag coefficient of the performer. It should be remembered that at velocities attained by a rapidly moving athlete, the effect of the retarding force of air can be several pounds. This force is in the opposite direction to the line of motion and tends to reduce horizontal velocity while the athlete is airborne. Since the purpose of a hurdling event is to maintain maximum possible horizontal velocity, any action which minimizes these retarding forces helps in a decrease of the total time for the race. Minimizing the total vertical lift of the performer's center of gravity also minimizes trajectory time in air. An excessive lift in this case not only normally reduces horizontal velocity but greatly increases the amount of time when the athlete is airborne, and he cannot exert further forces to move himself down the track. It should be observed in frames twenty-two and twenty-three that the athlete is clearing the hurdle with a minimum excess space. This also helps minimize the lifting of the center of gravity.

With respect to the **base of support** in this action, the two critical regions are the takeoff during frames seven through eleven and the recovery phase in frame thirty-two. In the sequence involving the takeoff, the important point to watch is the high degree of plantar flexion which helps lift the center of mass and determine the angle of projection. This is seen in frame twelve. Several points should be noted with reference to the base of support during the time of landing. Very critical is the fact that the landing is made with the foot pointed straight forward in the direction of motion. This means that there is no dissipation of force in an unintended direction. Secondly, the landing is also made with plantar flexion in order to absorb downward momentum with a minimum shock to the remainder of the body. Finally, it should be noted that the center of mass is almost directly over the point of support by the time the body reaches the full weight-bearing position. This means that forces from that point of support have no component in the backward direction to slow horizontal motion. The subsequent plantar flexion supplies a force to accelerate the runner horizontally as he moves into the running phase to approach the next hurdle. This is seen in frames thirty-one and thirty-two.

With respect to the **head and cervical spine,** it is the stabilization or complete lack of motion throughout this sequence which is of importance. As was indicated earlier, any excess motion would indicate a case of disequilibrium or a situation where energy was being placed into nonproductive movement.

Observation of the **right arm** of this performer indicates one of the shortcomings of cinematographic analysis of a single event. Since the event can be seen from only one view, there are likely to be hidden segments of the body. In this case, it will be noted that from frames twelve through twenty-nine, the arm is virtually hidden. Actually, in this case, the fact that it cannot be seen is significant since it means the athlete is dynamically stabilizing the arm with a shoulder extension and slight elbow flexion during the flight phase of this performance. This helps stabilize the lumbar-thoracic region in the midposition by not contributing any extraneous torques from motion at the right shoulder.

Motion of the **left arm,** on the other hand, is used to counter the strong torque being generated by motions of the legs. Left-arm motion must begin before the athlete becomes airborne. A strong diagonal adduction of the **left shoulder** is observed in frames one through twelve, with the shoulder remaining stabilized thereafter until frame eighteen. The purpose of this initial motion is to provide a torque which counters the torque produced by motion of the right leg and also to provide a small amount of lift during the termination of the upward component of diagonal adduction. Utilization of an extreme range of motion in this diagonal adduction would again result in an excessive raising of the center of gravity, resulting in a prolonged time of flight.

In frames eighteen through thirty-two, the **left shoulder** undergoes a ballistic diagonal abduction which again serves two purposes. First, the torque generated by this diagonal abduction tends to balance the countertorque being generated by the forward motion of the right leg in coming over the hurdle. Secondly, the downward vertical component of the diagonal abduction is tending to provide a slight lift to maintain the center of mass over the hurdle during the final part of this trajectory. It will be noted that this combination of moves leaves the arms in the proper position for running immediately upon impact with the track following the flight portion of the hurdle. This can be observed in frames twenty-nine and thirty. This decreases the time necessary to go into linear acceleration during the running phase and again decreases the total time of the race.

Another observation which can be made with respect to the **hands** is the position of the fingers throughout the various frames recorded in this motion. A tightly clenched fist is quite often an indication of excessive internal tension within the muscular structure. This normally leads to a decreased performance characteristic. Another indication of this condition can often be found in the position of the mouth and jaw muscles. This performer is remarkably free of internal tensions for an event such as the 120-yard high hurdles.

Cinematographic data are particularly helpful in the motions of the **knee and hip joints,** since these are quite complex and ballistic in this event. Frames five through twelve are particularly significant in the contribution of the right leg to the lifting phase of the takeoff. It should be noted in frames seven through eleven that the knee joint is extremely flexed in order to obtain the maximum possible angular velocity through conservation of angular momentum and accelerating torque at the hip joint. This extreme angular motion of the right hip joint is necessary in getting the performer airborne as soon as possible and in providing the major portion of vertical lift necessary for this event. This high rotational velocity is also important as an aid to extreme hip flexion observed during the initial portion of the flight phase toward the hurdle. This extreme flexion can be seen in frames thirteen and fourteen. During these frames, knee extension necessary to bring the right foot over the hurdle can be observed. The observation of frames nine and ten during the lift phase reveals a very small flexion at the knee and hip. This is important in indicating that the performer is hurdling and not jumping during takeoff. Frames eleven to thirteen indicate the plantar flexion governing the angle of projection into the air for the trajectory. Frames fifteen through twenty-nine indicate the ballistic diagonal adduction of the left hip joint which serves the purpose of bringing the left foot over the hurdle following the pelvic region. It will be noted that this performer stops the diagonal adduction as the motion intersects the anteroposterior plane and immediately begins the extension movement of the hip and knee joints associated with the running phase. This can be observed in frames thirty-one and thirty-two.

The right knee is maintained in a nearly stabilized extension from frame sixteen through the culmination of this performance, and the right hip, approaching the landing point, moves into extension so the leg can serve as a lever for rotation as the performer moves into the running phase.

Examination of frames eight, fifteen, twenty-two, and twenty-eight can be used to indicate the synchronization of the beginning and terminating phases of arm and leg motions. This is an advantage which the basic cinematographic technique has over noncinematographic analysis. It is impossible even for the most experienced physical educator to observe close times of synchronization between widely separated body segments. However, this can be done quite easily on film.

Frames twenty-nine, thirty, and thirty-one indicate the motion of a second performer who is trailing behind the principal performer. The reader should compare these with frames twenty, twenty-one, and twenty-two. What are the differences in the styles of the two performers? At 32 frames/second, for example, how much difference in time is indicated which one might attribute to these differences in styles?

Earlier in this chapter the high jump was examined noncinematographically using the Fosbury Flop as shown in figure 8.3. In actions such as the high jump, cinematographic analysis is almost necessary because of the large number of motions which take place within a very limited time span. In the successful execution of the high jump, these motions need to be almost perfectly synchronized. This synchronization is difficult to determine noncinematographically. Thus, observations made during practice or meets need to be supplemented by cinematographic analysis at least at the basic level.

The preparatory run to the bar as shown in frames one through fifteen of figure 8.3 serves several purposes. Basically, the athlete at this point develops kinetic energy which will be partially converted into potential energy in lifting the center of gravity for passage over the bar. In addition, he is developing horizontal velocity which will carry him across the bar during the actual jumping phase. It should be noted that horizontal velocity developed during the run, as illustrated in frames one through seven, is greater than the optimum velocity for sequencing of motions to clear the bar. In frames eight to fifteen the athlete will actually suffer a deceleration as a result of the motions necessary to place him in the best position for jumping.

Also important in this run phase is the lowering of the **center of mass** as observed in frames eight, nine, ten, and eleven. The purpose of this, which is more pronounced in some jumpers than in others, is to provide a greater range of vertical motion while still in contact with the ground. It also places the athlete in a more stable form of equilibrium throughout the last stride onto the jumping foot. The backward lean of the lumbar-thoracic region, as shown in frames thirteen, fourteen, and fifteen, is actually a compensatory movement for ballistic anteroposterior motion of the arms.

During the initial part of the movement phase, the **lumbar-thoracic and pelvic regions** are stabilized but rotate through an angle of approximately ninety degrees as seen in frames nineteen to twenty-five. This is actually the time of maximum rise by the center of gravity of the performer. This angular motion is arrested by compensatory torques provided by the left arm and right leg. These are completed by frame twenty-six, with the performer's chest facing upward in the correct position for passing over the bar. At this point, as seen in frame twenty-six, the very important motion of hyperextension of the lumbar spine is initiated. This hyperextension is continued through frame thirty as the lumbar-thoracic portion of the body passes over the bar. It should be noted at this point that because of the low position of the legs during this phase and the extreme closeness of the remainder of the performer's body to the height of the bar, his center of gravity will actually lie at the bar level or below. One of the advantages of this form in the high jump is the fact that the performer can sometimes clear the bar without his center of gravity ever rising that high. The hyperextension of the lumbar spine serves the purpose of forcing the lumbar-thoracic region, the shoulders, and the cervical regions downward, with the resulting counterforce upward on the pelvic regions. As the athlete's pelvic area passes over the bar, he returns to an extension of the lumbar-thoracic spine as a preparation for motion by the legs and feet. It is the synchronization of the lumbar hyperextension and following extension with the horizontal velocity as the athlete is passing over the bar which enables him to clear the bar with a minimal raising of the center of gravity. It should be noticed throughout the movement phase that the horizontal motions of the performer include a component passing over the bar together with an almost equal component sliding along the bar. It is extremely important during the preparatory motions that both optimum magnitude and angle of horizontal motion be maintained in order to supply these components.

The critical frames with reference to the **base of support** for this high jumper are frames twelve through twenty. Frames twelve through fifteen illustrate what the performer normally calls the planting of the jumping foot. Frames fourteen and fifteen illustrate placement of the foot in a normal weight-bearing position in such a manner that horizontal momentum carries him into an optimum position for moving vertically. It should be noted at this point that the vertical lift arises from three sources: (1) actions of the arms upward, (2) action of the right leg moving upward, and (3) forceful extension of the left hip, knee, and ankle in raising the entire body. The counterforce necessary to application of all three of these movements is delivered by the ground onto the left foot. It is for this reason that the final placement of that foot with respect to the position of the other body segments is so vitally important. It might be noted in frames twenty and twenty-one that for this athlete the range of plantar flexion seems to be somewhat limited in the left ankle. This decreases the total lift which he is obtaining in this jump. With an increased range of motion, he would be able to remain in contact with the ground longer and provide still greater upward velocities to all three of the aforementioned segmental motions.

A sequence of photographs illustrates the stabilizing of the **cervical spine and the head** throughout the entire preparatory phase and initial portion of the movement phase. In frame nineteen there is the beginning of a lateral flexion to the right at the cervical spine. Beyond frame twenty-seven the angle of viewing completely hides this portion of the body. As discussed earlier in this chapter, it might lead to a better performance to combine a hyperextension of the lumbar spine and likewise a return to extension in the cervical spine at the time of return to extension in the lumbar spine. This combination would enhance the force-counterforce actions discussed in the reasoning behind the lumbar hyperextension.

During the preparatory phase, motion of the **arms** into a pronounced hyperextension is extremely important in the preparation for use of the arms as a lifting device. It should be noted in frames one to four that the arms are being held in an abducted position rather than participating in the natural running motion. The critical points for observation in this phase of the movement are frames twelve and thirteen where the arms are in an extreme bilateral hyperextension. The symmetrical nature of this motion is necessary in order to obtain a maximum lift without introducing an unwanted torque by a stronger motion of one arm than the other. The maximum extension should occur just before the time of planting the jumping foot as seen in frame thirteen. In frames thirteen to nineteen the arms are brought forward and upward into a bilateral shoulder-joint flexion. This provides a large amount of upward-directed momentum used by the body throughout the jumping process. As he exerts a force with the shoulder musculature to stop this upward motion of the arms, the resulting counterforce then provides a lift to the remainder of the body. During the time of flight over the bar, diagonal abduction of the left shoulder, together with extension of the left elbow joint, is used to provide the countertorque to stop rotation of the body. This is seen in frames twenty-seven, twenty-eight, and twenty-nine. This action, plus the diagonal abduction of the right shoulder, adds to flight stability during passage over the bar. A horizontal abduction of both shoulder joints accompanies the return to extension in the spine in preparation for landing. This is seen in frames thirty-one through thirty-four. In a sense, this lifting of the arms is forcing the total body downward before the legs have cleared the bar and, as such, detracts from the total performance. It is possible that the use of a total body tuck position in this latter phase could contribute slightly to the maximum possible height of the jump. Such a tuck would have to be initiated about frame thirty.

Frame seventeen indicates the **hip and knee flexions** which represent an optimum compromise between the range of upward motion available, power to be obtained from concentric contractions of the left knee extensors, and maintenance of an optimum horizontal velocity. While a greater range of motion and muscular force might be obtained through a higher degree of flexion at the left knee and hip joints, it would interrupt the summation of motions in such a way as to almost negate the preparatory phase.

The prime component of lift in the Fosbury Flop comes from the ballistic flexion of the right hip. It is the rapid upward motion of the right leg, interrupted in frame twenty, which provides the major portion of the upward component of momentum during the initial part of the movement phase. In the example shown, the ability to rapidly move this hip into flexion from the extension shown in frame thirteen is partially diminished by the failure to completely flex the knee joint during this motion. In frames fourteen through eighteen this joint is carried at about a 90-degree flexion where an angle of about 130 degrees should be possible for this type of motion. The reader should compare the motion of the right leg in this illustration with that of the hurdler discussed previously in which a more optimum use of this conservation of angular momentum was made. A higher degree of flexion reduces the total moment of inertia of the leg, thereby allowing a much greater acceleration with the same torque being produced at the hip. This, in turn, produces a larger upward velocity before the interruption, as indicated before in frame twenty.

Once airborne, the right leg returns to a partial extension at the hip in order to become symmetrical with the left leg, as in frame twenty-eight. As the lumbar-thoracic spine returns to extension in frame thirty-one, the hips begin the flexion necessary to allow the heels to clear the bar. This combination of hip flexion with partial knee extension completes the final phase of passage over the bar.

Figure 8.5 shows a sequence of film frames for a javelin thrower moving after his approach run through the crossover step into the culmination of the throw and follow-through.

In this sequence, the *preparatory phase* is extended from frames one through twenty. Actually, the preparatory phase would begin before frame one in the preliminary run which is not shown in these photographs. This extended preparatory phase is a necessary part of the javelin throw because of the complex relationship between the various segment motions which must be synchronized in order to achieve an optimum velocity and release angle of the javelin. Because of the length of the javelin, it is awkward to place the body in the correct position with the proper muscles on stretch in order to achieve a final optimum velocity. Also, this velocity needs to be directed at an angle between thirty and forty-five degrees above the horizontal, and the javelin needs to be tilted slightly above the line of motion in order to achieve the flight interaction with the air. This means that a very complex combination of rotational movements between the pelvic girdle, spinal column, and right shoulder joint must be used.

Following the extended preparation phase, the *motion phase* is extremely short. The motion phase occurs in frames twenty-one through twenty-five, a total time of about one-eighth of a second. After release following frame twenty-five, frames twenty-six to thirty show the beginning of the *follow-through*. The follow-through is designed only to prevent the javelin thrower from fouling by crossing the line. No formal recovery phase is required since the performance is completed with this one action.

The motions of the pelvic region and lumbar-thoracic spine are extremely important in the javelin throw during the final aspect of the preparatory phase and give an excellent example of the Serape Effect.

During the crossover-step portion of the preparatory phase, the coach should observe the magnitude of the vertical lift of the body. If this is excessive, it means that a portion of the kinetic energy gained during the initial run is being converted into vertical motion rather than being retained as horizontal motion. In the example, the maximum vertical position occurs near frame six but can be seen to be only four to six inches above the average vertical position throughout the sequence. Throughout the preparation phase, the **lumbar-thoracic spine** is held dynamically stable in lateral flexion combined with a slight rotation to the right. This stability exists through frame sixteen at which time both lateral flexion and rotation are increased as the muscles are placed on stretch in preparation for the motion phase. This lateral flexion of the lumbar-thoracic spine is important in order to correctly establish the subsequent angle of release of the javelin.

Frames seventeen through twenty illustrate the Serape Effect as used in this event. Left transverse pelvic rotation combined with right rotation of the lumbar-thoracic spine places the large, left spinal column rotators on stretch to optimize the subsequent lumbar-thoracic rotation as seen in frames twenty-one through twenty-six.

The importance of the left transverse pelvic rotation needs to be emphasized. Omission of this movement at the initiation of the motion phase will have an adverse effect on the velocity of the throwing limb as well as on the subsequent velocity and horizontal distance traversed by the javelin. This left transverse rotation of the pelvic girdle is the initial movement in the Serape Effect. The torque produced by this motion results in a countertorque by the lumbar-thoracic spine which gives optimum rotation of the upper portion of the body. These **pelvic and spinal column motions** not only place large spinal-rotator musculature on stretch, but also subsequently increase the total range of motion through which force can be placed against a javelin. Frames seventeen through

Figure 8.5. The javelin throw as executed by Janis Lusis, USSR. Preparatory phase: frames 1–20. Motion phase: frames 21–25. Follow-through: frames 26–30.

twenty of figure 8.5 are considered a classic example of the use of the Serape Effect in the javelin throw.

The placement of the **base of support,** especially during the final step, is important in allowing the proper set of rotations to take place without loss of either linear or angular momenta. The final placement of the right foot in this sequence is observed in frame thirteen. It would appear that during this performance, placement was made with the foot somewhat far forward with respect to the center of gravity of the performer. As observed in frame thirteen, the backward lean of the performer would mean that any forces being transferred from the ground would have a horizontal component which would tend to cancel a part of the horizontal velocity gained during the run. It probably would be better if the landing could occur with the total body position being more as observed in frame fourteen.

Placement of the left foot during the final weight-shifting process, as observed in frame twenty, is very important. The foot must be to the left of the midline of the body and pointed in the intended direction of the throw in order to provide stability and allow pelvic and spinal rotations to occur. Foot placements need to be made with a timing which allows a smooth shifting of weight from one to the other with minimum loss of horizontal velocity.

The **head and cervical spine** are maintained in a relatively stable position through most of the preparatory phase, as indicated in frames one through twenty. In frames twenty-one through twenty-five, an extreme cervical rotation is observed. This adds to the rotation of the lumbar-thoracic region and also aids in diagonal adduction of the right shoulder joint. This is another example of the use of a torque and countertorque principle in order to ultimately increase the total velocity of the throwing limb. At the point of release seen in frame twenty-six in this sequence, the performer is not looking in the direction the javelin will fly. If he attempts to look in the direction of motion too soon, the summation of motions critical to this event will be interrupted. The head does not return to the position which allows the performer to observe javelin flight until frame twenty-eight, or approximately one-tenth of a second *after* release.

The prime duty of the **left arm** throughout this performance is to help provide balance and add to the torque-countertorque sequence of motions within the final throwing phase.

In frames one through ten, the left shoulder is in a position of diagonal adduction as an aid to equilibrium of the body during this phase of the performance. In frames eleven through twenty-one, the left shoulder is diagonally abducted, and the left elbow moves into extension. This places muscles on stretch and aids in the final production of torque within the spinal column for rotation of the lumbar-thoracic spine and the final medial rotation and diagonal adduction of the right shoulder. In frames twenty-two through thirty, although the left arm is hidden by the body, the left shoulder is adducted through the lateral plane in order to provide a balance mechanism to offset ballistic motions of other body segments. Flexion occurs at the left elbow as a result of the ballistic motion of the right arm through the crossed-extensor reflex.

Throughout the initial phases of the performance, through frame sixteen, the **right arm** is diagonally abducted in a stable position. The wrist is also stabilized in slight hyperextension in order to maintain the desired angle for the javelin with respect to the horizontal. Any wobbling motion of the javelin during the preparatory phase results not only in inefficient uses of energy by the performer, but also may contribute to poor flight characteristics of the javelin after release. Since orientation of the javelin is so critical and a spin about the longitudinal axis must be given in the final phases, it is highly important that the orientation of the javelin during the preparatory phase be a fixed part of the performance.

Frames seventeen through twenty-five provide an example of development of angular momentum through diagonal adduction of the right shoulder joint through the high diagonal plane. There is a subsequent increase in limb velocity by a decrease of the moment of inertia through flexion at the right elbow. This flexion is observed in frames twenty-three and twenty-four of the sequence. Also occurring in frames twenty-four and twenty-five is the medial rotation of the right shoulder joint. This provides a final velocity increase prior to release of the javelin. As in previously described throwing motions, it is necessary to observe that this medial rotation takes place *before* the *release* of the object. If it is delayed until the follow-through phase, it cannot contribute any forces and increase velocity of the sport object. At that point, medial rotation of the throwing limb would only contribute to the aesthetic aspect of the performance.

During the crossover, diagonal action of the **legs,** the performer in this sequence is minimizing vertical lift while maintaining a horizontal velocity by an inversion of the left transverse tarsal and subtalar joints. A complete plantar flexion of the left ankle at this point would provide an undesired vertical component of velocity. This would result in a loss of horizontal velocity. During the landing on the right foot, as observed in frames thirteen through fifteen, it is necessary that the right knee joint undergo flexion. This motion is eccentrically controlled by the right quadriceps muscle group. This places these muscles on stretch for subsequent powerful extension of the right knee joint observed in frames eighteen through twenty-one. This knee extension provides the push against the ground and precedes the pelvic rotation so vital to the Serape Effect. Frame twenty shows the leg position which provides the optimal horizontal force component for initiating this rotation. At the same time, there is a minimizing effect on any vertical component of motion at this stage of the performance. If the performer simply pivots through this step, it will be extremely difficult to obtain the necessary pelvic rotation to provide an optimum Serape Effect and subsequent ballistic rotations.

In frames eighteen through twenty, the left hip is placed in slight flexion, with the knee stabilized in an extended position. This provides the fulcrum over which the final rotation takes place. As the body moves forward, the hip gradually returns to an extended position.

The javelin throw is an excellent example of the concept of a sequence of motions timed to produce a skilled performance as described in earlier chapters. An optimum performance requires a force generated from the right leg which provides a rotation for the pelvic region. In turn, this produces rotations of the lumbar-thoracic spine followed by diagonal-plane motions at the shoulder and a flexion at the elbow. All these motions must be performed in proper sequence in order to obtain a maximum performance.

SUMMARY

Within this chapter there was a discussion of the two most commonly used types of biomechanic analysis, noncinematographic analysis and basic cinematographic analysis. These two levels of biomechanic analysis will be utilized by teachers of physical education and by athletic coaches the majority of time during day-to-day relationships with students. The intermediate cinematographic analysis technique, which is discussed in chapter nine, will not be utilized as extensively in the daily teaching-coaching process.

Four examples of noncinematographic analyses were presented: (1) sprint start, (2) shot put, (3) high jump, and (4) hurdling. The primary purpose for presenting the sprint start as a noncinematographic analysis was to accentuate a performance where linear acceleration is the critical factor. In shot-putting, it is essential that rotational body motions be controlled to provide linear motion for the shot through maximum force application through the time of release. High jumping involves a smooth transition or transfer of horizontal to vertical motion. In contrast, hurdling involves maintenance of a maximum horizontal velocity while minimizing vertical lift. A segmental analysis approach was stressed in each of these examples.

The examples of hurdling and high jumping were continued through the basic cinematographic level. In addition, an example of javelin throwing was added at the basic cinematographic analysis level. In javelin throwing, the important factor is to control linear body motion as well as rotational body motions in order to achieve optimum flight characteristics for the javelin.

Chapter 9

Intermediate Cinematographic Analysis and Biomechanic Research

The first two levels on the biomechanic analysis hierarchy, noncinematographic and basic cinematographic analyses, are the most frequently used by the physical educator. These are the analytic levels which require utilization of subject matter from biomechanics on a daily basis during the teaching-coaching process.

INTERMEDIATE CINEMATOGRAPHIC ANALYSIS

As the name implies, intermediate cinematographic analysis involves transitional elements from the first two levels on the analysis hierarchy and an initial progressive step of an academic nature into the biomechanic research level. Intermediate cinematographic analysis can also be used extensively in teaching-coaching situations to objectify observations from the first two levels which tend to be more subjective. Unlike the first two analytic levels, mathematical computations are used during intermediate analysis to enhance precision and clarify observations made by the teacher or coach. As a result of these computations, considerably more time is required to undertake an intermediate-level analysis as compared to a basic cinematographic analysis. It is this time element which reduces extensive use of intermediate cinematographic analysis by busy teachers and coaches. However, it is a functional and practical technique for potential use as an instructional adjunct in class and/or athletic situations when time permits.

Filming Recommendations

Intermediate cinematographic analysis can be conducted from any film made during instructional or athletic situations. It is fully recognized that this type of film often has limitations, especially when compared to the filming criteria used for research purposes. *Observations and calculations must take these limitations into account, but this does not negate the use of film of this type for instruction utilizing biomechanic subject matter.*

Some photographic limitations can be minimized for game film if plans and preparations are made for the filming process in advance:

1. Place the camera operator in a fixed position at a right angle and known distance to the photographic field. The most difficult quantitative measurements are those where the performer is moving either toward or away from the camera. The distance of the camera from the photographic field should be great enough to minimize the rotational components of the camera during the filming process. If possible, distances from the camera to the photographed subjects should be known. Also, the camera should be on a tripod as often as possible to minimize vertical and horizontal errors.

2. Filming speeds in frames per second must be known. Most sport performances can be filmed for intermediate analysis at filming speeds ranging from sixteen to eighty frames per second. Sport skills involving high-velocity ballistic actions of limbs should be filmed at sixty-four to eighty frames per second. Game film for team sports such as basketball and football can be filmed at speeds of sixteen to thirty-two frames per second. However, if a football coach, as one example, wants to make detailed observations of his passer during a game, filming speed on the passing downs should be increased to sixty-four or eighty frames per second.

3. Known scales in feet or meters should be included in film backgrounds when possible. As an example, vertical and horizontal distance lines can be painted on the face of spectator stands next to a track. Film of runners or

hurdlers would include the runner as well as these known distance marks on the stands. This would facilitate analyses of such factors as vertical and horizontal velocities and accelerations.

4. If possible, include a large clock with a sweep hand at least once per filming within the photographic field. Most swimming teams have large interval training clocks with sweep hands which can be included in the film background for swimming or any other sport. This serves as a check on the calibration of film speed within the camera. Spring-driven cameras tend to lose frame speed as they wind down; consequently, they should be wound frequently. Electric-powered cameras are recommended, but not all athletic areas or fields have electric outlets readily available. Battery-powered cameras are available which do not limit the mobility of the operator.

Extracting Numerical and Graphic Information from Film

There are several differences between intermediate cinematographic analysis and biomechanic research. During intermediate cinematographic analysis, ordinary game or performance film is usually utilized to extract data. This means that there are some limitations of control over such things as viewing angle, perspective, scale, filming speed, and other factors which would be carefully controlled under research conditions. In the film sequences analyzed as examples of the intermediate cinematographic analysis level in this chapter, an attempt is made to show what type of numerical data could be obtained from typical film taken of athletes in action. The user of this type of film must accept the fact that there is an accuracy loss one would not have when working to extract data from research film, but this accuracy loss is not great enough to negate its use for *instructional purposes*. For example, the accuracy of our input data for the performance film analyzed in this chapter was estimated to be ± 5 percent when compared to film meeting research criteria. With this small loss of accuracy of the input data, no intermediate results should be interpreted as being more accurate from a truly scientific point of view. Thus, rounding of numbers, approximations, and other mathematic and cinematographic factors are not particularly significant unless they introduce an error of greater than ± 5 percent. This degree of accuracy loss is probably typical of what the physical educator working with game film would expect in most situations. The accuracy loss, however, could be greater or lower depending upon the precision control during filming. At the intermediate cinematographic analysis level, the numerical results of the analysis can be used to support or refute prior qualitative analyses. Such results, with their loss of scientific precision, limit the validity of their use to produce research findings.

How should findings of an intermediate level analysis be utilized? The immediate objective for a physical educator working with students in class situations or with student-athletes should be to utilize the findings of the biomechanic analysis to improve sport performances of those students and help them reach their potentials as performers. This objective is not of immediate concern to the research investigator. Therein lies another major difference between what is described herein as intermediate cinematographic analysis and biomechanic research. Subject matter from biomechanics can no longer be considered the exclusive property of the research investigator. The relationship of biomechanics subject matter to skill development is too important not to be utilized in day-to-day teaching and coaching situations. It can and should be utilized regularly by professional physical educators working with students of both sexes, all ages, and on every level of the performance continuum from the adapted physical education student to the Olympic athlete preparing for international competition.

Intermediate cinematographic analysis has two functions. First, it offers the practical objective of using biomechanics in the teaching-coaching situation. Second, it provides an introduction for the interested student into some of the methods and procedures of biomechanic research.

One of the principal problems in intermediate cinematographic analysis is the transformation from information on film to numbers which can be used in the calculation of physical quantities. There are a variety of ways in which this may be accomplished, depending on the type of action being analyzed.

In order to accurately transfer information from the picture on the film into a set of numbers, it is usually necessary to enlarge the image. This may be accomplished by projection on a screen by use of such instruments as Vanguard and Kail projectors. Any projector used for this purpose must be capable of *sustained single-frame projection*. This is necessary because of the time it takes for making measurements from film.

Measurements on the projected image can either be made directly or redrawn and graphed in a way that will allow further analysis. If only a few measurements are needed from each frame, it is usually more efficient and easier to make direct ruler measurements on the projected image. For example, in the sequence on hurdling given and discussed in chapter eight, measurements can be made directly from the pictures on the distance from the takeoff point to the hurdle and from the hurdle to the landing point. Using the measured height of the hurdle as a scaling factor, it is possible to calculate the actual flight distance during this performance. In this example, a measurement will show that the horizontal distance from the takeoff point to the base of the hurdle is almost exactly twice the measured distance of the hurdle height. Since a high hurdle is 42 inches in height, this means that the takeoff point was almost exactly 7 feet in front of the hurdle. Similar measurements will give a distance to the landing point of approximately 4.45 feet. Of course, these distances should not be expected from every high hurdler, but it is possible to determine rather quickly from film this type of performance parameter for any hurdler.

If, however, a series of measurements are needed on each frame or if comparative measurements between successive frames are to be used, it is usually more efficient to redraw the essential parts of the image in a more permanent form. In order to do this efficiently, a person must be familiar with the basic subject matter from anatomic kinesiology listed in chapter two. Rather than make a detailed contour drawing of the performer on a frame-by-frame basis, it is necessary only to mark positions of specific landmarks and/or joints. These can be used for subsequent analysis. Such a drawing is shown in figure 9.2.

Figure 9.2 represents a portion of the right lower limb movement of the hurdler as seen in figure 9.1 and discussed in chapter eight. *Approximate positions* of the center of the right hip and knee joints and the medial malleolus of the right tibia were recorded from frames eight through sixteen of figure 9.1. The recording of information from successive frames on a single drawing is extremely useful for calculation of rotation and linear velocities and accelerations.

It is useful to show the projected image either on a screen with a graphic scale or on a piece of graphing paper. If care is taken to adjust the size of the image to the graphing scale, positions can be read most conveniently. It is easier to construct a set of numbers by comparison to a graphic scale than it is to make actual measurements with a ruler. It should be noted that in such a drawing, angles can be measured directly by use of a protractor. Angles measured in this manner do have some built-in error. This will be discussed later in this chapter.

It is also necessary to include in the drawing some part of the known scale factors from the film in order to be able to properly scale the physical motion.

Figure 9.1. Hurdling trajectory

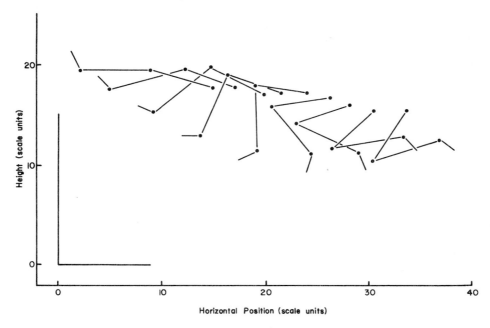

Figure 9.2. Lower limb segments of hurdler in figure 9.1

In figure 9.2, the primary scale factor was the forty-two-inch height of the hurdle. This scale factor was chosen because the hurdle is located at the same distance from the camera as the hurdler. This provides a known linear dimension.

Intermediate cinematographic analysis is often avoided because of the mathematical calculations involved. In most cases, the mathematical computations are not of a complex variety. They require only a few steps of multiplication or division, but they are usually performed on a large amount of data. As a consequence, it becomes an extremely time-consuming procedure if performed by hand. Most school districts or universities will have at least a desk-type calculator which can perform these multiplications and divisions. In fact, it is becoming quite common in many school systems to have either a computer terminal facility or a small self-contained desk-top computer capable of performing repetitive calculation. Use of such instruments can provide considerable saving of time for the type of calculation involved at this level of analysis. It is only necessary to tell the computer one time what actions are to be taken with the data, and from then on the results of any performance are simply entered as new data. This elimination of time as an inhibiting factor should ultimately lead to a greater use of biomechanic analysis at this level for the physical educator who has a background in computer operation.

Examples of Intermediate Cinematographic Analysis

In this section, examples of calculated information have been made from the film sequence of the hurdler as seen in figure 9.1. Also, selected parameters were analyzed from the film sequence of the discus throw (fig. 9.8). These were selected to show contrasting types of motions. Hurdling is basically a linear body motion, but it involves certain rotational aspects. In contrast to this, the discus throw is primarily a rotational body motion. A complete calculation of all body segments, velocities, accelerations, and other physics parameters would be an exhausting task. It is usually necessary to limit calculations to specific body parts or portions of the performance during intermediate cinematographic analysis. The experience and expertise of the coach will determine the specific areas of the performance in need of quantitative analysis. The choice of actions for intermediate analysis will normally be made on the basis of problems observed during basic cinematographic or noncinematographic analyses.

In the hurdling sequence, motions of the right lower limb during knee extension before reaching the hurdle are of prime concern. Also, motions of the head, left shoulder, and left hip as a linear trajectory in crossing the hurdle are important. On the right lower limb, angular positions and velocities as well as linear velocities were calculated. In regard to the head, shoulder, and hip, calculations are presented to indicate the vertical position and horizontal velocities of these three major body segments.

Figure 9.3 is a table of numbers used in the transformation from the scale drawing given in figure 9.2 to the actual spatial coordinates of the approximate joint centers of the hip and knee as well as the medial malleolus. In this case, the information from the various frames was projected and recorded on a scaled paper with magnification to the point that the height of the hurdle represented fifteen scale units. This gave a scaling factor of fifteen units equal to 42 inches—3.5 feet. The number in the upper portion of the figure represents numbers as read from the graph paper. The lower portion of figure 9.3 presents

Frame Number	8	9	10	11	12	13	14	15	16
Scale position (scale units)									
Hip									
Horizontal	33.5	30.4	28.0	26.2	24.2	21.3	19.8	17.0	14.8
Vertical	15.5	15.5	16.8	16.7	17.1	17.0	17.0	17.7	17.6
Knee									
Horizontal	30.3	26.3	23.0	20.5	19.0	16.3	14.7	11.8	8.8
Vertical	10.5	11.7	14.0	15.8	17.8	18.8	19.8	19.5	19.3
Ankle									
Horizontal	36.7	33.3	29.0	24.4	19.4	13.7	9.2	5.0	2.2
Vertical	12.6	12.8	11.2	11.0	11.3	12.8	15.2	17.3	19.2
Space position (feet)									
Hip									
Horizontal	7.82	7.09	6.53	6.11	5.65	4.97	4.62	3.97	3.45
Vertical	3.62	3.62	3.92	3.90	3.99	3.97	3.97	4.13	4.11
Knee									
Horizontal	7.07	6.14	5.37	4.78	4.43	3.80	3.43	2.75	2.05
Vertical	2.45	2.73	3.27	3.69	4.15	4.39	4.62	4.55	4.50
Ankle									
Horizontal	8.56	7.77	6.77	5.69	4.53	3.20	2.15	1.17	0.51
Vertical	2.94	2.99	2.61	2.57	2.64	2.99	3.55	4.04	4.48

Figure 9.3. Changes from scale to space coordinates of the hurdler

corresponding spatial coordinates. The horizontal coordinate represents distance from the hurdle, while the vertical coordinate is the height of the body segment above the ground. Conversion between upper and lower numbers was simply a matter of multiplying each number by the factor 3.5 divided by 15.

Figure 9.4 indicates angular positions and velocities of the femur and tibia-fibular segments of the right lower limb and the angle formed at the knee. These can be measured directly from figure 9.2, or they can be calculated by the vector equation given in chapter three. The second part of figure 9.4 indicates the apparent length of the femur and tibia-fibular segments as calculated from the recorded landmark positions. This calculation was made primarily to check for errors in the recording of the landmark positions. Since these two lengths should remain relatively fixed, a calculation indicating a large discrepancy provides a check against any errors made in the earlier portion of the analysis. For example, it might be noted that the lengths of the tibia-fibular segment vary between 1.51 and 1.67 feet in all frames except frame eleven. The lower figure of 1.44 feet in that frame probably indicates about a three-fourth-inch error in the location of the malleolus. A progressive error in the measurement of such fixed lengths may indicate corrections necessary due to the camera angle during filming.

The final portion of figure 9.4 indicates angular velocities corresponding to these motions. In calculating angular velocity, a filming speed of 32 frames/second was utilized. This means that there is a time interval of $\frac{1}{32}$ of a second between any two frames. Velocity is then calculated by dividing the change of angle between frames by the time necessary for change to occur. It can be noted from these figures that the highest angular velocities are reached by the tibia-fibular segment. This portion of the lower limb benefits from hip flexion and knee extension forces. It can also be noted that maximum elevation of the femur segment (hip flexion) is achieved in frame fourteen, and in the final two frames the femur segment is actually returning to the horizontal.

Figure 9.5 presents the calculated numbers for linear velocities of the three landmark positions. Again, these velocities require the use of the film speed of thirty-two frames per second to determine the time interval over which linear changes of position occur. They are expressed, in this case, in terms of horizontal and vertical components, as well as the total speed of the landmark position.

One interesting factor in these calculations is the extremely low values for the vertical component of velocity for the hip joint throughout the motion. Most of these values can be attributed to slight variations in the location of landmark positions during the graphic analysis phase. At this film speed, an error of one-half inch in location of a landmark position produces a velocity error of 1.3 ft/sec ($\frac{1}{2}$ inch $\times$ 32 = 16 inches = 1.3 feet). This problem of errors in velocities and accelerations is increased immensely for analyses made at higher film speeds. This is one reason why accurate studies of higher order accelerations require the techniques of biomechanic research.

Frame Number	8	9	10	11	12	13	14	15	16
Segment orientation									
Femur									
Length (ft)	1.39	1.30	1.33	1.35	1.23	1.24	1.36	1.29	1.40
Angle (°)	32.7	46.9	60.7	81.0	97.5	109.7	118.6	109.0	106.1
Tibia-fibula									
Length (ft)	1.57	1.65	1.55	1.44	1.51	1.52	1.67	1.66	1.54
Angle (°)	−108.2	−99.0	−64.8	−37.0	−5.0	22.2	50.1	72.1	89.3
Knee flexion (°)	39.1	34.1	54.5	62.0	77.5	93.5	111.5	143.1	163.2
Angular velocity (rev/sec)									
Femur	1.26	1.23	1.80	1.47	1.08	0.79	−0.85	−0.26	
Tibia-fibula	0.82	3.04	2.47	2.95	2.51	2.39	1.96	1.53	
Knee	−0.44	1.81	0.67	1.38	1.42	1.60	2.84	1.78	

Femur and tibia-fibular angles were measured clockwise with the vertical downward position representing zero degrees.
The knee flexion angle represents the angle between the femur and the tibia-fibula.

Figure 9.4. Angular positions and velocities of the hurdler

Frame Number	8	9	10	11	12	13	14	15	16
Hip velocity									
Horizontal	23.4	17.9	13.4	14.7	21.8	21.2	20.8	20.2	
Vertical	0	9.6	−0.6	2.9	−0.6	0	5.1	−0.6	
Total speed	23.4	20.3	13.5	15	21.8	21.2	21.4	20.3	
Knee velocity									
Horizontal	29.8	24.6	18.9	11.2	20.2	21.8	21.8	22.4	
Vertical	9.0	17.3	13.4	14.7	7.7	7.4	−2.2	−1.6	
Total speed	31.1	30.1	23.2	18.5	21.6	23.9	21.9	22.5	
Ankle velocity									
Horizontal	25.3	32.0	34.6	37.1	42.6	33.6	31.4	21.2	
Vertical	1.6	−12.2	−1.3	2.2	11.2	17.9	15.7	14.1	
Total speed	25.3	34.2	34.6	37.2	44.0	38.1	35.1	25.4	

All velocities in feet/second.

Figure 9.5. Linear velocities of the hurdler

Figure 9.6 represents a slightly different technique of recording information from film. In this case, only the landmark positions were recorded without the drawing of segments between. In recording these landmarks, the head position was chosen arbitrarily from a point on the zygomatic arch. The *approximate centers* of the shoulder and hip joints were also used. Other landmarks often used for recording positions of the head and shoulder are the tragus of the ear and the lateral aspect of the acromion process of the scapula. Without involving numeric calculations, the plot of these points indicates their relative horizontal and vertical motions during the initial part of the hurdling process.

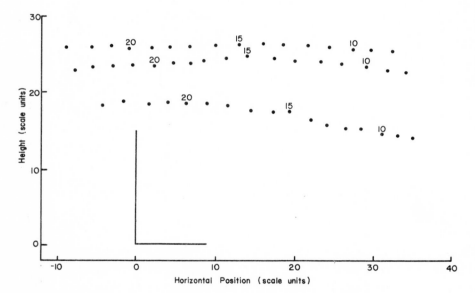

Figure 9.6. Anatomic landmarks indicating the hurdler's trajectory. Top line of dots is the head, center line is the shoulder, and bottom line is the hip. Numbers are frame numbers for these positions.

A table similar to figure 9.3 was prepared from figure 9.6 to allow for a transformation of scaling factors from the drawing into actual spatial positions of these landmarks. The lines indicating the vertical spatial positions from this table are indicated in figure 9.7. Horizontal velocity data, calculated from the

Frame Number	8	9	10	11	12	13	14	15	16	17	18	19	20	21	22	23	24
Height above ground (feet)																	
Head	5.9	5.95	5.97	6.02	6.07	6.11	6.14	6.11	6.07	6.02	6.02	6.02	5.97	6.07	6.02	6.02	
Shoulder	5.25	5.25	5.44	5.53	5.55	5.60	5.67	5.76	5.67	5.60	5.53	5.53	5.44	5.46	5.43	5.41	5.30
Hip	3.22	3.31	3.34	3.55	3.55	3.66	3.80	4.04	4.04	4.06	4.20	4.27	4.29	4.32	4.27	4.26	4.25
Horizontal velocity (ft/sec)																	
Head			20	21.4	21.3	21.1	21.7	21.3	21.8	20.5	20.2	18.7	19.5	20.2	19.8		
Shoulder			20.3	22.7	21.6	22.4	22.4	21.5	20.2	17.4	16.8	16.6	17.9	18.9	18.7		
Hip				17.4	16.4	17.2	17.2	15.1	18.3	19.6	23.9	19.4	18.5	19.4	19.8		

Figure 9.7. Vertical position and horizontal velocity data of the hurdler

horizontal spatial positions, are also presented. It is interesting to note that in the numeric calculation of the vertical position of the head, the total variation throughout this part of the hurdling process was from 5.90 feet in frame eight to 6.14 feet in frame fourteen. This represents a total rise of the head of less than three inches throughout the clearance of the forty-two-inch-high hurdle! While the shoulder shows a slightly larger variation throughout the process, part of this vertical motion can be attributed to the diagonal adduction of the upper limb as a portion of the torque-countertorque process. The vertical position of the center of the hip joint during passage over the hurdle was calculated to be between fifty and fifty-two inches. This is only eight to ten inches above the hurdle itself. When the diameter of the thigh musculature is considered, this is excellent hurdle clearance with minimal vertical lift.

In the calculation of the horizontal velocity components, intervals of one-eighth of a second centered on the indicated frames were used. This use of longer time intervals than the filming speed diminishes the "scatter" in calculated velocities resulting from small errors in the location of positions of anatomic landmarks. For example, between frames eight and twelve, the horizontal position of the head changes from 7.54 feet to 5.04 feet. This represents a change of 2.5 feet in one-eighth of a second (4 frames at 32 frames/second). Therefore, the average velocity during this interval is 20 ft/sec ($2.5 \times 8 = 20$). The next average is taken between frames nine and thirteen, and this procedure is followed throughout this portion of the analysis.

By diminishing the "scatter," it is easier to analyze the changes in total motion occurring, as opposed to apparent changes simply due to errors in the data reduction process. It will be noted that throughout this portion of the hurdling process, the apparent velocities of the head and shoulders are greater than the average velocity of the pelvic area. This is due to the fact that the hurdler's position at the beginning of these frames was almost upright. At the end, lumbar flexion had actually caused the head and shoulders to move a greater horizontal distance than the pelvic girdle. The variations in horizontal velocity observed at the shoulder and hip joints can be correlated on the sequence of photographs with the ballistic movements of the accompanying limbs. It will be noted that all of these velocities indicate a forward body velocity of approximately 20 ft/sec. The average velocity for this high hurdler throughout the race is between 23 and 25 ft/sec. This means that this athlete reduces horizontal velocity very little in clearing the hurdle. This is one criterion for championship hurdling form.

It should be noted that there are a large number of other measurements or extensions of the presently shown calculations which could be presented from the knowledge of velocities and time intervals between frames. Accelerations can be calculated if the physical educator has measurements of the mass of the performer's various body segments. These can be combined with the velocities and accelerations to make calculations of energy, linear momentum, and angular momentum. However, such calculations are probably of more interest to the biomechanic researcher than the practicing coach.

It needs to be emphasized that numbers obtained in intermediate cinematographic analysis serve to objectify observations made at the first two levels of analysis. For example, in the basic cinematographic analysis of this performance in chapter eight, it was noted that there was very little extraneous motion of the head throughout the flight phase. The numerical calculations showed quantitatively the amount of motion present, i.e., the subjective evaluation was objectified. It was also stressed in earlier discussions of this event that maintenance of horizontal velocity was a prime concern in the hurdling process. The intermediate analysis provides numerical measurement of this horizontal velocity to substantiate the earlier observation. Also, since this performer is of championship caliber and shows few performance problems, data obtained from this type of calculation can be used as quantitative standards by a coach to compare and contrast with similar data collected from film of other hurdlers.

Figure 9.8 shows a film sequence of a championship discus performer. This differs from the hurdle example because the action occurs within a relatively small spatial environment and is primarily rotational in nature. Techniques for the discus throw utilize (1) a combination of body and upper-limb rotations to produce a high velocity of the discus, (2) release of the discus at the proper flight angle, and (3) the proper flight orientation of the discus to achieve optimum interaction with air. If these technique factors are followed, maximum distance of discus flight will be attained. In order to successfully perform this type of discus technique, a sequence of rotational motions must be timed to provide an optimum velocity and angle of release of the discus.

Intermediate cinematographic analysis of the frames in figure 9.8 provides the reader with examples which differ from the parameters analyzed previously on the hurdler. Measurement of angles and positions in this performance is much more difficult and, therefore, much less precise than in the previous example. In the case of the hurdler, motions of interest were all perpendicular to the line of observation by the camera. For this reason, the important changes of position could be accurately measured from one frame to another. In the discus example, the important changes are those in the direction in which certain segments of the body are oriented. The determination of these directions is less precise than determinations of spatial positions. These filming limitations must be recognized, and they simply have to be accepted during intermediate cinematographic analysis. In order to achieve precision in the measurement of joint angles, triaxial procedures must be utilized. Actual performances in competitive situations and film taken during games differ from film taken of a performance in a laboratory. Although these limitations are evident, there is still a possibility of gaining considerable information about a performer's actions which can be used for instructional or coaching purposes. *This practicality objective for using subject matter from biomechanics is very important relative to enhancing the quality of instruction in physical education.*

Figure 9.8. The discus throw as performed by Jay Silvester, U.S.A. Olympic team

Courtesy Visual Track and Field Techniques, 292 So. LaCienaga Blvd., Beverly Hills, Calif. 90211

In estimating the directions the following system was used:
0° toward observer
90° to right of picture
180° away from observer
270° to left of picture

Scale for height of discus determined from chain link fence in background.

Frame Number	7	8	9	10	11	12	13	14	15	16	17	18	19	20
Pelvic direction (°)	135	150	165	190	230	250	270	300	320	350	0	20	50	70
Lumbar-thoracic direction (°)	90	120	150	170	210	230	245	260	290	320	340	0	20	40
Head direction (°)	150	165	180	190	230	260	280	300	330	10	30	60	75	90
Right upper limb direction (°)	320	340	350	30	100	120	135	150	180	200	220	250	260	270
Discus height (scale units)	20.5	19	19	16	13	12	12	11.5	—	13	13	15	16	18

Frame Number	21	22	23	24	25	26	27	28	29	30	31	32	33	34
Pelvic direction (°)	90	120	150	180	200	220	240	260	290	320	350	0	0	10
Lumbar-thoracic direction (°)	60	80	110	140	150	160	180	210	250	280	320	0	10	30
Head direction (°)	120	150	170	180	200	220	240	250	270	310	0	30	50	70
Right upper limb direction (°)	290	310	340	0	20	40	70	90	130	180	220	250	280	310
Discus height (scale units)	20	23	24	25	24	23	20	17	13	—	14	19	25	31

Figure 9.9. Table of basic angular and height data for the discus performance

To begin the analysis of this performance, a set of data was extracted from the frames shown in figure 9.8. Directions of orientation were determined for (1) the pelvic girdle, (2) lumbar-thoracic spine, (3) cervical spine and head, and (4) the right upper limb. The latter was oriented with respect to the earth. The numbers within figure 9.9 were assigned with reference to the discus circle using the following criteria: (1) 0 degrees represents the direction toward the observer or camera, (2) 90 degrees is to the right of the frame, (3) 180 degrees represents the direction away from the observer, and (4) 270 degrees represents the direction to the left of the frame. In addition, the vertical height of the discus in each frame was measured with reference to the scale of the chain link fence in the background of the frame. Because the fence is farther away from the camera than the performer, the two-inch mesh cannot be used directly for scaling. However, the size of the discus (Diameter = 8.75 inches) can be used to establish the true scaling factor between motions in the planes of the performer and the fence. In the case of this sequence, the scaling factor was such that the diagonal distance across one of the mesh squares represents 2.9 inches. Figure 9.9 provides angular and height data which were determined from frames seven through thirty-four of figure 9.8.

The parameters chosen for analysis from this sequence were the (1) relative rotations within the pelvic girdle, lumbar-thoracic spine, and right shoulder joint of the performer, and (2) rotational velocities obtained at these body segments. These parameters are described in figures 9.10 and 9.11.

The position of the cervical spine and head in this performance is important from biomechanic and psychologic points of view. Rotations in the cervical spine can be used to supply a torque-countertorque effect to increase the angular velocity of the lumbar-thoracic region. Therefore, a large angle of rotation of the cervical spine is required preceding the final phase of the performance. When this is suddenly decreased, the countertorque follows. From a psychologic point of view, there is a strong tendency to want to see the direction in which one is moving. This human trait can be observed in the discus thrower. He not only rotates the cervical spine, but the eyes are also rotated. This is observed in frames thirteen through eighteen of figure 9.8.

The cervical angle listed in figure 9.10 is simply the difference in orientation between head and lumbar-thoracic spine directions as given in figure 9.9. In essence, figure 9.10 provides ranges of motion associated with cervical rotation for each frame of the sequence.

Frame Number		7	8	9	10	11	12	13	14	15	16	17	18	19	20
Angle															
Cervical	(°)	60	45	30	20	20	30	35	40	40	50	50	60	55	50
Lumbar-thoracic	(°)	45	30	15	20	20	20	35	40	40	30	20	20	30	30
Shoulder	(°)	40	50	70	50	20	30	20	20	20	30	30	20	30	40

Frame Number		21	22	23	24	25	26	27	28	29	30	31	32	33	34
Angle															
Cervical	(°)	60	70	60	40	50	60	60	40	20	30	40	30	40	40
Lumbar-thoracic	(°)	30	40	40	40	50	60	60	50	40	40	30	0	−10	−20
Shoulder	(°)	40	40	40	50	40	30	20	30	30	10	10	20	0	−10

For explanation of angles, see text.

Figure 9.10. Table of joint angles and ranges of motion for the discus performance

Frame Number	7	8	9	10	11	12	13	14	15	16	17	18	19	20
Velocity (rev/sec)														
Pelvic	1.96	1.60	2.40	2.49	2.40	2.04	2.04	2.40	1.78	1.78	1.78	2.04	2.04	2.04
Lumbar-thoracic	2.67	2.40	2.67	2.40	2.22	1.51	1.78	2.22	2.40	2.04	1.78	1.78	1.78	1.78
Right upper limb	1.78	2.40	3.40	3.40	3.11	1.51	1.78	1.96	2.04	2.04	1.78	1.51	1.16	1.51

Frame Number	21	22	23	24	25	26	27	28	29	30	31	32	33	34
Velocity (rev/sec)														
Pelvic	2.40	2.67	2.40	2.04	1.78	1.78	2.04	2.40	2.67	2.67	0.89	0	0.89	
Lumbar-thoracic	2.04	2.40	2.04	1.51	1.16	1.78	2.67	2.93	3.29	3.29	3.56	0.89	1.78	
Right upper limb	2.04	2.04	2.04	1.78	2.04	2.04	2.67	3.29	3.82	3.82	2.93	2.67	2.67	
Right upper limb (Corrected)										3.82	3.82	3.89	3.94	3.94

Figure 9.11. Table of angular velocities for the discus performance

Likewise, the difference between the orientation of the lumbar-thoracic body segment and the pelvic girdle is presented in figure 9.10 as the lumbar-thoracic angle. This rotation is especially important because it places the critical muscles on stretch for the final execution of the Serape Effect. This strong muscle action provides rotational acceleration of the lumbar-thoracic spine, and this motion is primarily responsible for the ultimate velocity of the discus.

The shoulder angle given in figure 9.10 decribes the relative orientation between the lumbar-thoracic segment and the right upper limb. The numbers were chosen so a zero-degree angle was arbitrarily established as any position of the right upper limb lying in the lateral plane. The number of degrees shown in each frame in the table, therefore, represents the angle in which the right upper limb is *deflected posteriorward* through either diagonal or transverse planes. The negative number given for the shoulder in frame thirty-four represents a ten-degree anterior deflection, while the negative numbers for the lumbar-thoracic angle in frames thirty-three and thirty-four represent a rotation of the lumbar-thoracic spine beyond the stabilized position of the pelvic girdle at that point in the performance.

Figure 9.11 represents the angular velocities of the pelvic girdle, lumbar-thoracic spine, and right upper limb. These were calculated by taking the difference in orientation between successive frames and utilizing the 32 frame/sec filming speed to transfer the differences in angular position into angular velocity. In order to smooth out the "scatter" due to errors in determining precise angle positions, the average motion over a three-frame interval centered at the indicated frame was used. For example, in the three frames centered on the interval between frames eight and nine, there was a total change of orientation by the pelvic girdle of 55 degrees. This is an average of 18 degrees per frame. In other words, a total of 55 degrees of rotation occurred between frames seven and ten. Multiplying this average of 18 degrees per frame by 32 (the filming speed of the camera) and dividing by 360 provides the average velocity at this interval in revolutions per second. The calculation gives the value of 1.60, which is seen in the line for the pelvic velocity between frames eight and nine in figure 9.11. In this way, average velocities during each interval of the pelvic girdle, lumbar-thoracic spine, and right upper limb were determined.

Information about a performance such as this can be absorbed by most individuals more efficiently if it is presented in the form of a graph rather than a table of numbers. Therefore, in figures 9.12 and 9.13, information from the two previous tables has been plotted in graphic fashion to show the correlations between joint angles and angular velocities at various times in the performance. It can be seen that both the cervical and lumbar-thoracic angles progressively develop to a maximum about frame twenty-eight. This decreases rapidly as the lumbar-thoracic spine is accelerated rotationally to its final peak velocity as noted in figure 9.12.

The graph of the velocity data shows certain items of interest. During the very early part of the performance, the rotational velocity of the throwing limb reaches a peak between frames ten and eleven. This, ironically, represents a rotational velocity nearly as high as the final velocity seen near the time of release. However, as can be observed in the frames of figure 9.8, the discus is not being held as far from the center of rotation of the body as it is in the final rotation, and the angular position at this point is not one in which the elevated trajectory could be given to the discus. Discus throwers, especially those at the secondary-school level of education, who release the discus during the early stages of the throw at this early peak of velocity of the throwing limb may obtain fair results. However, they will never reach their ultimate potential as discus throwers. One psychologic problem for the athlete and the coach at the secondary-school level seems to be that a large and strong performer can win points for the team in meets without ever developing to his full potential. Here is where the coach must interject his own philosophic view regarding the role of athletics in education. Points now or excellence later?

From the table in figure 9.11 and the graph in figure 9.13, there is an apparent decrease of angular velocity by the right upper limb in the final frames. This apparent decrease comes from the fact that the angles were measured with reference to the horizontal discus circle. In these final frames, the right upper limb is moving through a diagonal plane. Therefore, it has only a component of its motion apparent relative to the circle. The corrected numbers given in the final line for these frames represent the change from the horizontal component to the total motion in that frame. The dotted lines given for the motion of the right upper limb in the graph on figure 9.13 indicates the same set of numbers.

It will be noted in the final portion of figure 9.13 that there is a succession of maximal rotational velocities reached by the various body segments. The maximum velocity for the pelvic region occurs about frame thirty-one. The lumbar-thoracic spine achieves maximum velocity about frame thirty-three, and maximum velocity of the throwing limb occurs between frames thirty-three and thirty-four at the time of release. It is this excellent sequencing of motion which

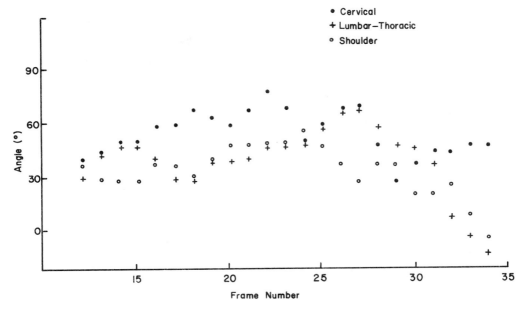

*Figure 9.12. Sequential joint angles during the discus perform-
ance.*

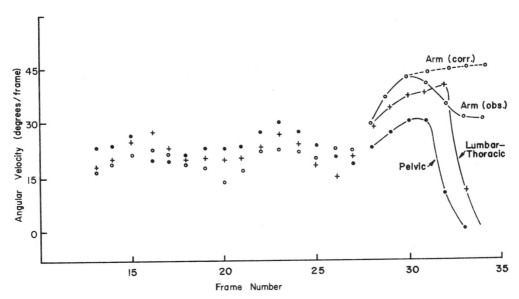

*Figure 9.13. Sequential angular velocities during the discus per-
formance.*

must be observed in a ballistic-type skill of this nature. This is a classic example of summation of motion.

It will be noticed in frame thirty-three of figure 9.8 that this performer actually leaves the ground prior to release of the discus. This is allowable as a result of his excellent throwing style. A man of this size and moment of inertia is capable of accomplishing this without any loss to either body stability or final velocity of the discus. In contrast to this, such an action might not be advisable for smaller or younger performers who are not as tall, strong, and skilled in this very difficult event. They should have both feet in contact with the ground when the discus is released to take advantage of the force-counterforce principle.

BIOMECHANIC RESEARCH

Conducting biomechanic research requires extensive multidisciplinary professional preparation at both undergraduate and graduate levels. This would include course work in mathematics through calculus, advanced physics, computer science, human engineering, and other related science course work. As a consequence, the most advanced analytic step in the hierarchy, biomechanic research, is beyond the scope of this book except to inform the reader that this level does exist and logically follows after the student has attained an understanding of the first three levels of biomechanic analysis. *Most professional physical educators will utilize the first three levels of biomechanic analysis within the hierarchy and be consumers as opposed to producers of biomechanic research.*

The purpose of this section is to present the biomechanic research level in a very brief and introductory manner. A few basic concepts about research as well as some of the instrumentation utilized in biomechanic research are presented to give the reader some insight into the potential scope and depth of biomechanic research projects. The interested and academically qualified student is encouraged to pursue this area of biomechanics.

Research involves controlled observations in which systematic investigations are conducted to seek new truths in an academic discipline. The results of such investigations serve to establish facts from which generalized principles can be developed. In the field of biomechanics, these principles can ultimately serve as guides for action and conduct of programs of sport, exercise, and dance.

Biomechanic research usually involves descriptive analyses performed at several levels of sophistication. *Biomechanic research is conducted to solve delimited motion problems, accurately describe motion, and discover new knowledge about neuromuscular performances.* The most commonly researched parameter is the relationship between space and time relative to human performances. Recordings of motions of various body parts and segments moving through space in several directions and at different velocities concurrently require complex research techniques. Facilities for obtaining data from which descriptive analyses can be conducted require excellent equipment and a large financial outlay. Extensive man-hour involvement must also be an important consideration. As a result, only a small number of biomechanic research facilities are in operation in colleges and universities throughout the United States.

Cinematography

Cinematographic procedures serve as the most common "tool" of biomechanic research for physical educators. In general, the cinematographic procedure outlined previously in this chapter under the heading "Intermediate Cinematographic Analysis" has many of the same components as biomechanic research. The main difference lies in the precision of measurement to obtain accurate information for analysis. Another difference lies in the fact that a researcher tends to delimit his study, to a considerable extent, in the laboratory situation; whereas analyses on the lower levels of the hierarchy are concerned with the totality of the skill in the game situation. Furthermore, the research worker is not concerned about immediate utilization of the findings of the investigation for instructional purposes.

Cinematographic data obtained during biomechanic research situations are more precise than data obtained during intermediate cinematographic analysis of game film. Control and precision are characteristics of research. These factors must be considered strengths; however, they are also weaknesses when athletic skills are studied. The reader should consider the following question in this respect: Is a performance of a shot-putter, as one example, filmed in a sterile laboratory situation in front of mirrors, on unusual surfaces, and with the performer wired for determination of joint angles and muscle-action potentials the same type of performance seen in competition? The superficiality of the testing situation would appear to be a logically significant limitation of biomechanic research techniques applied to athletic skills when compared with the other levels of cinematographic analyses discussed earlier in this chapter and in chapter eight. When possible and feasible, cinematographic data for research purposes should be collected on performers in competitive situations.

Specialized camera mechanisms which offer exceptionally high and precisely maintained filming speeds are available for the biomechanic researcher. These are necessary tools for accurate measurements involving ballistic motions. While cameras which produce very high filming-speed rates can be purchased, it must be remembered that utilization of filming speeds above 100 frames per second introduces special lighting and synchronization problems. In the context of research, no details must be omitted in the development of the experimental procedure and design.

Recording three-dimensional action on two-dimensional film constitutes another limitation of cinematography. This is due to the function of parallax. *Parallax is the apparent displacement of an observed object due to a change in the position of the observer.* Because most biomechanic analyses involve measurement of angles formed by limbs and body segments moving at joints, parallax must be overcome, many times, in planes of motion not parallel to the film if accurate joint angles are to be determined. Unless the angle formed by two levers is in a plane of motion perpendicular to the line of observation by the camera, the *actual angle* of that joint will be different from that observed on film.

In research situations, parallax must be considered. To do this, three views of any given angle must be photographed to ascertain the actual angle of any given joint motion. This may be accomplished by using three synchronized cameras to film the performance. Or, it can be accomplished with one camera utilizing several mirrors set at strategic angles within the laboratory. The three-camera or the multiple-mirror technique using one camera must provide photographs of a given angle in which the visual axis *(the visual axis being a straight line perpendicular to the film surface)* of each photograph is perpendicular to the others. The measured angles from these three views are averaged, and this yields the actual angle. This method of determining accurate joint angles during biomechanic research is known as *triaxial analysis.*

When filming a performer in the standing position, the three-camera technique involves placement of two cameras approximately at waist height of the performer, with their visual axes in a perpendicular relationship to each other. The third camera is placed above the performer with its visual axis perpendicular to the other two axes.

Figure 9.14 illustrates mirror placement in a laboratory setting in which only one motion-picture camera is used for triaxial analysis. The photographic area shown involves six mirrors ranging in size from five feet by five feet to five feet by eight feet. Mirrors A and B are positioned in such a way that the images produced in mirrors A′ and B′ are representative of the two visual axes which would be produced by using two cameras whose visual axes lie perpendicular to each other. Mirror C, the overhead mirror, produces an image in mirror C′. This is representative of the visual axis which would be produced by an overhead camera. The image in mirror C′ is perpendicular to the visual axes of the other two cameras. It can be seen through this very limited discussion of triaxial analysis that it would be difficult to utilize this procedure in the competitive situation while taking game film.

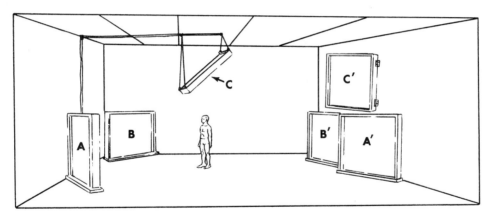

Figure 9.14. Triaxial cinematographic analysis mirror setting—a tool for biomechanic research.

Through the use of a dichroic mirror placed in front of the motion-picture camera lens, a clockface and grid may be superimposed over the image of the performer being photographed (fig. 9.15). Camera speeds may be checked accurately by placing a clock with a sweep-second hand in the photographic field. A grid may be used to provide reference points for measurements. In addition, placement of a carpenter's level in the scene provides a reference to the horizontal. It also allows for the presence of an object of known length.

Figure 9.15. Use of a dichroic mirror.

Electrogoniometry

Electrogoniometry provides accurate measurement of joint angles and ranges of motion through the use of recorded signals produced by an external electric source. Two lever arms hinged to form a joint are attached to a performer across joints of the limbs or body segments as shown in figure 9.16. The recorder produces a visual record of the number of degrees through which the

Figure 9.16. Utilization of the electrogoniometer to determine ranges of motion of joints during biomechanic research.

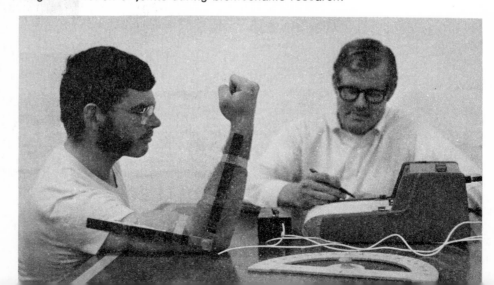

levers move. The utilization of the electrogoniometer in research situations is a good procedure to check or determine ranges of motion and joint angles.

Force Measurement

Force relationships in various performances may be measured and recorded by the use of force plates. When three strain gauges or transducers are utilized, force can be measured through the three cardinal planes of the body. No appreciable movement of the platform on which the performer applies force is necessitated during the measurement. Through the use of multiple strain gauges and subsequent mathematical calculations, force in any direction may be determined. The research implications in sport are unlimited for force and counterforce determinations.

Electromyography

The degree and amount of muscle-action potentials being produced during a muscle contraction may be measured by electromyography. These data can be translated into the approximate amount of internal force being exerted during any motion with or against gravity. Correlations between force-time analyses and electromyographic information add to the depth of study of total performance.

It is recommended that cinematographic studies of athletic skills also include synchronized electromyographic extraction of data. Figure 9.17 shows the physiograph being utilized to obtain electromyographic data from a subject performing work on a bicycle ergometer during a research project to determine the efficiency of various bicycle-seat settings for the sport of cycling.

Figure 9.17. Obtaining muscle action potentials through the use of electromyography.

Stroboscopic Analysis

The production of multiple images on one photographic print may be accomplished with a stroboscopic light and still-camera apparatus. The camera shutter is opened while a light source is made to produce intermittent light. The changes of rate of the intermittent flashes of light vary the number of images produced in sequence in a given period of time. The resultant photograph may be used to provide data for calculating space-time relationships of body segments or parts.

Computer Analysis

Because biomechanic research relies mainly on cinematographic techniques, photographic data reduction methods become necessary to handle the large amount of information produced from high-speed motion-picture photography. Quantitative information used to calculate such factors as velocities and accelerations may be obtained through the use of motion analyzers with automatic readout systems (fig. 9.18). The film image is projected in such a way that measurements of X and Y coordinates, angles, time, and other information may be obtained from the film. This information is then fed into a computer, as shown in figure 9.18, for an analysis of the data.

Biomechanic research techniques generate data at a prodigious rate. These data, combined with the more complex analyses required for such items as parallax corrections and accurate scaling, require an overwhelming amount of computation. For these reasons and others, the use of computer techniques in biomechanic research becomes a necessity rather than a convenience. Most research groups in universities have access to a large computer facility either through time-sharing terminals or card-punch machines within their laboratories. Furthermore, computer-center personnel, especially in universities, have data reduction and computer skills to help analyze accumulated data. These services must be utilized during biomechanic research. Many new uses are being designed for computers in biomechanic research; consequently, the student planning to work in this field should arrange to take considerable course work related to cybernetics.

The main objective of this book is to assist the student with a functional understanding of noncinematographic, basic cinematographic, and intermediate

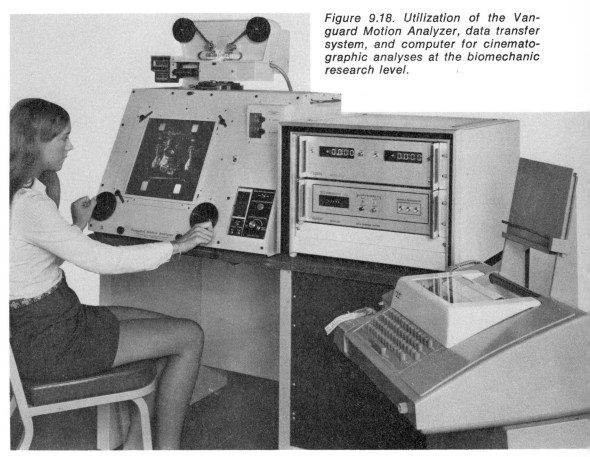

Figure 9.18. Utilization of the Vanguard Motion Analyzer, data transfer system, and computer for cinematographic analyses at the biomechanic research level.

Courtesy Vanguard Instrument Corp., Mehlville, L.I., N.Y.

cinematographic analyses. The first two levels should be used extensively by physical educators in daily teaching-coaching situations. Intermediate cinematographic analysis can be applied in teaching-coaching situations on a less frequent basis when the coach wants to objectify observations made elsewhere. Biomechanic research logically follows for interested students with adequate professional preparation in this area. Each level on the biomechanic analysis hierarchy is designed to increase the degree and precision of controlled observations of performers in classes or in athletic or research situations. Biomechanic subject matter should be utilized to enhance the quality of instruction in all aspects of physical education. The subject matter of biomechanics is no longer considered the exclusive property of the research investigator.

CONVERSION TABLES FOR MECHANICAL UNITS

This appendix has been compiled to provide conversion factors between the most commonly used sets of units for the description of human body motion. All possible conversion factors are not presented.

Although the pound is technically a unit of force and the kilogram a unit of mass, these units are both in common usage as force and mass units. Therefore, the conversions for both have been included. It should be remembered, however, that when using many formulae for the interactions of biomechanics, a correction factor is needed if mass is expressed in pounds, or force is expressed in kilograms.

Interconversions within the metric system have not been given because they are always expressed in terms of powers of 10. The following list of prefixes indicates the most commonly used factors:

Mega	1,000,000	10^6
Kilo	1,000	10^3
Centi	0.01	10^{-2}
Milli	0.001	10^{-3}
Micro	0.000001	10^{-6}

	To Change From	To	Multiply By
DISTANCE	feet	meters	0.3048
	yards	meters	0.9144
	meters	feet	3.28
	meters	yards	1.094
	miles	kilometers	1.609
	kilometers	miles	0.621
	inches	centimeters	2.54
	centimeters	inches	0.3937

	To Change From	To	Multiply By
VELOCITY	In all conversions using only the form distance/sec, the conversion factors are the same as in the "Distance" section above.		
	miles/hour	feet/second	1.467
	miles/hour	meters/second	0.447
	miles/hour	kilometers/hour	1.609
	feet/second	miles/hour	0.682
	meters/second	miles/hour	2.237
	kilometers/hour	miles/hour	0.621
ACCELERATION	feet/second^2	meters/second^2	0.3048
	meters/second^2	feet/second^2	3.28
	miles/hour per second	feet/second^2	1.467
	miles/hour per second	meters/second^2	0.447
	meters/second^2	miles/hour per second	2.237
	feet/second^2	miles/hour per second	0.682
FORCE	pounds	newtons	4.45
	pounds	kilograms	0.454
	kilograms	newtons	9.8
	kilograms	pounds	2.2
	newtons	kilograms	0.102
	newtons	pounds	0.225
MASS	pounds	kilograms	0.454
	pounds	slugs	0.0311
	kilograms	pounds	2.2
	kilograms	slugs	0.0685
	slugs	pounds	32.174
	slugs	kilograms	14.59
PRESSURE	pounds/inch^2	kilograms/cm^2	0.0703
	pounds/inch^2	kilograms/meter^2	703
	pounds/inch^2	newtons/cm^2	68.947
	pounds/inch^2	dynes/centimeter^2	0.689
	kilograms/cm^2	pounds/inch^2	14.22
	kilograms/meter^2	pounds/inch^2	0.00142

	To Change From	To	Multiply By
ENERGY	foot-pounds	Joules	1.356
	foot-pounds	kilocalories	0.00032
	Joules	foot-pounds	0.738
	Joules	kilocalories	0.000239
	kilocalories	foot-pounds	3087.4
	kilocalories	Joules	4186
POWER	foot-pounds/second	watt	1.356
	foot-pounds/second	horsepower	0.0018
	watt	foot-pound/sec	0.738
	watt	horsepower	0.00134
	watt	kilocalories/sec	0.000239
	horsepower	foot-pounds/sec	550
	horsepower	watts	745.2
	horsepower	kilocalories/sec	0.167
	kilocalories/sec	foot-pounds/sec	0.858
	kilocalories/sec	watt	4186
	kilocalories/sec	horsepower	0.00156
MOMENTUM	slug-feet/sec	pound-feet/sec	32.174
	slug-feet/sec	kilogram-meters/sec	4.45
	pound-feet/sec	slug-feet/sec	0.0311
	pound-feet/sec	kilogram-meters/sec	0.138
	kilogram-meters/sec	slug-feet/sec	0.225
	kilogram-meters/sec	pound-feet/sec	7.227

IMPULSE To convert between the pound-second, newton-second, and the kilogram second, see the conversion factors under "Force" for the pound, newton, and kilogram.

One pound-second of impulse produces a change of momentum of 1 slug-foot/sec. One newton-second of impulse produces a change of momentum of 1 kilogram-meter/sec.

ANGLE	radians	degrees	57.296
	radians	revolutions	0.159
	degrees	radians	0.0175
	degrees	revolutions	0.00278
	revolutions	radians	6.28
	revolutions	degrees	360

	To Change From	To	Multiply By
MOMENT OF INERTIA	slug-feet^2	pound-feet^2	32.174
	slug-feet^2	kilogram-meter^2	1.3558
	pound-feet^2	slug-feet^2	0.0311
	pound-feet^2	kilogram-meter^2	0.0421
	kilogram-meter^2	slug-feet^2	0.738
	kilogram-meter^2	pound-feet^2	23.70
TORQUE	pound-feet	meter-newtons	1.356
	pound-feet	meter-kilograms	0.138
	meter-newtons	pound-feet	0.737
	meter-newtons	meter-kilograms	0.102
	meter-kilograms	pound-feet	7.23
	meter-newtons	meter-kilograms	9.8

ANGULAR MOMENTUM   The units of angular momentum are slug-feet^2-radians/sec, pound-feet^2-radians/sec, and kilogram-meter^2-radians/sec. The conversion factors are the same as given under "Moment of Inertia" for slug-feet^2, pound-feet^2, and kilogram-meter^2.

MUSCLES MOST INVOLVED IN JOINT MOVEMENTS

Muscles[1]	Proximal Attachment	Distal Attachment

I. *Subtalar and Transverse Tarsal Joint Musculature*—(Articulatio Subtalaris and Articulatio Tarsi Transversa)*

A. Inverters

1. Tibialis anterior	Condylus lateralis of the tibia and upper two-thirds of the lateral aspect of the tibia.	Medial aspect of the os cuneiforme mediale and base of the first metatarsal bone.
2. Tibialis posterior	Lateral portion of the posterior aspect of the tibia and from the upper two-thirds of the medial aspect of the fibula.	Tuberositas ossis navicularis with fiber connections to the three cuneiformia, cuboideum, and bases of the II, III, and IV metatarsalia.
3. Extensor hallucis longus	Middle one-half of the anterior aspect of the fibula.	Phalanx distalis of the great toe (dorsal surface).
4. Flexor hallucis longus	Lower two-thirds of the posterior aspect of the fibula.	Phalanx distalis of the great toe (plantar surface).
5. Flexor digitorum longus	Posterior surface of the tibia; tendon passes posterior to the malleolus medialis and divides into four tendons.	Phalanx distalis of ossa digitorum pedis II, III, IV, and V (plantar surface).

B. Everters

1. Extensor digitorum longus	Condylus lateralis of the tibia and upper three-fourths of the anterior aspect of fibula and divides into four tendons.	Phalanx media and distalis of the ossa digitorum pedis II, III, IV, and V (dorsal surface).
2. Peroneus tertius (fibularis tertius)	Lower one-third of the anterior surface of the fibula.	Basis ossis metatarsalis V (dorsal surface).
3. Peroneus longus (fibularis longus)	Caput fibulae and upper two-thirds of the lateral aspect of the fibula; tendon runs posterior to the malleolus lateralis.	Basis ossis metatarsalis I and the lateral aspect of the os cuneiforme inermedium (plantar surface).

1. To avoid duplication, the proximal and distal attachments for each muscle will only be presented the first time the muscle appears on the movement list.

* Anatomic nomenclature used in this appendix is consistent with the third edition of *Nomina Anatomica,* 1968 printing.

MUSCLES MOST INVOLVED IN JOINT MOVEMENTS—*Continued*

Muscles	Proximal Attachment	Distal Attachment
4. Peroneus brevis (fibularis brevis)	Lower two-thirds of the lateral surface of the fibula; tendon runs posterior to the malleolus lateralis.	Tuberositas ossis metatarsalis V lateral aspect.

II. *Talocrural Joint Musculature*—(Articulatio talocruralis)

A. Dorsiflexors
  1. Tibialis anterior
  2. Extensor hallucis longus
  3. Extensor digitorium longus
  4. Peroneus tertius (fibularis tertius)

B. Plantar Flexors

1. Gastrocnemius	Two heads attach to the condylus medialis and condylus lateralis at the posterior aspect of the femur.	Tendo calcaneus (Achillis).
2. Soleus	Caput fibulae and upper one-third of the posterior aspect of the fibula.	Tendo calcaneus (Achillis).

  3. Peroneus longus (fibularis longus)
  4. Peroneus brevis (fibularis brevis)
  5. Flexor digitorum longus
  6. Flexor hallucis longus
  7. Tibialis posterior

MUSCLES MOST INVOLVED IN JOINT MOVEMENTS—*Continued*

Muscles	Proximal Attachment	Distal Attachment

III. *Knee Joint Musculature*—(Articulatio genus)

   A. Extensors

Muscles	Proximal Attachment	Distal Attachment
1. Rectus femoris	Spina iliaca anterior inferior and anterior aspect of the acetabulum.	Tuberositas tibiae via the quadriceps femoris tendon.
2. Vastus lateralis	Upper portion of the linea intertrochanterica of the femur; anterior and inferior borders of the trochanter major of the femur and upper half of the labius laterale of the linea aspera.	Tuberositas tibiae via the quadriceps femoris tendon.
3. Vastus medialis	Lower half of the linea intertrochanterica of the femur and the labium mediale of the linea aspera.	Tuberositas tibiae via the quadriceps femoris tendon.
4. Vastus intermedius	Anterior and lateral aspects of the upper two-thirds of the femur.	Tuberositas tibiae via the quadriceps femoris tendon.

   B. Flexors

Muscles	Proximal Attachment	Distal Attachment
1. Semitendinosus	Tuber ischiadicum of os ischii.	Posterior, medial aspect of the condylus medialis of the tibia.
2. Semimembranosus	Tuber ischiadicum of os ischii.	Posterior, medial aspect of the condylus medialis of the tibia.
3. Biceps femoris	*Caput longus:* tuber ischiadicum of os ischii. *Caput breve:* labium laterale of the linea aspera of the femur.	Caput fibulae and condylus lateralis of the tibia.
4. Sartorius	Spina iliaca anterior superior.	Upper portion of the medial aspect of the tibia anterior to the semitendinosus.
5. Gracilis	Upper half of the crista pubica.	Inferior to the condylus medialis of the tibia immediately superior to the semitendinosus.

MUSCLES MOST INVOLVED IN JOINT MOVEMENTS—*Continued*

Muscles	Proximal Attachment	Distal Attachment
6. Popliteus	Condylus lateralis of the femur.	Posterior surface of the upper and medial one-third of the tibia.
7. Gastrocnemius		
C. Medial Rotators		
1. Semitendinosus		
2. Semi-membranosus		
3. Popliteus		
4. Sartorius		
5. Gracilis		
D. Lateral Rotator		
1. Biceps femoris		

IV. *Hip Joint Musculature*—(Articulatio coxae)

A. Flexors		
1. Psoas major	Each processus transversus of the five vertebrae lumbales and from the bodies of the intervertebral fibrocartilages of the last of the vertebrae thoracicae and all vertebrae lumbales.	Trochanter minor of the femur.
2. Iliacus	Upper two-thirds of the fossa iliaca and labium interum of the crista iliaca.	Lateral to the psoas major on the trochanter minor of the femur.
3. Rectus femoris		
4. Tensor fasciae latae	Anterior aspect of the labium externum of the crista iliaca and the spina iliaca anterior superior.	Laterally into the tractus iliotibialis superficial to the trochanter major of the femur. The tractus iliotibialis attaches to the proximal and lateral aspect of the tibia.
5. Pectineus	Between the tubercular pubicum and pecten ossis pubis.	Linea pectinea leading from the trochanter minor to the linea aspera of the femur.

MUSCLES MOST INVOLVED IN JOINT MOVEMENTS—*Continued*

Muscles	Proximal Attachment	Distal Attachment
B. Extensors		
1. Gluteus maximus	Linea glutea posterior of the ilium and a portion of the posterior aspect of the crista iliaca.	Upper fibers into the posterior fibers of the tractus iliotibialis and lower fibers into the ruberositas glutea on the corpus femoris.
2. Biceps femoris (caput longum)	*Caput longum:* tuber ischiadicum of os ischii.	Caput fibulae and condylus lateralis of the tibia.
3. Semitendinosus		
4. Semi-membranosus		
C. Abductors		
1. Gluteus medius	From the area of the facies glutea of the ilium between the crista iliaca and linea glutea posterior above and linea glutea anterior below.	Major trochanter of the femur.
2. Gluteus minimus	Beneath the gluteus medius from the area of the facies glutea between the linea glutea anterior and linea glutea inferior of the ilium.	Fossa trochanterica on the anterior aspect of the major trochanter of the femur.
D. Adductors		
1. Adductor brevis	Ramus inferior ossis pubis.	Upper aspect of the linea aspera of the femur.
2. Adductor longus	Cristas pubica.	Linea aspera of the femur between the vastus medialis and adductor magnus.
3. Adductor magnus	Ramus inferior ossis pubis, ramus ossis ischii, and inferior aspect of the tuber ischiadicum.	Linea aspera and tuberculum adductorium of the femur.
4. Gracilis		
E. Diagonal Adductors		
1. Iliopsoas		
2. Rectus femoris		

MUSCLES MOST INVOLVED IN JOINT MOVEMENTS—*Continued*

Muscles	Proximal Attachment	Distal Attachment
3. Pectineus		
4. Adductor magnus		
5. Adductor longus		
6. Adductor brevis		
F. Diagonal Abductors		
1. Gluteus maximus		
2. Semitendinosus		
3. Semi-membranosus		
4. Biceps femoris	Caput longum only.	
5. Piriformis	Anterior aspect of the sacrum and the foramina sacralia pelvina.	Upper aspect of the major trochanter of the femur.
6. Obturatorius internus	Surround the foramen obturatum and attaches to the ramus ossis ischii and ramus inferior ossis pubis.	Medial aspect of the major trochanter of the femur above the fossa trochanterica.
7. Gemellus superior	Outer aspect of the spina ischiadica.	Medial aspect of the major trochanter of the femur.
8. Gemellus inferior	Upper aspect of the tuber ischiadicum.	Medial aspect of the major trochanter of the femur.
9. Quadratus femoris	External border of the tuber ischiadicum.	Linea intertrochanterica of the femur.
10. Obturatorius externus	Medial aspect of the foramen obturatum, ramus inferior ossis pubis, ramus superior ossis pubis, and the ramus ossis ischii.	Fossa trochanterica of the femur.
11. Gluteus medius		
G. Medial Rotators		
1. Tensor fasciae latae		
2. Gluteus medius—anterior fibers		
3. Gluteus minimus		

MUSCLES MOST INVOLVED IN JOINT MOVEMENTS—*Continued*

Muscles	Proximal Attachment	Distal Attachment
H. Lateral Rotators		
1. Gluteus maximus		
2. Gluteus medius—posterior fibers		
3. Six lateral rotators		
a. Piriformis		
b. Obturatorius internus		
c. Gemellus superior		
d. Gemellus inferior		
e. Quadratus femoris		
f. Obturatorius externus		
V. *Spinal Column and Rib Cage Musculature*—(Columna Vertebralis)		
A. Lumbar and Thoracic Flexors: (vertebrae lumbales and vertebrae thoracicae)		
1. Rectus abdominis	Crista pubica.	Anterior on the cartilages of ribs five through seven and on the lateral aspect of the processus xiphodeus.
2. Obliquus externus abdominis	Anterior half of the labium externum of the crista iliaca and the linea alba.	Inferior borders of the lower eight ribs.
3. Obliquus internus abdominis	Anterior two-thirds of the labium internum of the crista iliaca and lateral half of the inguinal ligament and the lumbodorsal fascia.	Inferior borders of the lower four ribs and the linea alba.

MUSCLES MOST INVOLVED IN JOINT MOVEMENTS—*Continued*

Muscles	Proximal Attachment	Distal Attachment
B. Lumbar and Thoracic Extensors		
1. Erector spinae		
a. Iliocostalis lumborum	Inferior borders of ribs seven through twelve (posterior)	Crista sacralis intermedia spinosus of the vertebrae lumbales and the lower two vertebrae thoracicae, labium interum of the crista iliaca to the crista sacralis lateralis.
b. Iliocostalis thoracis	Superior aspects of ribs one through six (posterior).	Superior aspects of ribs seven through twelve (posterior).
c. Longissimus thoracis	Each processus transversus of the twelve vertebrae thoracicae and the adjacent ribs four through twelve.	Integrated with the iliocostalis lumborum and attaches to each processus transversus of the five vertebrae lumbales.
d. Spinalis thoracis	Processus spinosus of the upper four to eight vertebrae thoracicae.	Each processus spinosus of vertebrae lumbales four and five as well as each processus spinous of vertebrae thoracicae eleven and twelve.
C. Right Lateral Flexors of the Lumbar and Thoracic Spine		
1. Right obliquus internus abdominis		
2. Right obliquus externus abdominis		
3. Right rectus abdominis		
4. Right erector spinae		

MUSCLES MOST INVOLVED IN JOINT MOVEMENTS—*Continued*

Muscles	Proximal Attachment	Distal Attachment

D. Left Lateral Flexors of the Lumbar and Thoracic Spine
   1. Left obliquus internus abdominis
   2. Left obliquus externus abdominis
   3. Left rectus abdominis
   4. Left erector spinae
E. Right Spinal Rotators of the Lumbar and Thoracic Spine
   1. Right obliquus internus abdominis
   2. Left obliquus externus abdominis
   3. Right erector spinae
F. Left Spinal Rotators of the Lumbar and Thoracic Spine
   1. Left obliquus internus abdominis
   2. Right obliquus externus abdominis
   3. Left erector spinae

MUSCLES MOST INVOLVED IN JOINT MOVEMENTS—*Continued*

Muscles	Proximal Attachment	Distal Attachment
G. Cervical Flexor		

1. Sternocleido-
    mastoideus
	Sternal head: anterior manu-
	   brium sterni.
	Clavicular head: medial third of
	   the anterior aspect of the clavi-
	   cle.
		Processus mastoideus and linea
		nuchae superior.

H. Cervical Extensors		
1. Erector spinae		
a. Iliocostalis cervicis	Third through sixth ribs pos- teriorly.	Each tuberculum posterius of each processus transversus of the fourth, fifth, and sixth vertebrae cervicales.
b. Longissimus cervicis	Each processus transversus of vertebrae thoracicae one through five.	Tuberculum posterius of each processus transversus of vertebrae cervicales two through six.
c. Longissimus capitis	Processus transversus of vertebrae thoracicae one through five and the processus articularis inferior of vertebrae cervicales one through four.	Processus mastoideus.
d. Spinalis cervicis	Ligamentum nuchae and the processus spinous of the seventh vertebrae cervicales.	Processus spinous of the axis ver- tebra.
e. Spinalis capitis	Same as spinalis cervicis.	Same as spinalis cervicis.
I. Right Lateral Flexors of the Cervical Spine		
1. Right sterno- cleidomastoideus		
2. Right erector spinae		
J. Left Lateral Flexors of the Cervical Spine		
1. Left sterno- cleidomastoideus		
2. Left erector spinae		

MUSCLES MOST INVOLVED IN JOINT MOVEMENTS—*Continued*

Muscles	Proximal Attachment	Distal Attachment
K. Right Cervical Rotation 1. Left sterno-cleidomastoideus 2. Right erector spinae		
L. Left Cervical Rotation 1. Right sterno-cleidomastoideus 2. Left erector spinae		
VI. *Shoulder Girdle Musculature*		
A. Scapular Abductors		
1. Pectoralis minor	Upper, anterior aspects of ribs three through five.	Medial aspect of the processus coracoideus of scapula.
2. Serratus anterior	Outer and lateral aspects of ribs one through nine.	The entire vertebral border of the scapula including the angulus superior and angulus inferior.
B. Scapular Adductors		
1. Trapezius (middle fibers)	Protuberatia occipitalis externa and medial third of the linea nuchae superior, ligamentum nuchae and each processus spinosus of all vertebrae thoracicae and the seventh vertebrae cervicales.	Posterior border of the lateral third of the clavicle, acromion and spina scapulae.
2. Rhomboidei		
a. Rhomboideus major	Each processus spinosus of the second through the fifth vertebrae thoracicae.	Angulus inferior of the scapula along the vertebral border to the spina scapulae.
b. Rhomboideus minor	Ligamentum nuchae, processus spinosus of the seventh vertebra cervicales, and processus spinosus of the first vertebra thoracicae.	Spina scapulae superior to rhomboideus major on vertebral border of the scapula.

MUSCLES MOST INVOLVED IN JOINT MOVEMENTS—*Continued*

Muscles	Proximal Attachment	Distal Attachment
C. Scapular Upward Rotators		
1. Trapezius (all parts)		
2. Serratus anterior (lower fibers)		
D. Scapular Downward Rotators		
1. Rhomboidei		
2. Pectoralis minor		
3. Levator scapulae	Processus transversus of the atlas, processus transversus of the axis. Each tuberculum posterius of the processus transversus of third and fourth vertebrae cervicales.	Vertebral border of the scapula between the angulus superior and the spina scapulae.
E. Scapulae Elevators		
1. Levator scapulae		
2. Trapezius (upper fibers)		
3. Rhomboidei		
F. Scapulae Depressors		
1. Trapezius (lower fibers)		
2. Pectoralis minor		
VII. *Shoulder Joint Musculature*—(Articulatio Humeri)		
A. Shoulder Flexors		
1. Deltoideus (anterior fibers)	Anterior aspect of the lateral one-third of the clavicula, acromion and spina scapulae.	Tuberositas deltoidea.
2. Pectoralis major (upper fibers)	Anterior and medial one-half of the clavicula, anterior aspect of the sternum.	Crista tuberculi majoris.
3. Coracobrachialis	Processus coracoideus.	Medial aspect of the corpus humeri.

MUSCLES MOST INVOLVED IN JOINT MOVEMENTS—*Continued*

Muscles	Proximal Attachment	Distal Attachment
4. Biceps brachii (caput breve)	*Caput breve:* Processus coracoideus. *Caput longum:* Tuberculum Supraglenoidale of the scapula.	Tuberositas radii.
B. Shoulder Extensors 1. Pectoralis major (lower fibers)		
2. Latissimus dorsi	Each processus spinosus of vertebrae thoracicae seven through twelve, all vertebrae lumbales and vertebrae sacrales; posterior aspect of the crista iliaca; lateral on the labial externum of the crista iliaca and from the lower four ribs posteriorally.	Suleus intertubercularis of the humerus.
3. Teres major	Angulus inferior of the scapula.	Crista tuberculum minoris of the humerus.
4. Deltoideus (posterior fibers)		
5. Triceps brachii (caput longum)	*Caput longum:* tuberculum infraglenoidale of the scapula. *Caput laterale:* posterior aspect of the corpus humeri adjacent to the upper part of the sulcus for the radialis nerve. *Caput mediale:* margo medialis of the corpus humeri below the radial nerve sulcus.	Olecranon of the ulna.
C. Shoulder Abductors 1. Deltoideus		
2. Pectoralis major (upper fibers when arm is above horizontal)		
3. Supraspinatus	Fossa supra spirata.	Tuberculum majus of the humerus.

MUSCLES MOST INVOLVED IN JOINT MOVEMENTS—*Continued*

Muscles	Proximal Attachment	Distal Attachment
D. Shoulder Adductors		
1. Latissimus dorsi		
2. Teres major		
3. Pectoralis major (lower fibers)		
4. Triceps brachii (caput longum)		
E. Shoulder Medial Rotators		
1. Subscapularis	Medial two-thirds of the fossa subscapularis.	Tuberculum minus of the humerus.
2. Teres major		
3. Latissimus dorsi		
4. Pectoralis major		
F. Shoulder Lateral Rotators		
1. Infraspinatus	Upper two-thirds of the fossa infraspinata.	Tuberculum majus of the humerus.
2. Teres minor	Axillary border of the upper two-thirds of the scapula.	Tuberculum majus of the humerus and upper, medial aspect of the corpus humeri.
G. Shoulder Horizontal Abductors		
1. Deltoideus (middle and posterior fibers)		
2. Infraspinatus		
3. Teres minor		
4. Triceps brachii (caput longum)		
H. Shoulder Horizontal Adductors		
1. Deltoideus (anterior fibers)		
2. Pectoralis major		
3. Coracobrachialis		

MUSCLES MOST INVOLVED IN JOINT MOVEMENTS—*Continued*

Muscles	Proximal Attachment	Distal Attachment

    4. Biceps brachii
       (caput breve)

I. Shoulder High
  Diagonal Abductors
    1. Deltoideus
       (posterior fibers)
    2. Infraspinatus
    3. Teres minor
    4. Triceps brachii
       (caput longum)

J. Shoulder High
  Diagonal Adduction
    1. Deltoideus
       (anterior fibers)
    2. Pectoralis major
       (lower fibers)
    3. Coracobrachialis
    4. Biceps brachii
       (caput breve)

K. Shoulder Low
  Diagonal Abduction
    1. Deltoideus
       (posterior)
    2. Infraspinatus
    3. Teres minor
    4. Triceps brachii
       (caput longum)

L. Shoulder Low
  Diagonal Adduction
    1. Deltoideus
       (anterior fibers)
    2. Pectoralis major
       (upper fibers)
    3. Coracobrachialis
    4. Biceps brachii
       (caput breve)

MUSCLES MOST INVOLVED IN JOINT MOVEMENTS—*Continued*

Muscles	Proximal Attachment	Distal Attachment

VIII. *Elbow Joint Musculature*—(Articulatio Cubiti)

A. Elbow Flexors

1. Biceps brachii

2. Brachialis	Anterior and lower half of the corpus humeri.	Tuberositas ulnae and processus coronoideus.
3. Brachioradialis	Upper two-thirds of the lateral processus supracondylaris of the humerus.	Lateral aspect of the base of the processus styloideus on the radius.

B. Elbow Extensor

1. Triceps brachii

IX. *Radio-Ulnar Joint Musculature*—(Articulatio Radioulnaris)

A. Pronators

1. Pronator teres	*Caput humerale:* epicondylus medialis of the humerus. *Caput ulnare:* medial aspect of the processus coronoideus on the ulna.	Middle and lateral aspect of the corpus radii.
2. Pronator quadratus	Volar surface of the lower aspect of the corpus ulnae.	Above the incisura ulnaris of the radius.

3. Brachioradialis

B. Supinators

1. Supinator	Epicondylus lateralis of the humerus and crista supinatoris of the ulna.	Dorsal and lateral aspects of the corpus radii.

2. Biceps brachii

3. Brachioradialis

X. *Wrist Joint Musculature*—(Articulatio Radiocarpea)

A. Wrist Flexors

1. Flexor carpi radialis	Epicondylus medialis of the humerus.	Bases of metacarpalia I and II.
2. Flexor carpi ulnaris	*Caput humerale:* Epicondylus medialis of the humerus.	Pisiforme, hamatum and metacarpus V.

MUSCLES MOST INVOLVED IN JOINT MOVEMENTS—*Continued*

Muscles	Proximal Attachment	Distal Attachment
	Caput ulnare: Medial aspect of the olecranon and upper two-thirds of the dorsal aspect of the ulna.	
3. Palmaris longus	Epicondylus medialis of the humerus.	Transverse carpal ligament and the palmar aponeurosis.
4. Flexor digitorum superficialis	*Caput humeroulnare:* Epicondylus medialis of the humerus. *Caput radiale:* Tuberositas radii.	Via four tendons into each side of phalanx media of the four fingers.
5. Flexor pollicis longus	On the volar surface of the radius below the tuberositas radii and epicondylus medialis of the humerus.	Base of the phalanx distalis of the thumb.
B. Wrist Extensors		
1. Extensor carpi radialis longus	Lower third of the lateral supracondylar ridge of the humerus.	Radial and dorsal aspects of the basis of metacarpus II.
2. Extensor carpi radialis brevis	Epicondylus lateralis of the humerus.	Radial and dorsal aspects of the basis of metacarpus III.
3. Extensor carpi ulnaris	Epicondylus lateralis of the humerus.	Ulnar side of the basis of metacarpus V.
4. Extensor digitorum	Epicondylus lateralis of the humerus.	Via four tendons to the dorsal surface of the phalanx distilas of each digit.
5. Extensor indicis	Dorsal aspect of the corpus ulnae.	Via the extensor digitorum tendon to the index finger.
6. Extensor digiti minimi	Common extensor tendon and adjacent muscles.	Via the extensor digitorum tendon to the dorsal aspect of the phalanx proximalis of the little finger.
7. Extensor pollicis longus	Middle third of the dorsal aspect of the corpus ulnae.	Base of the phalanx distalis of the thumb.
C. Radial Flexors		
1. Flexor carpi radialis		
2. Extensor carpi radialis longus		

MUSCLES MOST INVOLVED IN JOINT MOVEMENTS—*Continued*

Muscles	Proximal Attachment	Distal Attachment
3. Extensor carpi radialis brevis		
4. Extensor pollicis brevis	Dorsal aspect of the corpus radii and the interosseus membrane.	Base of the phalanx proximalis of the thumb.
5. Abductor pollicis longus	Lateral and dorsal aspect of the corpus ulnaris, interosseus membrane and middle third of the dorsal aspect of the corpus radii.	Radial aspect of the basis of metacarpus I.

D. Ulnar Flexors
  1. Flexor carpi ulnaris
  2. Extensor carpi ulnaris

XI. *Metacarpophalangeal* (Articulationes metacarpophalangeae) *and Interphalangeal* (Articulationes interphalangeae manus) *Musculature*

A. Flexors

1. Flexor digitorum profundus	Volar and medial aspects of the upper three-fourths of the corpus ulnae, processus coronoideus and upper half of the interosseus membrane.	Basis of each finger's phalanx distalis.

  2. Flexor digitorum superficialis
  3. Flexor pollicis longus

B. Extensors
  1. Extensor digitorum
  2. Extensor indicis
  3. Extensor digiti minimi
  4. Extensor pollicis longus
  5. Extensor pollicis brevis

bibliography

This bibliography contains selected books on biomechanics, anatomic kinesiology, cinematography, physics, anatomy, exercise physiology, and related areas. These books should be available in most university or college libraries.

1. ADRIAN, M.; TIPTON, C. M.; and KARPOVICH, P. *Electrogoniometry Manual.* Springfield, Ill.: Springfield College, 1965.
2. AMAR, JULES. *The Human Motor.* New York: E. P. Dutton and Co., 1920.
3. AMERICAN ACADEMY OF ORTHOPEDIC SURGEONS. *Measuring and Recording of Joint Motion.* Chicago: The Academy, 1965.
4. ANDERSON, T. McCLURG. *Human Kinetics and Analyzing Body Movements.* London: William Heinemann Medical Books, Ltd., 1951.
5. ARISTOTLE. *Progressions of Animals,* IX. Translated by E. S. Forster. Cambridge: Harvard University Press, 1945.
6. BADE, EDWIN. *The Mechanics of Sport.* Kingswood: Glade House, 1962.
7. BARHAM, JERRY N., and THOMAS, WILLIAM L. *Anatomical Kinesiology.* London: The Macmillan Co., 1969.
8. BARNETT, C. H.; DAVIES, D. V.; and MacCONAILL, M. A. *Synovial Joints, Their Structure and Mechanics.* Springfield, Ill.: Charles C Thomas, Publisher, 1961.
9. BASMAJIAN, J. V. *Muscles Alive. Their Functions Revealed by Electromyography.* Baltimore: The Williams and Wilkins Co., 1962.
10. BEEVOR, C. *The Croonian Lectures on Muscular Movements.* London: Macmillan, Ltd., 1903.
11. BERNSTEIN, N. *The Co-ordination and Regulation of Movements.* New York: Pergamon Press, 1967.
12. BOURNE, G. H. B., ed. *The Structure and Function of Muscle.* New York: Academic Press, Inc., 1960.
13. BROER, M. R. *An Introduction to Kinesiology.* Englewood Cliffs, N.J.: Prentice-Hall, Inc., 1968.
14. ———. *Efficiency of Human Movement.* Philadelphia: W. B. Saunders Co., 1973.
15. ———. *Laboratory Experiences: Exploring Efficiency of Human Movement.* Philadelphia: W. B. Saunders Co., 1973.
16. ———, and HOUTZ, SARA J. *Patterns of Muscular Activity in Selected Sport Skills: An Electromyographic Study.* Springfield, Ill.: Charles C Thomas, Publisher, 1967.
17. BROWN, ROSCOE C., and KENYON, GERALD S., eds. *Classical Studies on Physical Activity.* Englewood Cliffs, N.J.: Prentice-Hall, Inc., 1968.

18. BRUNNSTROM, SIGNE. *Clinical Kinesiology.* Philadelphia: F. A. Davis Co., 1966.
19. BUNN, JOHN W. *Scientific Principles of Coaching.* Englewood Cliffs, N.J.: Prentice-Hall, Inc., 1972.
20. CAMPBELL, E. J. M. *The Respiratory Muscles and the Mechanics of Breathing.* London: Lloyd-Luke (Medical Books) Ltd., 1958.
21. CANNA, D. J., and LORING, E. *Kinesography.* Fresno: The Academy Guild Press, 1955.
22. CHESTERMAN, W. D. *The Photographic Study of Rapid Events.* London: Oxford University Press, 1951.
23. CLOSE, J. R. *Motor Function in the Lower Extremity: Analyses by Electronic Instrumentation.* Springfield, Ill.: Charles C Thomas, Publisher, 1964.
24. COCHRAN, ALASTAIR, and STOBBS, JOHN. *The Search for the Perfect Swing.* New York: J. B. Lippincott Co., 1968.
25. COOPER, JOHN M., ed. *C.I.C. Symposium on Biomechanics.* Chicago: Athletic Institute, 1971.
26. ———, and GLASSOW, RUTH B. *Kinesiology.* St. Louis: The C. V. Mosby Co., 1972.
27. ———, and SIEDENTROP, D. *The Theory and Science of Basketball.* Philadelphia: Lea and Febiger, 1969.
28. COUNSILMAN, JAMES E. *The Science of Swimming.* Englewood Cliffs, N.J.: Prentice-Hall, Inc., 1968.
29. DE VRIES, HERBERT A. *Physiology of Exercise for Physical Education and Athletics.* Dubuque, Ia.: Wm. C. Brown Co. Publishers, 1966.
30. DUBOIS, J., and SANTSCHI, W. R. *The Determination of the Moment of Inertia of Living Human Organisms.* New York: John Wiley, 1963.
31. DUCHENNE, G. B. A. *Physiology of Motion.* Translated by E. B. Kaplan. Philadelphia: W. B. Saunders Co., 1959.
32. DUVALL, ELLEN NEALL. *Kinesiology: The Anatomy of Motion.* Englewood Cliffs, N.J.: Prentice-Hall, Inc., 1959.
33. DYSON, GEOFFREY H. G. *The Mechanics of Athletics.* London: University of London Press, 1964.
34. ELFTMAN, H. *Skeletal and Muscular Systems: Structure and Function in Medical Physics.* Chicago: Year Book Publications, 1944.
35. EVANS, F. GAYNOR, ed. *Biomechanical Studies of the Musculo-skeletal System.* Springfield, Ill.: Charles C Thomas, Publisher, 1961.
36. ———. *Studies on the Anatomy and Function of Bone and Joints.* New York: Springer-Verlag, 1966.
37. FALLS, HAROLD B., ed. *Exercise Physiology.* New York: Academic Press, 1968.
38. FINLEY, F. RAY. *Kinesiological Analysis of Human Locomotion.* Eugene: University of Oregon Press, 1961.
39. FRANKEL, VICTOR H., and BURSTEIN, ALBERT H. *Orthopaedic Biomechanics.* Philadelphia: Lea and Febiger, 1970.
40. FROST, HAROLD M. *An Introduction to Biomechanics.* Springfield, Ill.: Charles C Thomas, Publisher, 1967.
41. GANSLEN, R. V., and HALL, K. G. *The Aerodynamics of Javelin Flight.* Fayetteville: University of Arkansas Press, 1960.
42. GANSLEN, R. V. *Mechanics of the Pole Vault.* St. Louis: John S. Swift Co., Inc., 1963.
43. GOLDSMITH, WERNER. *Impact.* New York: St. Martin's, 1961.

44. GRAY, HENRY. *Anatomy of the Human Body*. Philadelphia: Lea and Febiger, 1973.
45. GRAY, J. *How Animals Move*. London: Cambridge University Press, 1960.
46. HALL, MICHAEL C. *The Locomotor System: Functional Anatomy*. Springfield: Charles C Thomas, Publisher, 1965.
47. HALLIDAY, D., and RESNICK, R. *Physics for Students of Science and Engineering*. Part I. New York: John Wiley, 1965.
48. HAWLEY, GERTRUDE. *An Anatomical Analysis of Sport*. Cranbury, N.J.: A. S. Barnes, 1940.
49. HEMMING, GEORGE W. *Billiards Mathematically Treated*. London: Macmillan, 1899.
50. HERTEL, HEINRICH. *Structure-Form-Movement*. New York: Reinhold Publishing Corp., 1966.
51. HICKMAN, C. N.; NAGLER, F.; and KLOPSTEG, PAUL E. *Archery: The Technical Side*. Redlands, Calif.: National Field Archery Association, 1947.
52. HILL, A. V. *Muscular Movements in Man*. New York: McGraw-Hill Book Co., 1927.
53. ———. *Living Machinery*. New York: McGraw-Hill Book Co., 1927.
54. HOLLINSHEAD, H. W. *Functional Anatomy of the Limbs and Back*. Philadelphia: W. B. Saunders Co., 1960.
55. HOWELL, A. BRAZIEIR. *Speed in Animals: Their Specialization for Running and Leaping*. New York: Hafner Publishers, 1965.
56. HYZER, WILLIAM G. *Engineering and Scientific High Speed Photography*. New York: The Macmillan Co., 1963.
57. JENSEN, CLAYNE R., and SCHULTZ, GORDON W. *Applied Kinesiology*. St. Louis: McGraw-Hill Book Co., 1970.
58. JOHNSON, WARREN R., ed. *Science and Medicine of Exercise and Sports*. New York: Harper and Row, Publishers, 1960.
59. JONES, F. W. *Structure and Function as Seen in the Foot*. London: Bailliere, Tindall and Cox, Ltd., 1949.
60. JOSEPH, J. *Man's Posture Electromyographic Studies*. Springfield, Ill.: Charles C Thomas, Publisher, 1960.
61. KARAS, V., and STAPLETON, A. *Application of the Theory of the Motion System in the Analysis of Gymnastic Motions*. New York: S. Karger, 1968.
62. KELLEY, DAVID L. *Kinesiology: Fundamentals of Motion Description*. Englewood Cliffs, N.J.: Prentice-Hall, Inc., 1971.
63. KENEDI, R. M., ed. *Symposium on Biomechanics and Related Bioengineering Topics*. New York: Pergamon Press, 1965.
64. LEVENS, ALEXANDER. *Graphical Methods in Research*. New York: John Wiley, 1965.
65. LIPOVETZ, F. J. *Basic Kinesiology*. Minneapolis: Burgess Publishing Co., 1952.
66. LOGAN, GENE A. *Adapted Physical Education*. Dubuque, Ia.: Wm. C. Brown Co. Publishers, 1972.
67. ———, and McKINNEY, WAYNE C. *Kinesiology*. Dubuque, Ia.: Wm. C. Brown Co. Publishers, 1970.
68. LUCAS, D. B., and INMAN, V. T. *Functional Anatomy of the Shoulder Joint*. Berkeley: University of California Medical School, 1963.
69. MACCONAILL, M. A., and BASMAJIAN, J. V. *Muscles and Movement: A Basis for Human Kinesiology*. Baltimore: The William and Wilkins Co., 1969.

70. MAREY, ETIENNE J. *Movement.* Translated by Eric Pritchard. London: William Heineman, Ltd., 1895.

71. MASCELLI, JOSEPH V., and MILLER, ARTHUR. *American Cinematographer Manual.* Hollywood: American Society of Cinematographers Holding Corporation, 1966.

72. MASSEY, BENJAMIN H., and others. *The Kinesiology of Weight Lifting.* Dubuque, Ia.: Wm. C. Brown Co. Publishers, 1959.

73. METHENY, ELEANOR. *Body Dynamics.* New York: McGraw-Hill, Inc., 1952.

74. MONTAGU, M. F. A. *A Handbook of Anthropometry.* Springfield, Ill.: Charles C Thomas, Publisher, 1960.

75. MOREHOUSE, L. E., and COOPER, J. M. *Kinesiology.* St. Louis: The C. V. Mosby Co., 1950.

76. MORRIS, ROXIE. *Correlation of Basic Sciences with Kinesiology.* New York: American Physical Therapy Association, 1955.

77. MORTON, D. J., and FULLER, D. D. *Human Locomotion and Body Form.* Baltimore: The Williams and Wilkins Co., 1952.

78. MUYBRIDGE, EADWEARD. *The Human Figure in Motion.* New York: Dover Publications, Inc., 1955.

79. O'CONNELL, ALICE L., and GARDNER, ELIZABETH B. *Understanding the Scientific Bases of Human Movement.* Baltimore: Williams and Wilkins Co., 1972.

80. PLAGENHOEF, STANLEY. *Fundamentals of Tennis.* Englewood Cliffs, N.J.: Prentice-Hall, Inc., 1970.

81. ————. *Patterns of Human Motion: A Cinematographic Analysis.* Englewood Cliffs, N.J.: Prentice-Hall, Inc., 1971.

82. POSSE, N. *The Special Kinesiology of Educational Gymnastics.* Boston: Lothrop, Lee and Shepard Co., Inc., 1890.

83. RASCH, PHILIP J., and BURKE, ROGER K. *Kinesiology and Applied Anatomy.* Philadelphia: Lea and Febiger, 1972.

84. REBIKOFF, DIMITRI, and CHERNEY, PAUL. *A Guide to Underwater Photography.* New York: Greenberg, 1955.

85. RODAHL, K., and HORVATH, S. M. *Muscle as a Tissue.* New York: McGraw-Hill, Inc., 1962.

86. RUCH, T. C., and PATTON, H. D., eds. *Physiology and Biophysics.* Philadelphia: W. B. Saunders Co., 1965.

87. SCOTT, M. GLADYS. *Analysis of Human Motion.* New York: Appleton-Century-Crofts, 1963.

88. SKARSTROM, W. *Gymnastic Kinesiology.* Springfield: F. A. Bassette Co., 1909.

89. ————. *Kinesiology of Trunk, Shoulders and Hip.* Springfield, Ill.: Charles C Thomas, Publisher, 1946.

90. SLOCUM, D. B., and BOWERMAN, WILLIAM. *The Biomechanics of Running.* Clinical Orthopaedics No. 23. Philadelphia: J. B. Lippincott Co., 1962.

91. STEINDLER, ARTHUR. *Mechanics of Normal and Pathological Locomotion in Man.* Springfield, Ill.: Charles C Thomas, Publisher, 1935.

92. ————. *Kinesiology of the Human Body under Normal and Pathological Conditions.* Springfield, Ill.: Charles C Thomas, Publisher, 1955.

93. STODDARD, J. T. *The Science of Billiards.* Boston: Butterfield, 1913.

94. STRASSER, H. *Lehrbuch der Muskel und Gelenkmeckanik.* Berlin: J. Springer, 1913.

95. STREETER, V. L. *Fluid Mechanics.* New York: McGraw-Hill, 1966.

96. THOMPSON, CLEM W. *Kranz Manual of Kinesiology.* St. Louis: The C. V. Mosby Co., 1969.
97. TRICKER, R. A. R., and TRICKER, B. J. K. *The Science of Movement.* New York: American Elsevier Publishing Co., Inc., 1967.
98. VREDENBREGT, J., and WARTENWEILER, J., eds. *International Seminar on Biomechanics.* Baltimore: University Park Press, 1971.
99. WADDELL, J. H., and WADDELL, J. W. *Photographic Motion Analysis.* Chicago: Indust. Lab. Publ., 1955.
100. WARTENWEILER, J.; JOKL, E.; and HEBBELNICK, M., eds. *International Seminar on Biomechanics.* New York: S. Krager, 1968.
101. WEBSTER, F. A. M. *Why? The Science of Athletics.* London: John F. Shaw and Co., Ltd., 1936.
102. WELLS, KATHARINE F. *Kinesiology.* Philadelphia: W. B. Saunders Co., 1971.
103. WILLIAMS, M., and LISSNER, H. R. *Biomechanics of Human Motion.* Philadelphia: W. B. Saunders Co., 1962.
104. WRIGHT, W. *Muscle Function.* New York: Paul B. Hoeber, Inc., 1928.